THE COLLECTED AWARD PAPERS

THE GRALNICK FOUNDATION
PORT CHESTER, NEW YORK
1966

PREFACE

THE Gralnick Foundation was created as a public charitable trust in March of 1956 under the laws of the State of New York with Alexander Gralnick, M.D. as its Grantor. Its funds were, and continue to be intended for the following purposes: 1) to support medical research "particularly in the field of mental health, including that devoted to improving the general understanding of mental illness and the treatment procedures in psychiatry"; 2) to aid "the mental hygiene movement generally and those organizations specifically endeavoring to forward the mental hygiene of the community"; 3) to aid "schools, both public and private, devoted to the advanced training of psychiatrists, particularly in psychoanalysis"; 4) to aid "clinics devoted to the psychiatric care of the community"; 5) to aid "medical school and hospital programs which are devoted to the advancement of psychiatric research, training and treatment"; 6) to grant "scholarships for worthy individuals whose main interest is medicine and psychiatry"; and 7) to aid "publications in the field of psychiatry."

In support of one of its aims, namely, the advancement of training and research, the Foundation offered cash awards to training schools offering post-graduate psychiatric and psychoanalytic training. The faculty of the school selected the graduating doctor who wrote the best thesis or research paper of his class as the recipient of the annual award. The papers they have selected during the past eight years are herein published in slightly abridged form.

In the main, the recipients are medical doctors who have had residency training in psychiatry and were in the process of gaining postgraduate education in psychiatry and psychoanalysis at the time of the award. The school at which they were receiving this training is listed in the case of each paper. The following schools have thus far given one or more awards: Columbia University College of Physicians and Surgeons, New York Medical College, the William Alanson White Institute, the American Institute for Psychoanalysis, and the Postgraduate Center for Psychotherapy.

In addition to awards for the studies that appear in this volume of collected papers, the Foundation has made extensive grants for outstanding research and clinical accomplishment. The Foundation also has granted awards to medical students to encourage an interest in psychiatry. A record of these grants appears in the annual report of the Foundation.

The papers making up the text of this book may represent the first efforts of their authors at making contributions to the literature of the discipline they have chosen. It is in this respect that The Gralnick Foundation, with its offering of competitive awards, makes an important contribution to psychoanalytic education; it invites students in training for this discipline in psychiatry to write competitively for an award, which is outwardly material in nature; but inwardly the award thus offered is more than material. It is an invitation to participate, even though in many cases the participation is premature, in that aspect of the *substance* of the field which, it is hoped, will one day be the heritage of many of the competitors and award-winners.

In offering these awards, The Gralnick Foundation is making a substantial contribution to psychiatric and psychoanalytic education. It is not to be expected that any of the papers printed in this volume will be of great importance in themselves. What is, however, of the greatest importance is that several workers are making a beginning contribution to the literature of this discipline, and they might not have been able to do so without the vision and insight of The Gralnick Foundation and its Trustees in making these awards possible.

William V. Silverberg, M.D.
Trustee
New York City, N. Y.

TABLE OF CONTENTS

Suicide In Denmark

by Herbert Hendin, M.D.
College of Physicians and Surgeons,
Columbia University

Herbert Hendin, M.D.

Dr. Hendin is currently affiliated with Harlem Hospital where he is engaged in a study of psychosocial problems of the American Negro. He is a Fellow of the American-Scandinavian Foundation, and in 1964 was honored by the Association for Psychoanalytic Medicine, Psychoanalysis and Social Research, for his study of Suicide and Scandinavia.

WHILE the high suicide rate in Denmark has received considerable world-wide attention in the last decade, the Danes themselves have been aware of, and concerned with, the problem for a much longer time. There is fairly good statistical evidence that the suicide rate in Denmark has been appreciably higher than that in most of the rest of Europe over the past hundred years. Nevertheless, the Danish suicide rate of 22 per 100,000 while relatively high when compared with that of the United States (10.5 per 100,000) and England (almost the same as the United States rate) and absolutely high when compared with that of countries like Ireland (2.5 per 100,000) or Holland (6 per 100,000), is equalled by the suicide rates in Switzerland, Austria, West Germany and Japan. However, with the possible exception of Japan, the Danish suicide rate is the most publicized. Certainly, it is only in Denmark, and it is perhaps characteristically Danish, that visitors on tourist buses—after being told by their guides about Danish silverware, and about Tuborg and Carlsberg beer—are told about the high suicide rate in the country.

Then, too, the suicide rate in Denmark has received added publicity because it has been caught up both inside and outside Denmark in the arguments for and against the form of socialism being practiced in Denmark. Such discussions have usually been of little value. Certainly, suicide is a measure of social tension within a given society. Studying the motivations of suicidal patients in that society will throw a good deal of light on what the sources of those tensions are; and this was one of the major purposes of this study. However, suicide is only one barometer of social tension. Crime, alcoholism, homosexuality and neurosis are also such barometers. You cannot take a look at one such factor without reference to all the others. For example, the Danish homicide rate is strikingly low; and while the suicide rate is twice that of the United States, the United States homicide rate is ten times that of Denmark.

Partly in self-defense, partly because it is true, the Danes point to the fact that they keep more accurate statistics and feel less need to conceal suicide than do the inhabitants of Catholic countries. These, say the Danes, are factors responsible for their higher suicide rate. They do have an excellent statistical bureau; and they are able to keep more detailed records for their four and a half million people, who change residence relatively infrequently, than we in the United States could ever hope to achieve. However, when all this is said, statistical accuracy is not responsible for the difference in suicide rates between Denmark and England or the United States, and the Danish statisticians, sociologists and psychiatrists are fully aware of this. Furthermore, the need to conceal suicide in Catholic countries is in itself an indication of a greater religious and social shame attached to suicide; and it would not be surprising if this were reflected in an actually lower suicide rate as well as in any tendency toward concealment of the suicides that do occur.

Many excellent statistical studies on the problem of suicide have been done and are being done in Denmark. The interested reader of this paper will be referred to several of these in the bibliography. However, since the purpose of this study was psychological or psychosocial, no detailed summary of this work will be given here. It will be sufficient to note just a few salient points. In common with most other countries, the rate is higher in men than women, higher in the old than in the young, higher in the divorced and separated than in the married, and higher in the city population than in that of the towns or rural areas.

This raises the question of whether a disproportionate number of any one of the groups just named is responsible for the high suicide rate. Perhaps, for example, a greater proportion of elderly people in the population in comparison with other countries, or a greater proportion of divorced people in the population in comparison with other countries, is responsible for the higher suicide rate in Denmark. This is not, however, the case. While a divorced person in Denmark is ten times more likely to kill himself than one who is married, the percentage of divorced suicides in comparison with married suicides is just too small to change the rate significantly. Thus, by and large, a comparison of divorced people in Denmark with divorced people in the United States or married people in Denmark with married people in the United States, will show the same ratio of higher suicides in Denmark compared to the United States. Nor does the fact that the United States has a large Negro population with a low suicide rate cause the difference, since the United States Negro population is small in comparison to the whole population. The United States rate, if figured purely for whites, is about 11.1 per 100,000 in comparison to 10.5 per 100,000 when Negroes are included in the rate.

In this study 25 suicidal patients were personally seen, usually for several interviews. Five more nonsuicidal patients were similarly seen. Five other suicidal patients were seen with the help of an interpreter. The interview technique was psychoanalytic in nature, that is, it relied as much on what the patient unwittingly revealed as on what he actually said. This proved practical only when an interpreter was not necessary. Despite the serious and dedicated co-operation of the interpreter, interviews by interpreter had much less success. Fortunately, an extremely high percentage of the Danish people, including those of relatively little general education, speak English fluently. (English is a compulsory language from the beginning of school in Denmark.) Finding English-speaking patients was not too difficult, because of the splendid co-operation of the psychiatric departments of all the major hospitals in Copenhagen.*

It must be noted that only 30 days were spent actually seeing patients and that the writer was relatively unfamiliar with the institutions and attitudes of the Danes. Fortunately, however, the writer's unfamiliarity with the customs of the Danes allowed him to discover a sophisticated use of guilt among many of the suicidal patients interviewed and to find that the arousal of guilt is the major form of discipline Danish parents use on their children.

Discussion of the problem of guilt leads, naturally enough, to the whole question of aggression and how it is handled, ex-

---

* The writer wishes to express appreciation to some of those who made this work possible:

First, to the following heads of the departments of psychiatry in Copenhagen for their permission and co-operation with regard to the writer's seeing patients in the hospitals and out-patient clinics: Dr. Carl Clemmensen of the Bispebjerg Hospital; Dr. Einar Geert-Jorgensen of the Frederiksberg Hospital; Dr. Villars Lunn of the Rigshospital; Dr. Mogens Ellerman of the Military Hospital; Dr. Fini Schulsinger of the Kommunehospital.

Then to Dr. Grethe Paerregaard, Dr. Andre Myschetzky, Dr. Aage Gjersoe and Dr. Gidrun Brun of the Bispebjerg Hospital and to Dr. Lass Sonne and Dr. Paerregaard of the Rigshospital for their help and advice. Also to Dr. Herlof Andersen of the Frederiksberg Hospital, Dr. Hagens and Dr. Smith of the Bisperbjerg Hospital and Dr. H. Renotorff of the Rigshospital who were particularly helpful in finding patients. The writer wishes also to thank Dr. Ostergade, psychologist at Rigshospital, for her time and patience. Also, Miss Kirsten Rudfeld of the Sociological Institute of the University of Copenhagen; Miss Marie Lindhardt and Miss Karen Dreyer of the Statistical Section of the National Health Service, all of whom have been, and are, working with the problem of suicide and who were extremely helpful and co-operative.

pressed or controlled. In general, far less overt destructiveness or violence is seen among Danish patients than will be seen among American patients. Even in the United States, on a disturbed ward consisting entirely of schizophrenic patients, where so many adaptive controls have broken down, patients of Scandinavian origin are more apt to be those who are mute than those who are actively enraged and throwing things.

The incredibly low homicide rate in comparison with the United States is further evidence of this. In a recent year, there were only 28 homicides in the entire country, 13 of whom were children killed in connection with their parents' suicides.

The Danish child, while indulged in many ways, is not permitted anything like the aggressiveness toward parents and siblings that is tolerated from an American child. Danish children, as a consequence, appear to Americans exceedingly well disciplined and well behaved, while American children often seem like monsters to the Danes.

If there is a socially acceptable outlet for Danish aggression it is in the sense of humor. The Danes are very fond of teasing and are proud of their perceptiveness for humor. Their humor will often contain aggressive barbs, though clothed in such a manner as to get the point across without being provocative enough to cause open friction.

However, while a great deal has been written about the importance of aggression turned inward with regard to suicide, it is far from the whole story with regard to suicide in general, and also very far from the whole story with regard to suicide in Denmark. Other countries, such as England, for example, curb aggression and have a low homicide rate without the high Danish suicide rate.

The whole dependency constellation, which has its own unique character in Denmark, is equally important and very much at the crux of the whole Danish vulnerability to depression and suicide. As one Danish psychiatrist put it to the writer, you can, in a way, divide Denmark into two groups: those who are looking for someone to take care of them, and those who are looking for someone to take care of. There is more truth than might be imagined in that succinct statement.

The Danish child's dependence on his mother is far more encouraged than that of the American child. Danish mothers are most apt to boast how well their children look, how well they eat and how much they weigh. They are far less likely to boast of activities of the child that in any way tend to separate him from the mother, such as how fast the child can walk or talk or do things by himself. The child is fondled, coddled and hugged more often, and probably to a later age, than in general in the United States. In addition, the American mother will often not curb her child's aggressiveness—out of the fear that she may damage his initiative. The Danish mother is much less ruled by this concern, and the child's aggressiveness is strictly checked and is, in a sense, part of the price he pays for his dependence. In addition, the very checking of the child's aggressiveness serves, in turn, to increase and foster this dependence. This appears to make the separation from the mother, when it does come, all the harder to bear. Many seek to return to the maternal relationship, either directly or through a mother substitute, while others achieve this kind of gratification vicariously through attending to the needs of the first group.

The search for dependence results in greater need of the sexes for each other and more moving toward each other, with less fear and more ease, than is perhaps the case here in the United States. This is heightened by the fact that up to now there is relatively a small amount of the competition in the relationship between men and women that is so common in the United States. Of course, expectations of dependent gratification from the opposite sex are often disappointed, and this is a major cause for the termination of relationships, and a major factor in Danish divorces.

Marriage involves many economic sacrifices and is not entered into lightly or viewed as the cure-all for personal problems. There is far less pressure on the unmarried to get married, and, as a consequence, less panic in girls of 23 to 28 who are unmarried, than one sees in the United States. Unmarried couples often live together and marry when a child is expected.

Within the family, the pattern of the passive father and more forceful mother is seen more and more. Danish preoccupation with pointing out this pattern in the United States is probably a reflection of their own anxieties about it. One patient who spoke of the submissiveness of men and women in the United States had himself been ruled all his life by his wife.

The Danish husband is very often in the position of a privileged oldest child. He has usually little to do with the discipline of the children. Resentment on the part of the fathers at the birth of children is rather common. Even more striking evidence of the dependency anxieties we are concerned with here is the widespread loss of potency or loss of sexual interest on the part of the husband after the birth of the first child.

Frigidity among Danish women appears as widespread as in the United States. This is despite their very feminine manner, their noncompetitiveness with men and the fact that they are permitted to have at least slightly more sexual freedom during adolescence though no more during childhood. (The attitude of the Danish mothers toward heterosexual play or masturbation in their children is generally to prohibit it and at the same time to deny its existence—very much as American mothers do.) However, female frigidity does not appear to be of the guilt-ridden nature common in the United States 30 years ago or of the competitive origin common today. Rather it appears due to the woman's dependent longings and to her image of herself as a little girl rather than a grown woman.

Consistent with the dependency constellation, is a far greater prevalence of depression as the outstanding symptomatology in psychiatric patients than one sees here. Of course, many of the Danish patients diagnosed as having endogenous or psychogenic depression would be considered here to be schizophrenic. But regardless of who is right in diagnosis, an American psychiatrist is bound to be struck by the predominance of depressive symptoms in patients that he considers schizophrenic.

In working with suicidal patients in the United States, fantasies of reunion with a lost love object after death are not uncommon. But in Denmark they are so much more common as to be almost the rule. This is despite the fact that most Danes interviewed tended to stress "not being religious" with almost some pride. However, the Lutheran version of the afterlife is universally taught in their schools, and the idea of reunion after death is often heard by the child from his parents, even before school. Evidently, even if formal religion is later rejected, the potential for the idea of afterlife and reunion with loved ones after death remains. Such fantasies were not only more common but were more openly and consciously expressed by Danish patients than by American patients, in whom they generally have to be ascertained from dreams. Certainly, the hold of such ideas is consistent with the dependency constellation previously discussed.

The best and most perceptive prototypes of Danish reunion-in-death fantasies are found in the Hans Christian Andersen fairy tales.

There is "The Little Match Girl" who, while freezing to death in the cold, lights her matches and sees the image of her grandmother who is the only person who ever loved her and with whom she is reunited after her death.

There is "The Steadfast Tin Soldier" who can only be united with his ballerina doll in the fire that destroys both of them.

The Andersen stories are a gold mine of information with regard to these fantasies of death, dying and afterlife. Suicide itself is almost directly taken up in "The Old Street Lamp." The lamp fears decomposition. It is relieved of this fear when it obtains the power to kill itself, so to speak, by turning to rust in one day. (Suicidal patients often do feel a sense of mastery over all sorts of anxieties, including fears of death, from the feeling of control and power over a situation that they obtain through the idea that they can at will end their lives.) The lamp, like many patients and nonpatients, finally decides not to use this power and that, even though a new existence might be better, it will not seek it.

since there are others (the watchman and his wife) who care about it and whom it must consider.

Rebirth fantasies are often associated with reunion-after-death fantasies. The famous "Ugly Duckling" is very much such a rebirth story. It appeals to the idea that, while in the present life one may be unloved and unwanted, in some future existence one's whole state can be very different, that is, the duckling is reborn as a swan. While the actual dying does not take place in the story, the psychological idea of the rebirth is there, nonetheless.

By and large the love-death theme—the idea that without love there will be death but perhaps in death the desire for love will be gratified—runs through the Andersen stories. The boy who is in bondage to "The Snow Queen" is emotionally frozen, has a "heart like ice," and can obtain pleasure in reason only. It is only by the strength of the love of little Gerda and her faith that he can be returned to normal.

Nor should it be assumed that these are the universal themes of all fairy tales. For example, the Andersen tales are by and large not competitive or performance tales. Neither giants nor dragons have to be killed by the hero to achieve success.

Other Danish attitudes with regard to death have certain features in common with our own. Death is as taboo a subject of conversation in Denmark as in the United States, if not more so. With children, as here, the parents are uncomfortable when the child brings it up. The Danes, however, do not use their funerals as an occasion for grief or mourning; they find them painful and wish them over as soon as possible. They are often uncomfortable being around a bereaved person. They expect a short period of bereavement and then that discussion of the death should stop. This is in keeping with their sensitivity and anxiety with regard to a separation from, the loss of, or the abandonment by, a source of dependency gratification. Several of the psychiatrists, psychologists and sociologists concerned with the problem expressed the feeling that, from their own personal experiences, a longer period of grieving would probably be a better safety valve.

With regard to the Danish attitude toward suicide itself, the taboo on it as an act does not seem so great as in the United States, and is probably much less severe than in Catholic countries. The patients who make suicide attempts and fail express less shame at having made the attempts than do similar patients in the United States. They are equally or more apt to express shame at not having successfully completed the act. While a wife or husband of the suicidal patient may feel some shame, the attitude of those around is, in general, to feel sorry for the suicide and pity him. Early church teachings that suicide is immoral do not appear to have any strong hold—a fact admitted to the writer by a Danish clergyman who has seen a great number of religious families in this situation. Then, too, there is bound to be a lessening of a taboo with regard to suicide when so many Danes have known personally friends and relatives who have killed themselves or made suicide attempts. Suicide does not have to become institutionalized—that is, approved of and even expected by society in certain situations as in Japan—for it to be a known and not uncommon, if not acceptable and traditional expression of unhappiness.

To sum up these factors: It should be stressed that by far the most common precipitating situation for suicide in Denmark is the loss of dependency-gratification through death, separation or divorce, or most often through the deterioration of a relationship. Working with, and reinforcing the effect of Danish dependency, are the control and suppression of aggression and familiarity with the use of personal suffering as a technique for arousing guilt in others and insuring desired gratification. The patterned control of aggression, and the use of guilt-arousing techniques would predispose to the use of suicide as a method of dealing with the frustration and anger generated by dependency loss. Then must be noted the frequency of fantasies concerning gratification after death—a fact which is consistent with the dependency desires—and finally the lesser degree of shame in Denmark attached to the act of suicide.

It should not be assumed that every social and character pattern that is important with regard to suicide is significantly present in Denmark. The Danish child is not particularly encouraged toward competitiveness. The characteristic attitude is that one should not stand out too much in any direction and anyone who violates this rule, whether the child at school or the adult at work, is subject to a good deal of envy and dislike. In light of all that has been said here of Danish family life, upbringing and attitudes, it is not surprising that the Danes were not extremely performance conscious, as are the Germans, and that success did not have the life-and-death meaning in Denmark that has been described in countries like Germany, Switzerland and Japan.

What role does Danish socialism play in fostering the national attitude toward competition and dependency? Certainly many of these attitudes antedated the social and economic changes of the last few decades in Denmark. However, Danish socialism may give expression to and reinforce these qualities and attitudes in the national character; and these qualities and attitudes, in turn, undoubtedly shape the particular form that the social reforms take.

Government concern for the individual gives a kind of permission for the overt expression of the longing to be taken care of. Even the tone of the letters to the newspapers in Denmark indicates a feeling of passively-endured injustice, with regard to personal economic problems in particular, and reflects a lesser feeling of responsibility for one's personal destiny than Americans are accustomed to. This attitude is a source of concern to the Danes themselves.

Certainly all the social welfare agencies give an outlet to those wishing to care for the dependent needs of others. There is a greater concern than in the United States on the part of those administering help (whether it be medical care or economic aid), with the welfare of everyone, and there is a tendency to feel personally responsible for the suffering of anyone. In discussing this at a seminar in Copenhagen one doctor gave the writer an illustration with which all concurred: that the entire country can experience a wave of guilt in reading a newspaper account of a man who died in his room and whose body was undiscovered for several days. This means to the Danes that he was lonely, uncared for, and probably without friends; and all tend to feel personally responsible.

We do not know for sure how a particular people hits upon a particular set of institutions and attitudes for regulating their lives, bringing up their children, and so on, out of the different alternatives that may be available to them. We do know that once they choose a particular way, it will have a profound effect on their character and attitudes.

However, psychosocial studies are still much in their infancy for one to pass judgement as to better or to worse ways of doing things, or for one to make any very definitive suggestions with regard to doing them differently, either in our own country or abroad. For the present, our job is to accumulate more knowledge as to the ways in which different social institutions and customs produce different individual characters and attitudes.

In this regard, the Scandinavian countries have a special interest. The relatively greater homogeneity of the people in each of their countries than in the United States would make the study of the differences among the Scandinavian countries and between these countries and ourselves a particularly fruitful source of information. Also, the Scandinavian countries are pioneering in many new social and economic areas that the rest of the world is interested in. Some of their ideas and plans have been, and will be followed by other countries. If we can learn something from the inevitable difficulties they are bound to have from going first, we can only be grateful, and trust that they will not begrudge the fact that our paths have been made easier by their own pioneering.

BIBLIOGRAPHY

DREYER, K.: "Comparative suicide statistics," *Danish Med. Bull.*, 6: 3, 65-81, May 1959.

HENDIN, H.: "Suicide," *Psychiat. Quart.*, 30: 2, 267-282, April 1956.

MYSCHETZKY, A.: "Suicidal and accidental intoxications," *Danish Med. Bull.*, 5: 4, 131-137, May 1958.

Paerregaard, G.: "Attempted suicide and suicide in Copenhagen" (not yet completed).

Rudfeld, K.: "Social statistics study of suicide in Denmark for year 1956" (unpublished as yet).

United States Department of Health, Education and Welfare: "Suicide–death rates by age, race and sex, United States–1900-1953." *Vital Statistics–Special Reports,* 43: 30, August 22, 1956.

United States Department of Health, Education and Welfare: "Homicide death rates by age, race and sex, United States–1900-1953." *Vital Statistics–Special Reports,* 43: 31, August 23, 1956.

World Health Organization: "Mortality from suicide." *Epidemiological and Vital Statistics Report,* 9: 4, 1956.

The Bereavement Reaction: A Special Case of Separation Anxiety Sociocultural Considerations

by George R. Krupp, M.D.
New York Medical College

George R. Krupp, M.D.

Dr. Krupp is Research Fellow in Psychiatry with the Downstate Medical Center, State University of New York. He is engaged in private practice and, since writing the paper published here, has continued to specialize in the area of bereavement.

THE famous patient Anna O. (Breuer and Freud, 1895, p. 21), whose therapy ushered in the science of psychoanalysis, was a case of mourning reaction. Her illness was set into motion by the sickness of her father, "of whom she was passionately fond." She began improving under treatment, but when "her adored father" died, she quickly retrogressed. Through catharsis and development of a transference neurosis (Jones, 1953, p.224), she recovered to a large extent. In the case of Fraulein Elizabeth von R. (Breuer and Freud, 1895, p.135), who "nursed to the end three or four of those whom she loved," Strachey notes that "Freud anticipates the work of mourning in his account of her 'work' of recollection" (p.162). In 1895 in a letter to Fliess, Freud (1895) further anticipates Abraham (1911, 1924) as well as his own classic "Mourning and Melancholia" (1917) by stating: "The affect corresponding to melancholia is grief–that is, longing for something that is lost" (p.105). He considered the loss in depression as one of the subject's instinctual life–loss of libido.

It was to be expected that Freud and so many other analysts would be concerned with the mourning reaction when we consider that mourning is one form of a separation reaction or separation anxiety. Anxiety has occupied a central position in psychoanalytic formulation since the beginning of psychoanalysis. In his *Introductory Lectures,* Freud (1916, p.401) states: "The problem of anxiety is a nodal point linking up all kinds of most important questions," and he focused attention on anxiety as the core problem in understanding psychological disorders. It is the "fundamental phenomenon and the problem of neurosis" (Freud, 1926). Anxiety still holds this key position today. In *Inhibitions, Symptoms and Anxiety* (1926) and in his *New Introductory Lectures* (1932),

Freud indicates that helplessness, fear of castration, fear of the superego, moral anxiety and fear of death all have their roots in earlier separation from the love object. Therefore, all later anxiety reactions signify in some sense a separation from the mother. "The danger of loss of object or of love corresponds to the dependence of the early years of childhood" (p.122).

A different view is taken by social psychologists and culturally oriented psychoanalysts who relate anxiety to man's "psychological isolation, his alienation from his own self and from his fellow men" (Fromm-Reichmann, 1955) and feel this is the "common fate of man." Actually, this represents another facet of the same problem of separation from the mother, but is expressed in terms of the milieu. This alienation from the world (transformed into terms of loss of values in life, loss of identity, and loneliness) relates it at once to anxiety and the primary loss of the mother. Klein (1934), Lewin (1950), and Heilbrunn (1955) move a step further than fear of loss of mother when they discuss the infant's projection of his own id aggression onto the threatening breast. Heilbrunn (1955) states that it is "the ever-existing threat of passive cannibalistic incorporation as the basic danger."

Recent psychological studies on monkeys, and observations of infants, indicate that the represented danger seems to reside in the loss of the whole mother rather than the breast (Bowlby, 1961). Undoubtedly, loneliness, fear of loss of mother, helplessness, and fear of being devoured are physiologically connected to the disturbance of homeostasis which the infant experiences.

The premise that anxiety may be related to helplessness and the primary loss of the mother, brings us back to bereavement. It raises the question of whether examination of the reaction to bereavement will clarify the dynamics of separation anxiety. In separation anxiety there is hope of reunion. In mourning, the hope is given up. Both anxiety and depression appear to be related to the infant's helplessness when separated from his mother. Why one person's infantile neurosis leads him to develop anxiety, and another's, depression, is not altogether clear. In fact, Freud (1926) raised a similar question: "When does separation from an object produce anxiety, when does it produce mourning and when does it produce, it may be, only pain?" He continues: "there is no prospect of answering these questions at present." [1] Nevertheless, he draws certain distinctions. "Pain is thus the actual loss of object and anxiety is the reaction to the danger which that loss entails. . . . Mourning is entrusted with the task of carrying out this retreat from the object."

Bereavement holds interest for us not only because of its relationship to anxiety and depression but also because of its relationship to all neuroses, changes, and emotional crises in a person's life history. Adolescence, for example, is a period when the individual is expected to reach genital primacy, relinquishing his childhood and parental attachments, and substituting nonincestuous love objects. In the adolescent, this loss of his past is, in our culture, associated with psychic pain, depression, and conflict which, if highly condensed, would be quite similar to the bereavement process. Even more dramatically, the bereavement reaction may be observed in menopausal depressions.

The term "bereavement reaction" is used in preference to "grief" or "mourning."[2] All of the terms used are heavily saturated with cultural assumptions. Bereavement embraces the appearance, behavior, attitudes and feelings of a person who has recently been separated by death from a loved one and who is endeavoring to give him up. While not entirely excluding external appearance and behavior, the word "grief" refers mostly to the inner emotions, attitudes, and thoughts of the mourner. Mourning refers more to the external rites, customs, or conventions of bereavement, although it is frequently used interchangeably with bereavement.

SOCIOCULTURAL FACTORS IN AMERICA

Almost all death customs and rites of today originated thousands of years ago, in many cases remaining remarkably unchanged. Thus, interment, cremation, and embalming; graves and cemeteries; preparation of the body for burial; expressions of grief, flowers, funeral processions, funeral orations; gravestones, epitaphs, and feasting—all made their appearance long before the Christian era (Hall-Quest, 1952). But the emotional reactions of our time and the past are different indeed. In the American family with its long childhood, there is considerable dependency on the parents. This breeds strong emotional attachments within the family, often fostering excessive involvement and pathological dependence. Substitutes are not readily acceptable psychologically. In fact, part of our culture encourages this, e.g., in the orthodox Jewish religion one is supposed to wait for a year before remarrying. Death is felt not only as an individual but also as a family crisis. The family organization is broken up, and feelings of anxiety and uncertainty possess its members.

The reaction to this great loss, however, does not produce the emotional outbursts, and tearing of the clothes and hair, so common to the ancients and preliterate[3] society. Everything in our culture conspires to erase death from our minds, even from our feelings. Death, though threatening and difficult to handle, has been made remote. American society, its movies, television, and mores represent a supreme effort to preserve youth, and deny aging and death. Though death has not been eliminated, it has been postponed.

Estranged by our advanced civilization from the basic realities of life (of which death is a part), we have lost contact with the daily struggle for life. We have less and less contact with nature, with the death of livestock, and with the slaughtering of animals for food. Death has become even more foreboding, frightening, repugnant, and mysterious.

Yet the bereaved person is supposed to behave well and make his state "less noticeable." A visit to the funeral "parlor," the banks of flowers heaped around the coffin, the make-up used on the deceased, the music, and even the words spoken by many ministers tend to deny death, the possibility that it is happening to ourselves and our loved ones. "Our unconscious does not believe in its own death; everyone is convinced of his own immortality" (Freud, 1915). When death occurs to a beloved person it is often imputed to accident or disease, not to inevitable natural causes. This is akin to the primitive concept that some blunder or magical occurrence caused the person to die.[4]

On the one hand, those dear to us have become fewer and fewer, closer and closer. On the other hand, death has faded from our lives. It is no longer seen daily and anticipated inevitably, but denied and driven from our minds.

Our behavior becomes extreme. When death does occur the deceased is overpraised: consideration for the dead is sometimes greater than consideration for the living. (One must follow the deceased's wishes even though one refused to do so when the deceased was alive.) The over-idealization of the departed one is similar to the over-idealization of the parent by the young child, or of the beloved in romantic love. Bowman (1959) states, "The behaviour of groups as they discuss funerals, funeral directors, death, corpses and the dying is as unpredictable and seemingly irrational as any of the many curious aspects of this subject. In tone, the discussions range from the sublime to the ribald, with the accent resting heavily on the latter." These irrational attitudes have a significant effect on the lives of people and the way in which they mourn.

SYMPTOMATOLOGY

In our culture, the bereavement reaction is influenced by the following factors: the relationship of the bereaved to the deceased, the degree of contact and emotional involvement and dependence (i.e., the extent of the loss[5]); the degree of ego strength and ambivalence (i.e., wish for the death, anger at the deceased for dying); availability of substitute resources (family, relatives, and friends); timeliness of the death (amount of preparation the bereaved has had); significantly, the amount of warning the deceased has had; and lastly, the effect of the death on the economic position and social status of the bereaved. The symptomatology of the bereaved person will be described according to four categories, which are not mutually exclusive. They are:

(1) alterations in emotional state, primarily in his feeling toward himself and the deceased; (2) alterations in physiology and physical state; (3) alterations in the relationship to people and all the environment; and (4) alterations in dreams. The symptoms occur in all three stages of bereavement: the beginning stage of protest—denial, weeping, clinging to lost object, hostility; the middle stage of disorganization—despair, apathy, aimlessness, etc.; the termination stage of reorganization (Bowlby, 1961).

Pathological reactions also occur, usually one of two types: either a too severe reaction, i.e., neurosis or psychosis; or absence of reaction.

Alterations in the Bereaved's Emotional State

After the original panic and uncontrollable crying (lasting from minutes to an hour or longer), contact with the environment and the people in it begins to be made. In the beginning phase of protest, the bereaved may be severely depressed, with altered sensorium and some sense of unreality. He is intensely preoccupied with the images of the dead one. The deceased's voice may be heard and the bereaved may at times sense or feel his presence. He may even see him. Usually there is preoccupation with guilt and self-berating for all the major and minor omissions committed. The bereaved is in great emotional pain, with a loss of interest in the external world as long as it does not recall the dead one. The loved one cannot be replaced, and all thoughts and energy are directed only toward him. At the same time efforts are made to recover him in hopes, fantasies, dreams, and actions. The world is poor and empty. Freud (1917) observed that there was no loss of self-esteem in grief. My experience has been that there is usually a considerable loss of self-esteem, accompanied by guilt, certainly in the early phase. This may be related to the hostility universally present.

The most poignant feeling is the deep sense of loss and the feeling of uselessness and emptiness. "I have nothing to live for now." Accompanying this admission of loss is an intense need to deny the loss.[6] It is seen most vividly in the bereavement dream when the dead person is dreamed of so clearly that the bereaved finds it hard to accept the fact of the death. There is a strong tendency to function as if the deceased is still alive. In fact, the bereaved is momentarily convinced that it is the death, not the dream, which is an illusion. These dreams, in addition to hallucinatory experiences, help explain why primitive and even civilized people feel the dead to return (the denial defense may well preserve the individual from complete disintegration under the full impact of the blow). Gradually as the "work of mourning" progresses, the waking feelings of disbelief and the dream imagery fuse with the hard facts of reality.

There may be great concern over the fate of the dead, especially their body condition. The concept of the rain and wind beating down on the deserted coffin, for instance, is a recurring painful thought that may persist for years.

The extent of self-reproach on the part of the bereaved depends to a large degree on his ambivalent feelings toward the dead one. This alternation of blame for his death, and anger at him, throws the bereaved into anxiety and depression. The anger produces guilt and expectations of punishment. When there was some neglect in reality, obsessional reproaches may be even more marked.

While attacking himself sadistically, the bereaved becomes disproportionately preoccupied with the wonderful qualities of the deceased. As in the state of romantic love, the loved one had no faults. The memory picture has little resemblance to reality. Retroactive falsification, idealization, memory lapses all seem to be defensive measures against hostile and inadmissible thoughts. One of these inadmissible thoughts may be the feeling of triumph over the dead one. Probably every death represents a triumph to those left behind—a triumph that the loved one is killed off and the person left is alive and victorious.

Alterations in Physical State

Since all physical states are accompanied by emotions, the bereaved person may give the impression of being ill. He feels weak, exhausted, agitated, and frequently sighs. These symptoms become particularly acute when new persons come into the room who apparently remind him anew of his loss. Disorganization characterizes his pattern of conduct. This may be manifested by a restlessness, an aimless search, and a type of agitation. This agitation with depression often is more evident than retardation in psychomotor activity. In fact, there is usually a flow of speech as well as action. For example, in one case of sudden death, the bereaved wife of a forty-five-year-old man carried on a constant barrage of orders and directions concerning the handling of the body, making preparations for the funeral, and commenting about the behavior of the deceased during the past days and weeks. She moved about with unusual rapidity and gave the impression of forcing herself to be extremely busy. This began about an hour after death, after the first phase of shock had passed. (Ten months later she still kept her husband's clothes in the closet, and also by her attitude indicated that she was still partly in the beginning state of denial.) One twenty-year-old son, after his father's death, anxiously spent the entire day phoning friends, relatives, and business associates to inform them of his father's death.

The digestive symptoms are well known. There is loss of appetite.[7] Food may taste like sand. There may be bulimia, particularly in adolescents.

One patient, a woman aged thirty-nine, whose mother had committed suicide fourteen years earlier, portrayed an example of overeating. The father was separated; there was a slightly younger sister, and an eighteen-year-old brother. In the eighteen hours that followed the loss, the patient showed no emotion, but set about informing the father of the loss (shielding him from the knowledge of the suicide), rehousing the children, arranging the funeral, etc. At the end of the eighteen hours, at noon, just before the funeral, the patient felt a sudden craving for a chocolate bar, a rare experience for her. In the ten months following the death, she gained fifteen pounds, gradually and almost unaware; she had never been overweight before. Further analysis revealed that the mother had been withdrawn since the patient's infancy, had rejected her, had involutional melancholia and was paranoid. There had apparently been great ambivalence hidden. The patient observed that since her mother's death, tension produced bulimia (to achieve relaxation through a distended stomach; or self-punishment when feeling self-hatred; or as an expression of hostility to consume or "chew out" her "enemies"). At the same time, the bulimia permitted the incorporating (thus preventing withdrawal) of the sweet-breasted mother who was so longed for in moments of helplessness. This patient recalled that she had been fed by the clock as an infant, crying as long as a half hour at a time for the breast, without being held, till the hour struck.

The amount and duration of weeping is to a large extent determined by the prevailing cultural and family attitude toward expression of feeling. Often a bereaved person exhibits considerable distress as he struggles to control crying in order to meet the demands of family and friends. In our culture great importance is attached to self-control, and symptoms may arise from fear of its loss. Bowlby (1961) considers weeping or rage reaction as attempts to recover the lost person: "When he weeps the bereaved adult is responding to a loss as a child does to the temporary absence of his mother." He notes that Darwin (1872) was the first who recognized that the expressions exhibited in grief are derived from the infant's screaming (for the absent mother).

Another interesting and recurring phenomenon is the acquisition of the symptoms belonging to the last illness of the deceased. The bereaved may assume the peculiarities of speech or gestures of the lost one. By such identification one can still possess the deceased.

Ulcerative colitis, rheumatoid arthritis, and asthma following separation or death of a loved one have been reported by Lindemann (1944). (This is particularly apt to occur when there is an absence of mourning.) In one series of forty-one patients with colitis, thirty-three had colitis in relationship to the loss; two developed bloody diarrhea at the funeral (Lindemann, 1945).

Alteration in Relationship to External World

In the beginning the mourner, inconsolable, has little contact with the people around him. Whatever warmth is present is usually closely related to dependency needs. Irritability, impatience, and veiled and open hostility replace former feelings. Some hide the hostility through excessive formality and withholding of emotion. Sometimes a furious hostility is developed against the doctor, surgeon, hospital, or one of the surviving family members. As Bowlby (1961) has pointed out, the accusation serves the function of attempting to recover the lost person. If someone did it, then unconsciously it is felt that it can be undone.

As the mourner notices more and more what goes on around him he may become even more angry and withdraw further. He notices the well-meaning comforting relatives in the background, who are busily engaged in renewing old friendships and relationships. He becomes angry at the good time they are having while he is suffering so much. He is also angry because they do not help him bring back the lost object. By their presence and their solicitation, however, as well as through problems that the bereaved must meet, he is forced back to reality even as he struggles to recapture the image of the dead one.

He may perform self-defeating acts such as giving money away and refusing to see people. He may find himself without friends, family, social status, or money. This social withdrawal may be a pathological expression of his need to control his angry feelings and expiate guilt.

It is generally assumed that sorrow is the prevailing disposition in the visitors to the bereaved. This is not always so. As communities grew larger, a single death produced less effect unless the member was some special symbol for the community.

Alteration in Dreams

The bereavement dream is part of the stage of protest but can occur at any stage. It is rich in expressions of the past, present, and future relationship with the deceased. As the work of bereavement progresses the dreams change in content and effect.

Mrs. C., age forty, was married to a man much older, but was quite happy in marriage. Her husband died suddenly. She was very grief-stricken in the beginning. Within forty-eight hours of the death she dreamed: "He appears and I have hurt my tooth. I told him. He was solicitous, like a father. I pointed in the back as if something there could be repaired." The patient woke up extremely disappointed when she realized it was only a dream. This dream indicates the lack of excessive ambivalence (or hostility) in the relationship and therefore prognosticates an uneventful bereavement action. This proved to be true.

Mrs. D., age thirty-eight, had been in analysis for two years when her husband died of a coronary thrombosis. She had anxiety states, phobias, depression, and feelings of lifelong rejection by both parents. There was also an increasing feeling of rejection by her husband, accompanied by much hostility on her part. Her guilt, sexual repression, and death wishes were just beginning to be resolved when her husband John died. She then was overwhelmed with feelings of guilt and suicidal preoccupation lasting for a period of ten months. For the first three months she did not leave the house except for essentials such as the analyst's appointments. During the first few weeks she dreamed: "I was in bed awake; John had not come home for several days. I heard steps in the hall and I hoped it was John. But no—it was a man with a handkerchief which he attempted to place on my face and smother me. He wore glasses and a white navy uniform. When he saw me looking at him, he put his handkerchief in his pocket, implying he wouldn't kill me. I woke up in panic and realized that unlike other dreams when you wake up and it isn't true, this one was true."

About four months after her husband's death, she had two dreams during one night. In the first, John had suffered a heart attack. In the second, she dreamed: "I was sitting on a staircase expecting it to break. It began to break. I held on to something and it broke too. From another room I heard the voices of John and his mother."

Toward the end of the bereavement period she dreamed that she was in a large room resembling a museum with many closed caskets. John was in a casket dressed in his navy uniform. At the foot of the casket was a citation. "I spoke to John and asked if there was a God and life after death. He sat up and said, 'Yes, there is something.' I was less afraid."

The above dreams occurred in an ambivalent woman who, during the working-through of the bereavement (and analysis), was able to recover. The dreams show the change in content and effect as she completed her mourning.

Mrs. E., age thirty-eight, when her wealthy father died, denied grief or any sorrow. About five weeks later Mrs. E. became increasingly depressed. The dynamics of the absent bereavement reaction was discussed in consultation. She vigorously denied any connection, paused, and then spontaneously told of a dream she had in which she heard the telephone ring, but on picking up the receiver all she heard was her father laughing loudly in a jeering way. This made her feel terrible. Her father had left her out of the will, although after the widow's death, the money would go to her children. She discussed her disappointment with this arrangement, and her feelings of anger that her father did not care and that he had the last laugh on her. With this, her depression lifted.

PATHOLOGICAL REACTIONS

Normal bereavement is a proportional emotional somatic response to a consciously recognized loss. It is self-limited and gradually subsides within a reasonable time—three to ten weeks. The reaction, however, may be replaced by a distorted picture which is pathological.

Exaggerated Reactions

1. One of the most common pathological reactions is the prolonged and intense one. The bereavement becomes chronic and the clinical picture merges into a true depression. The depression may be of such severe intensity and violence that it leads to dangerous self-destructive behavior. This is usually associated with anxiety and strong feelings that the mourner has no right to be alive. Nightmares, outbursts of fear and anger accompany the agitated depression. This may lead to suicide because of the feelings of guilt that the mourner must be punished, and that he must make amends by dying too.[8] Indeed, death is demanded of the mourner in his nightmare. As Anderson (1949) states, "such requests from loved objects seemed to imply not love, but rather the most intense and insatiable persecutory demands."

2. There may be complete ego breakdown leading to psychosis. When the intense rage is projected outward it may erupt in the form of paranoid and persecutory delusions. The panic is related to the ego's fear that the very object it mourns might return and harm him. The ego boundaries disintegrate and distinction between subject and object become less clear. The individual's hallucinatory world of attack and counterattack by internal and external evil objects may dominate him, waking or asleep.

3. Pathological identifications, i.e., the presence of symptoms that belong to the deceased, permit the mourner to retain the dead one as if alive. As in other hysterical symptoms, it represents both an unconscious gain and an unconscious punishment.

One patient, a young woman, developed a moderate chest pain which persisted for a year after her father's death from a heart attack. Another patient developed chest pains, anxiety, and fear of heart disease following her father's heart attack when she was twelve. After a while these symptoms diminished, only to return intermittently with increased intensity for the next twenty-five years during periods of tension. In addition, there has been a more or less chronic fear of and expectation of heart disease. Another patient was a nine-year-old boy whose father died suddenly of a cerebral hemorrhage when the boy was six. The father, shortly before his death, complained of a splitting headache, and with the palm of his hand pressed firmly down on the vertix of his head. The boy, who had witnessed the death, soon afterwards began to complain of headaches. Interestingly, several times a year, during periods of stress, he used the same words, "I have a splitting headache." At the same time he pressed the palm of his hand down on the top of his head.

Lifelong Alterations in Personality Structure

The death of a parent has a most violent and disrupting impact on a child's life. Such an event will have far-reaching consequences for the person's entire life. Such personality alterations are an extremely common finding in analytic practice.

One patient, whose father died when she was eleven, entered analysis with strong feelings that her otherwise satisfactory relationship with her husband would end in separation or disaster. She was concerned about his safety and health and would unconsciously set up obstacles in her relationship with him which would create guilt in herself. The obstacles and guilt seemed to bind and minimize her separation anxiety and allay her fears of his leaving her. Her infantile neurosis had otherwise been more or less successfully resolved. She came into analysis because of anxiety, following the loss of a new-born child, whose death she felt was due to gross neglect by the doctor delivering the baby. The theme of the analysis was her adolescent and still continuing reaction to her father's death. When this was worked through, in a relatively short time, her treatment was brought to a satisfactory conclusion.

Early parental loss seems to be implicated in the etiology of delinquency and schizophrenia (Glueck and Blueck, 1934; Barry, 1945). In both conditions reality testing is disturbed. Lewin (1950) has shown that persons with deceased parents may identify with them by means of sublimations, recreating their existence in the contemporary world. Through this type of internalized parental image they obtain immortality for the parents and themselves.

In *The Ego and the Id* (1923), Freud mentions, in his reference to depression, that object cathexis is replaced by an identification. "It may well be that identification is the general condition under which the id will relinquish its object." Fenichel (1945) too states that many persons who have lost a parent in early childhood "tend to establish along with their object relationships proper, extensive identifications, that is, to incorporate their objects."

Beres (1958), Kaufman (1960), and Alexrad (1960), all feel that the separation from a parent through death or other causes will be felt by the child as an act of rejection or aggression. The delinquent will project his "lost object onto the environment and set up an intensive interaction or rage against it like the melancholiac does with his introjected object" (Kaufman, 1960). One component of the delinquency may be related to the hostile identification with the lost parent. This would be similar to Anna Freud's (1936) concept of identification with an aggressor, which the delinquent (as well as others) may use to avoid further attack and depression. One aspect of juvenile delinquency seems to represent a group of defenses against helplessness, anxiety, and underlying depression.

Absence of Bereavement

The denial or postponement of emotion is one of the most frequent defense mechanisms utilized by the individual against anxiety or psychic pain. If the affect were to be fully released upon terminating a highly intense and interdependent relationship of our culture, disintegration might follow for the individual. However, complete absence of reaction must be considered pathological.

Freud (1918) writes that the Wolf Man experienced no grief on learning of his sister's death. Several months after her death he went to the region where she died. There he went to the grave of a famous poet (Bushkin) and mourned. This unusual behavior was understood when he realized that his father used to compare his sister's poems to those written by the poet.

Helene Deutsch (1937) corroborates the findings of Freud that the degree of ambivalence present determines whether bereavement is pathological or not. She cites four cases where there was a complete absence of bereavement. She observes: "first, that the death of a beloved person must produce a reactive expression of feeling in the normal course of events; second, that omission of such reactive responses is to be considered just as much a variation from the normal as excess in time or intensity; and third, that unmanifested grief will be found expressed to the full in some way or other." This has been my experience.

A thirty-three-year-old woman was referred to Family Service Agency because of her children's problems in adjustment. Her father, to whom she had been deeply attached, died overseas in the war. She felt no grief, could not believe he was really dead. A few months later she became promiscuous; shortly afterwards she married. For the next eighteen years she persisted in the fantasy that her father might not really be dead, and continued to look for him in restaurants and other public places. She had one intensely emotional but platonic extramarital relationship with a man who reminded her of her father. At the time of referral she was excessively preoccupied with this man and neglected her children. After a therapeutic relationship had been established, she discussed her feelings about her father and began to accept the idea that her father was dead. With this she began crying for the first time over the loss and finally began the work of mourning. She gave up her extramarital relationship and developed a more satisfactory relationship with her children. Her bereavement, postponed for eighteen years, when it did occur, brought catharsis and a mature approach to her problems.

Delayed bereavement reactions have been reported by others, e.g., Lindemann (1944), Hilgard et al. (1960). The latter, studying a random sample of adults from a metropolitan area, indicate that "grief at the death of a parent is recalled only in rare instances when such a death has been experienced prior to the age of nine."

There was more remembrance of the parents' bereavement reactions or of the funeral rituals. The ability to recall one's own grief after the age of nine to eleven illustrates the maturational changes in the ego's ability to tolerate pain and repress feelings. Patients in analysis who have lost a parent before the age of nine, however, do bring up the repressed painful memories which frequently become the core of the analysis.

HISTORICAL REVIEW

Mourning is another example where explanation of a pathological phenomenon (depression) has thrown light on normal processes. Although many psychoanalysts have discussed bereavement, their main interest has been in the psychology of depression. Only three—Freud, Lindemann, and Bowlby—have devoted considerable attention to the dynamics of the bereavement. Lindemann (1944) was the first psychoanalyst who fully studied and described bereavement in ordinary people. Bowlby is the only psychoanalyst who has extensively written on the bereavement process and who has compared bereavement in infants, animals, and adults.

In "Mourning and Melancholia" (1917), Freud directed attention to the structural similarity between mourning and depression, then illustrated the differences. "Mourning is regularly the reaction to the loss of a loved person or the loss of some abstraction which has taken the place of some one . . . the world becomes poor and empty" because of the real loss of the love object. "The fall in self-esteem is absent." In depression there is no real loss, but a psychic loss, and the depressed person "displays an extraordinary fall of self-esteem, a loss of the ego; the ego itself seems poor and empty." The mourner tends to cling to the lost loved object. The tie to the dead one is represented by the numerous separate memories of the past. Freud wrote: "Reality passes its verdict—that the object no longer exists—upon each single one of the memories and hopes through which the libido was attached to the lost object, and the ego, confronted as it were with the decision whether it will share this fate, is persuaded by the sum of its narcissistic satisfactions in being alive to sever its attachment to the nonexistent object." Carrying out this work of mourning is a painful and difficult task which is resisted by the person who maintains the illusion that the lost one still lives.

Abraham (1924) introduced the concept of a primal depression which develops in early childhood through disappointment in love. Using the framework of the libido theory, he stated that the depressed person regresses through the retentive and expulsive levels of the anal-sadistic stage, then steadily backward to a more primitive organization of the libido—the late oral-incorporative stage. In the normal process of mourning, the person reacts to a real object loss by producing a temporary introjection of the loved person.

Others have written on the subject of depression and mourning. Rado (1928) considered depression to be a cry for love, but the cry is directed toward the superego. The patient attempts by an expression of hostility to coerce the beloved person into giving protection and love. When the individual's rage does not get him love, expiation becomes a necessity, and the rage is turned inwards. He is torn between coercive rage and submissive fear in his effort to obtain maternal protection.

Melanie Klein (1934) agrees with Abraham and Freud that in normal and abnormal mourning there is a reactivation of an infantile depressive state. She relates this, however, to a still earlier stage in the child's development. What is being mourned is the breast which represents in the infants' mind love, security, goodness. These are felt to be lost by the baby because of its own greedy hostile impulses. Through the processes of projection and introjection there is fear that the ego will be destroyed by the bad internalized object, and with this a fear that the good internalized objects and he himself will be lost. The depressed person and the pathological bereaved person have never overcome the infantile depressive position. They are unable to establish good object relationships, or to feel secure within. "The person who gradually and successfully masters his grief does so through reinstating within himself his lost object as something that is good." Gero (1936), Jacobson (1937), and Masserman (1946), although emphasizing the early mother-child relationship, stress the genital conflicts in depression.

Stern et al. (1951) state that in twenty-five older persons experiencing bereavement, there was a relative paucity of overt grief and of conscious guilt feelings. There was, however, a great deal of overidealization of the deceased, self-isolation, preponderance of illness, and a displaced hostility toward living persons.

Anderson (1949) studied pathological bereavement reactions of 100 hospitalized patients with traumatic war neurosis. The reactions were not considered pure or static, and the clinical picture changed as mourning proceeded. His classification was as follows: anxiety states, 59 per cent; hysteria, 19 per cent; obsessional tension states, 7 per cent; and manic-depressive responses, 15 per cent.

Lindemann (1944) carried on an excellent extensive study on the symptomatology and management of 101 bereavement reactions following a violent disaster—the Coconut Grove Fire. He formulated the following signs for the bereavement reaction which he considered pathognomonic; somatic distress symptoms such as sighing respirations, weakness, and anorexia; sensorium generally somewhat altered and preoccupation with image of the deceased; feelings of guilt; lack of warmth; and irritability toward people; loss of normal pattern of conduct with change in daily routine. Interestingly, Lindemann implies that there is little relationship between an individual's previous neurosis and his bereavement reaction. This will be taken up later. Others, e.g., Bergler (1948), Brill (1944), Peck (1939), have reported individual cases of bereavement. Marris (1958) studied seventy-two cases of war widows. The sociologists Eliot (1954), Waller (1951), and Becker (1959) have written on bereavement and its relationship to the family and to social structure. Lehrman (1956), describing five cases where the reaction to untimely death was pathological, felt that the patient's childhood conditioning determined the clincial picture and that the pathological reactions "represent a defense against serious internal ego-threat."

Spitz (1945, 1946) has recorded firsthand observations on grief in infancy. Bowlby (1958, 1960, 1961) has written extensively on separation anxiety, grief in infancy, and on special problems of mourning. He suggests that the child's tie to the mother is best conceived as an outcome of a number of instinctual response systems mostly nonoral in character. These are part of the inherited behavior repertoire of man. Comparing bereavement in infants and adults, and animals, he offers evidence of an almost identical set and sequence of responses. After the initial stage of protest and demand, despair and disorganization set in, to be followed by a stage of reorganization. His thesis is that the significance of loss of breast has been exaggerated; when this loss appears to be of consequence, it is because it occurs contemporaneously with separation from the mother. The principal trauma to the child is loss of mother, and the processes connected with the depressive position are spread over a period from six months and continuing into and beyond the fourth year. Bowlby brilliantly notes that the instinctive response systems in bereavement are still focused on the original object with angry efforts to recover it. Successful resolution occurs only when there is a reorganization partly in connection with the image of the lost object, partly in connection with the new objects. Pathological bereavement is a fixation in the first phase of the bereavement process, and the individual, often without knowing it, is still striving to recover the object that has been lost.

DISCUSSION

Cross-cultural evaluation of mourning rituals in preliterate and contemporary society indicates certain institutionalized attempts to solve problems common to both. These are (1) loathing of the corpse and concern over its disposal; (2) fear of death; (3) desire for immortality both for the deceased and for the bereaved himself; (4) fear of the dead one; (5) impact of the loss on those closely related to him; (6) redistribution of the wealth. Preliterate man has a certain amount of perplexity and confusion in dealing with these problems because of the difficulty he has in making distinctions between living and dead, human and animal, and animate and inanimate. His lack of scientific knowledge and childhood conditioning interferes with his ability to comprehend these abstract concepts.

The man who has just died produces a social change more significant than birth, puberty, or marriage. There is a personal, family, and community loss. The daily expectation of thought and action are frustrated and the emotional interchanges involving the lost one are gone. No one can fill the hiatus. The remaining loved one attempts to restore the previous balance. Through adaptive biological mechanisms of weeping, and rage, and psychological defense mechanisms of denial, rationalization and identification, he attempts to retrieve the lost one. He may see the death couched in terms of will and motivation with anthropomorphic features, rather than a complete annihilation. At the moment of greatest sorrow, the funeral ritual forces those most concerned to participate in community activity. The integrity of the individual, family, and community is temporarily broken and the rites adjust the individual to the reality of death and realign communal unity. There is a forced catharsis and a transfer of interest from sentiment to activity. In addition, these rites often insure the soul passage and preservation in the hereafter. This reduces the impact of personal identification by suggesting immortality.

Thus, cultural action patterns in the form of mourning rituals allow for intensive working-through for society and individual object loss. The mourning ritual provides the community with a means of reintegrating the group and re-establishing the community morale. This is in contrast to the usual inhibited mourning of our own culture. Other cultural patterns and characteristics which aid the preliterate individual and group in the working-through of the loss are: (1) general proximity to life and death, and natural processes; (2) availability of substitute resources; (3) persistent belief that the beloved one is not really lost; (4) absence of overdependence, overattachment, and overidentification that contemporary culture fosters. The concept of "romantic love" is not present in preliterate society. Childhood dependence is usually minimal; the adolescent fulfills his libidinal desires soon after puberty and then usually achieves some kind of economic and social independence.

Preliterate society is characterized by a lack of emphasis on the uniqueness and importance of the individual. There is little choice and little range for identifications and, within this narrow range, there is a broader relationship with more people and an absence of self-awareness. Our society permits for greater freedom of choice of love object, emphasis on the uniqueness of the individual, greater range for identification, and greater awareness of self. However, there are fewer people to relate to, and a more intimate relationship develops among these. This intimacy of relationship to fewer people is the characteristic which makes bereavement so personally significant and anxiety-producing in our culture by connecting it with the long childhood dependency on mother. On the positive side, however, is the presence of a monogamous relationship of a highly developed and unusual kind. It is precisely in this kind of human relationship that man can obtain the highest development of his humanity and achieve great satisfaction and happiness. However, because of his great investment in the relationship, he can also be rendered most miserable.

Cross-cultural study of folklore of death and mourning rituals indicates that identification and incorporation mechanisms are a common component of grief. Roheim (1923) has emphasized that in some primitive societies bereavement is followed by an increase in sexual desire and eating of the dead person. In order not to lose the object of love cannibalism is practiced. Malinowski (1948) writes of the sarcocannibalism of the Melanesians who with feelings of dread and repugnance partake of the flesh of the dead person. Vomiting often occurs during this rite. The corpse is an object of horror as well as of tender love. The eating of courageous animals and slain enemies in an attempt to acquire their attributes, the totem feast and Holy Communion are additional examples of incorporation and identification. Bulimia, when present in mourning customs, may unconsciously be equated to eating the dead.

An understanding of identification mechanisms aids in the understanding of certain aspects of bereavement, particularly in our culture. Identification is a way of restoring a lost object. It develops in the growing infant as a countermeasure to frustration (anxiety). The infant tries himself to become that object to prevent further loss. Unless a loss occurs, identification could not occur. Identification refers to the mechanisms operating mostly unconsciously, by which an individual acquires the qualities and characteristics of persons to whom there is some emotional tie.

It seems that the ego is more ready to detach itself from an internalized object than from an external object because of its use of identification mechanisms in handling early losses. In healthy bereavement the introjection serves two functions: the object is retained and simultaneously the tie to the person now introjected is loosened. The bereavement becomes even more difficult when the previous relationship has been particularly ambivalent. Here the introjection may represent not only the need to preserve, but also an effort to destroy the object. This will initiate new guilt feelings. The anger at the introject may be projected outward, and the dreams may show fear of attack. Probably in every case of bereavement this will manifest itself to some degree. The mature person, with relatively "good" introjects, and resulting integrated autonomous self, seems to experience the bereavement directly related to the amount of loss felt. The pathological reaction can be understood by the extent of the "bad" infantile relationship, the partial identifications, and the profound ambivalence. The bereaved with a pathological reaction unconsciously feels he has killed off his adored loved one by his badness and hate and is thrown into anxiety and depression. Because of the intense need for the person and the guilt, he cannot let the person go and he remains fixated in his attempts to recover the lost person.

Bereavement practices vary as widely as other customs surrounding death. In fact, expressions of grief may often reflect society's taught responses as well as the individual's actual feelings. Durkheim (1915) writes that "mourning is not a natural moment of private feelings wounded by cruel loss; it is a duty imposed by the group. One weeps, not simply because he is sad, but because he is forced to weep. . . . Moreover, this obligation is sanctioned by mythical or social penalties." For example, in the code of Jewish Law (Ganzfried, 1927) one's parents are referred to as "relatives over whom one is compelled to weep and mourn vehemently." Each culture institutionalizes its own attitudes to death. This does not mean that everyone mourns the same way. "What is true is that in one culture he finds the one emotion already channelled for him," (Benedict, 1946).

It is of interest to see that identification following the loss of an object involves more than the taking-over of the object's physical traits or mannerisms. We often see how a Senator's wife or businessman's wife will take over her dead husband's ideals and pursuits. This is quite different from a depressive identification, which may lead to prolonged depression or suicide. Successful mourning is a process of the transfer of "interest" from the dead love object to the living world. When there is an absent or incomplete transfer, the work of mourning is made more difficult and pathology ensues. The bereavement dream, the physical state, the emotional state, the relationship to environment, the quality and amount of pathological symptoms are all indications of the degree of resolution of this process. Those people who have been able to maintain good object relationship before the loss will be able to maintain good relations to the lost one and others afterwards.

SUMMARY

Psychoanalysis, since its inception, has been concerned with problems of loss and restitution. How an individual reacts to the actual loss of a close relative or friend, of whose presence he has been bereaved, reveals much about the deprived individual and his culture. The experience of sustaining deprivation begins in infancy, when the loss of, or separation from, mother results in anxiety and in the setting up of a variety of compensatory defenses. Such grief in infancy is comparable to mourning in adults in that both represent reactions, passive and active, to the removal of a loved object. This paper is centered upon adult bereavement in contemporary

America (in its historical and comparative context), its symptomatology, pathology, and significance.

Cross-cultural evaluation of mourning rituals and bereavement practices indicates wide variations in coping with similar problems. Each culture provides specific institutionalized ways of handling loss. The individual's reaction is conditioned not only by the cultural milieu but also by his early infantile neurosis and by biological adaptive mechanisms. Certain areas of concern appear to be of universal importance: (1) loathing of the corpse and problems concerning its disposal; (2) fear of death; (3) desire for immortality, both for the deceased and for the mourner himself; (4) fear of the dead one (ghost); (5) loss of the dead person to family and community; (6) loss of love object to the mourner; (7) redistribution of the wealth.

In American culture, the death of a loved one often results in an extreme crisis, with accompanying anxiety, depression, and the reactivation of other infantile conflicts. Several factors may account for this reaction. The small, intimate family and the long period of dependence on parents result in overidentification and overdependence. The pressures in our society to preserve youth and repudiate aging and dying, coupled with urban estrangement from natural processes, all make death an alien and frightening figure, and one difficult to accept. Irrational behavior concerning dying, death, corpses, and funerals support this view. The function of the funeral rite is twofold: (1) to maintain the integrity of the community; (2) to force the individual to work through the loss. Mourning rituals express the ambivalence of the individual and society toward the deceased and protect against projected hostility. Permanence of the loss is denied and minimized as being only a change in communication. These and other defensive operations (i.e., identification mechanisms) assist the individual and society in the adaptation to the loss.

Bereavement is a normal manifestation; the difference between a healthy and pathological reaction can be compared to the difference between normal and neurotic behavior. The successful completion of mourning is a process of transfer of interest from the dead love object to the living world. Bereavement may even contain constructive elements which are disclosed as personality realignment occurs and hitherto latent resources develop.

Pathological bereavement is behavior in which unconscious factors predominate, and in which hostility, guilt, anxiety, and depression (all normally present in bereavement) are extreme both in degree and in duration. Pathology also ensues when there is an absence of transfer of interest, or when such transfer is incomplete or arrested. This represents attempts to recover the lost object.

The bereaved's emotional state, physical condition, relationship to the environment, bereavement dreams and the presence or absence of pathological symptoms are all indications reflecting the degree of resolution of the bereavement process. The bereavement reaction is also culturally determined as well as being a barometer of the quality of the love relationship existing between the bereaved and the deceased. Perhaps the best way of reacting constructively to death is to reflect that if one can learn to live with the living, then one can manage to live with the dead.

Bereavement, in a particular culture, is an expression of a biological adaptive reaction to loss of mother; an indication of an individual's degree of resolution of his infantile conflicts; and an occasion which a society utilizes to express its important cultural intentions.

FOOTNOTES

[1] It is interesting that Freud poses this question when at the same time he supplies the theoretical framework for an answer. It appears to me that the pertinent question is not the difference between anxiety, pain and mournings, but rather the difference between anxiety and depression. Both contain pain by definition and implication. Mourning, i.e., painful withdrawal of interest from the loved object, contains both anxiety and depression. The anxiety reaction to the loss of mother (helplessness, signal of danger) is biologically adaptive to anxiety or helplessness; but here the depression (fight, rage) is not expressed outwardly but internalized or inhibited, in the attempt to ward off further danger (loss) and at the same time recover the lost love object through incorporation. The depression is related to the adaptive mechanism of inhibition, which is another physiological method of responding to danger. The depressive reaction appears to be on a more integrative level than the anxiety reaction in coping with the danger. It is a defense against the anxiety. In this regard most patients seem to feel that pain is greater in severe anxiety or panic than in depression (as painful as this can be). Depression, then, is a defensive or adaptive mechanism (related to inhibition) of coping with anxiety, and is similar to other defense mechanisms such as conversion, etc., which are also defenses against anxiety. It follows that the depressed person has achieved a greater degree of integration or internal harmony than the anxiety-ridden person. The traumas may have occurred at a later period of psycho-sexual development, after more satisfactory attachments to love objects had been made and homeostatic mechanisms were more regularly established. Anxiety is helplessness with fear of danger. Depression is helplessness with internalized aggression or loss of self-esteem (Bibring, 1953).

[2] See Volkart (1957).

[3] The terms preliterate and primitive are used interchangeably throughout the paper.

[4] In primitive culture, death tends to be more often associated with youth than old age, as many people die young.

[5] There are exceptions to this as in the case of particular public figures, i.e., Abraham Lincoln, Rudolph Valentino, or Franklin D. Roosevelt, whose deaths produced a mass-mourning reaction. See Volkart (1957).

[6] Freud, in his paper "Splitting of the Ego in the Defensive Process," (1938), states, "he rejects reality and refuses to accept any prohibition; on the other hand, in the same breath he recognizes the danger of reality."

[7] Earlier psychoanalytic formulations emphasized the suicidal component in the anorexia. It seems more readily explained by the generalized inhibitions present. Animals also exhibit anorexia in mourning a loved animal or master.

[8] Hamlet is the classic story of the bereavement reaction ending tragically. Ambivalence, oedipal guilt, murder, psychosis, suicide, are all present (Sharpe, 1929).

BIBLIOGRAPHY

ABRAHAM, K. (1911), A Short Study of the Development of the Libido Viewed in the Light of Mental Disorders. *Selected Papers*. London: Hogarth Press, 1927.

——(1924), Notes on the Psychoanalytic Investigation and Treatment of Manic-depressive Insanity and Allied Conditions. *Selected Papers:* Hogarth Press, 1927.

ANDERSON, C (1949), Aspects of Pathological Grief and Mourning. *Int. J. Psychoanal.*, 30:48-55.

AXELRAD, S. (1960), Sociological Contribution to the Study of Early Super-ego Defect. Quoted by Kaufman (1960).

——& MAURY, L. (1951), Identification as a Mechanism of Adaptation. In: *Psychoanalysis and Culture,* ed. G. Wilbur & W. Muensterberger. New York: International Universities Press, Pp. 168-184.

BARRY, H. (1939), A Study of Bereavements: An Approach to Problems in Mental Disease. *Amer. J. Orthopsychiat.*, 9:355.

——(1945), Significance of Maternal Bereavement Before Age of Eight in Psychiatric Patients. *Arch. Neurol. Psychiat.*, 53:322.

BECKER, H. (1959) *Family, Marriage and Parenthood.* Boston: Health.

BENEDICT, R. (1946), *Patterns of Culture.* New York: Mentor Books.

BERES, D. (1958), Vicissitudes of Superego Functions and Superego Precursors. *The Psychoanalytic Study of the Child,* 13:324. New York: International Universities Press.

BERGLER, E. (1948), Psychopathology and Duration of Mourning in Neurotics. *J. Clin. Psychopathol.*, 3:478-482.

BIBRING, E. (1953), The Mechanism of Depression. In: *Affective Disorders,* ed. Pl. Greenacre. New York: International Universities Press, pp. 13-48.

BOWLBY, J. (1958), The Nature of the Child's Tie to His Mother. *Int. J. Psychoanal.,* 39:350-373.

——(1960), Grief and Mourning in Infancy and Early Childhood. *The Psychoanalytic Study of the Child,* 15:9-52, New York: International Universities Press.

——(1961), Processes of Mourning. *Int. J. Psychoanal.,* 42:317-340.

BOWMAN, L. (1959), *The American Funeral.* Washington, D.C.: Public Affairs Press.

BREUER, J. & FREUD, S. (1859), *Studies on Hysteria.* New York: Basic Books, 1957.

BRILL, A. A. (1944), Mourning, Melancholia and Compulsions. In: *Freud's Contribution to Psychiatry.* New York: Norton, pp. 168-184.

CAMPBELL, J. (1959), *The Masks of God: Primitive Mythology.* New York: Viking Press.

DARWIN, C. (1872), *The Expressions of the Emotions in Man and Animals,* London: Murray.

DEUTSCH, H. (1937), Absence of Grief, *Psychoanal. Quart.,* 6:12-22.

DEVEREUX, G. (1942a), Primitive Psychiatry, Funeral Suicide and the Mohave Social Structure. *Bull. Hist. Med.,* 11:522.

——(1942b), Social Structure and the Economy of Affective Bonds, *Psychoanal. Rev.,* 29:303-314.

DURKHEIM, E. (1915), *The Elementary Forms of the Religious Life.* London: Allen & Unwin.

ELIOT, T. D. (1954), Bereavement: Inevitable But Not Insurmountable. *Family, Marriage, and Parenthood.* Boston: Becker & Hill, 1955.

EPHRAIM, J. (1959), On Sudden or Rapid Whitening of the Hair. *Arch. Dermatol.,* 79-228.

FENICHEL, O. (1926), Identification. *Collected Papers,* 2:97-112, New York: Norton.

——(1945), *The Psychoanalytic Theory of Neurosis.* New York: Norton.

FORTES, M. (1949), *The Web of Kinship Amongst the Tallensi.* London: Oxford University Press.

FREUD, A. (1936), *The Ego and the Mechanisms of Defense.* New York: Oxford University Press, 1946.

FREUD, S. (1895), *The Origins of Psychoanalysis.* Garden City, N.Y.: Doubleday, 1957.

——(1900), The Interpretation of Dreams. *Basic Writings of Sigmund Freud.* New York: Modern Library, 1938.

——(1912-1913), Totem and Taboo. *The Basic Writings of Sigmund Freud.* New York: Modern Library, 1938.

——(1915), Thoughts for the Times on War and Death. *Collected Papers,* 4:288-319. London: Hogarth Press, 1950.

——(1916), *A General Introduction to Psychoanalysis.* New York: Permabooks, 1957.

——(1917), Mourning and Melancholia. *Collected Papers,* 4:152-170. London: Hogarth Press, 1950.

——(1918), From the History of an Infantile Neurosis. *Collected Papers,* 3:473-605. London: Hogarth Press, 1950.

——(1921), *Group Psychology and the Analysis of the Ego.* London: Hogarth Press, 1928.

——(1923), *The Ego and the Id.* London: Hogarth Press, 1940.

——(1926), *Inhibitions, Symptoms and Anxiety.* London: Hogarth Press, 1936.

——(1932), *New Introductory Lectures on Psychoanalysis.* New York: Norton, 1933.

——(1938), Splitting of the Ego in the Defensive Process. *Collected Papers,* 5:372-377. London: Hogarth Press, 1950.

FROMM-REICHMANN, F. (1955), Phychiatric Aspects of Anxiety. *An Outline of Psychoanalysis.* New York: Modern Library.

GANZFRIED, S. (1927), *Code of Jewish Law.* New York: Hebrew Publishing Company.

GERO, G. (1936), The Construction of Depression. *Int. J. Psychoanal.*, 17:423-461.

GLUECK, S. & GLUECK, E. (1934), *Five Hundred Delinquent Women.* New York: Knopf.

GRODDECK, G. (1923), *The Book of It.* New York: Nerv. Ment. Dis. Publishing Company.

HALL-QUEST, A. L. (1952), Death Customs and Rites. *Collier's Encyclopedia,* 6. New York: Collier.

HEILBRUNN, G. (1955), The Basic Fear. *J. Amer. Psychoanal. Assn.*, 3:447.

HILGARD, J. NEWMAN, M., & FISK, F. (1960), Strength of Adult Ego Following Childhood Bereavement. *Amer. J. Orthopsychiat.*, 30:788-798.

HOCART, A. M. (1931), Death Customs. *Encyclopedia of the Social Sciences,* 5. New York: Macmillan.

JACOBSON, E. (1937), Depression. The Oedipus Conflict in the Development of Depressive Mechanisms. *Psychoanal. Quart.*, 6:12.

JONES, E. (1953), *The Life and Work of Sigmund Freud,* 1. New York: Basic Books.

KANZER, M. (1935), Writers and the Early Loss of Parents. *J. Hillside Hosp.*, 1:148.

——(1957), Acting Out, Sublimation, Reality Testing. *J. Amer. Psychoanal. Assn.*, 5:663.

KAUFMAN, I. (1960), Child Therapy and Superego Development. *J. Amer. Psychoanal. Assn.*, 8:130.

KLEIN, M. (1934), A Contribution to the Psychogenesis of Manic-Depressive States. *Contributions to Psychoanalysis 1921-1945.* London: Hogarth Press, 1948.

KRUPP, G. R. & KLIGFELD, B. (1962), Bereavement Reaction. A Cross-cultural Evaluation. *J. Religion & Health,* 1:223-246.

LANDAUER, K. (1925), Aquivalente der Trauer. *Int. Z. Psychoanal.*, 11:194-205. Quoted by Fenichel (1945).

LEHRMAN, R. (1956), Reactions to Untimely Death. *Psychiat. Quart.*, 30:567.

LEWIN, B. D. (1950), *The Psychoanalysis of Elation.* New York: Norton.

LINDEMANN, E. (1944), Symptomatology and Management of Acute Grief. *Amer. J. Psychiat.*, 101:141-149.

——(1945), Psychiatric Aspects of Conservative Treatment of Ulcerative Colitis. *Arch. Neurol. Psychiat.*, 53:322.

LORENZ, K. (1954), *Man Meets Dog.* London: Methuen.

MALINOWSKI, B. (1948), *Magic, Science, and Religion.* Garden City, N.Y.: Doubleday.

MANDELBAUM, D. (1959), Social Use of Funeral Rites. In: *The Meaning of Death,* New York: McGraw-Hill.

MARRIS, P. (1958), *Widows and Their Families.* London: Routledge & Kegan Paul.

MASSERMAN, J. (1946), *Principles of Dynamic Psychiatry.* Philadelphia: Saunders.

MAY, R. (1955), Freud's Evolving Theories of Anxiety. In: *An Outline of Psychoanalysis.* New York: Modern Library.

MITRA, D. N. (1947), Mourning Customs and Modern Life in Bengal. *Amer. J. Sociol.,* 52:309-311.

PARTRIDGE, E. (1959), Origins (*Etymological Dictionary*). New York: Macmillan.

PECK, M. (1939), Notes on Identification in a Case of Depression Reactive to the Death of a Love Object. *Psychoanal. Quart.,* 8:1-17.

POWDERMAKER, H. (1960), Personal Communication.

RADO, S. (1928), The Problem of Melancholia. *Int. J. Psychoanal.,* 9:420-438.

ROCHLIN, G. (1953), Loss and Restitution. *The Psychoanalytic Study of the Child,* 8:288-309. New York: International Universities Press.

ROHEIM, G. (1923), Nach dem Tode Des Urvaters. *Imago,* 9:83-121.

SHARPE, E. F. (1929), The Impatience of Hamlet. *Int. J. Psychoanal.,* 10:270.

SOUTHHALL, A. W. (1960), Homicide and Suicide Among the Alur. *African Homicide and Suicide.* Princeton: Princeton University Press.

SPITZ, R. (1945), Hospitalization: An Inquiry into the Genesis of Psychiatric Conditions in Early Childhood. *The Psychoanalytic Study of the Child,* 1:53-74. New York: International Universities Press.

—-ibid. (1946), Anaclitic Depression. 2:313-342.

STERN, K., WILLIAMS G., & PRADOS, M. (1951), Grief Reactions in Later Life. *Amer. J. Psychiat.,* 108:289.

VOLKART, B. (1957), Bereavement and Mental Health, *Explorations in Social Psychiatry.* New York: Basic Books.

WALLER, W. W. (1951), *The Family, A Dynamic Interpretation.* New York: Dryden.

Formal Language Patterns As Defensive Operations

by Joseph Jaffe, M.D.
William Alanson White Institute

Joseph Jaffe, M.D.

Since writing this paper, the author has moved from private practice into research on normal and pathological communication. He is Director of Research at the William Alanson White Institute in New York City, and Assistant Clinical Professor of Psychiatry, College of Physicians and Surgeons, Columbia University. Dr. Jaffe is also an Associate Attending Psychiatrist at the New York State Psychiatric Institute.

PSYCHOANALYSIS is a "talking" therapy. The therapist listens to the content, the details of his patient's problems in living. Concurrently, he attends to the form or style of communication. "How" something is said may often be more significant than "what" is said. The identical events may be described humorously or fearfully, with conviction or tentatively. These qualities are conveyed by the rate, pitch and volume of speech, by pauses, hesitations, slips of the tongue and difficulties in articulation, by vocabulary, grammatical construction and word usage, as well as by accompanying facial expression, posture and gesture. Close attention to such formal aspects of communication enriches our understanding of the relation of language to emotional experience.

Certain formal language patterns serve an adaptive function for the speaker. The evidence for this is threefold; a) That the way of speaking has a necessary, compulsive quality, even if only for the moment, b) That interference with the form is accompanied by evidence of stress, or anxiety, c) That alteration of the pattern is attended by new and psychodynamically relevant information, or by change in emotional experience. The patient may or may not be aware of much of this. The way of communicating may constitute an ego defense or security operation that limits the patient's awareness, experience of anxiety, and spectrum of interpersonal relationships. These are familiar ideas to students of psychoanalysis. One of the earliest descriptions of resistance and defense is a catalogue of possible formal variations on a basic verbal theme. Freud wrote in 1895,

> . . . I always listen when I hear a patient talk so lightly of an idea. That the pathogenic idea should appear of so little importance on its reappearance is a sign of the successful de-

fense. One can infer from this, of what the process of defense consisted. Its object was to make a weak out of strong idea, that is, to rob it of its affect.

Among other signs, the pathogenic memories can also be recognized by the fact that they are designated by the patient as unessential, despite the fact that they are uttered with resistance. There are also cases where the patient seeks to disavow the recollections, even while they are being reproduced with such remarks as these: "Now something occurred to me, but apparently you talked it into me;" or "I know what you expect to this question, you surely think that I thought of this and that." An especially clever way of shifting responsibility is found in the following expression: "Now something really occurred to me, but it seems to me as if I added it, and that it is not a reproduced thought." . . .[13]

Later, both he and Ferenczi [14] reported striking differences in emotional effect when obscene words were used in the therapy, in place of their more polite equivalents. Here again was an instance of different forms of expression affecting the emotional impact of communication. However, the study of specific symbols has so preoccupied research workers in this field that analysis of style has been given insufficient emphasis.

OBSERVATIONS

1. Names and Forms of Address

This category of language patterns deals with questions of identity, status, intimacy and social distance.

Forms of address help to define the social situation. This function of language structure is more obvious in French and German where more than one form of personal pronoun exists for addressing one's partner, e.g. "tu" and "vous."

a) For the first two years of therapy a patient had rigidly said "Good evening, Doctor," at both beginning and end of the hour, and used this form of address during the sessions. In the third year he consistently used my first name. None of this was interpreted. At a stressful moment in his life, at the end of the third year, I gave him a prescription for a sedative. He was quite surprised to hear himself say, "Thank you, Doctor," and immediately asked, "Why did I call you that?" Answering his own question, he realized that he had stopped thinking of the therapy as a professional relationship, and that the prescription had interrupted the fantasy. In concurrent group therapy sessions, when talking about me, he used my first name when discussing positive feelings and my last name alone when voicing negative feelings.

b) A patient constantly referred to her "mother's father." My suggestion that she refer to him as "grandfather" resulted in unexpected anxiety. The first discussion of her strongly ambivalent feelings toward this man then occurred. She needed to feel unrelated to him because she currently identified him with me in the transference. The construction "my mother's father" rather than "my grandfather" maintained distance from these feelings.

c) A patient struggling to detach himself from an all-encompassing family situation began to refer to his parents as "Alice" and "William" rather than as "Mom" and "Dad." He said he did this quite consciously because it helped him to feel separate and to see them in perspective. Later in the analysis, when I referred abstractly to "father," the patient said, "You can say, 'your father' from now on. I don't need the protection of indirectness."

d) A patient's father had been described as a rather rejecting, withdrawn, disapproving person. When asked how she addressed her father in childhood, the name "Daddy-boy" was associated, with some embarrassment. This led to the omitted history of an earlier affectionate, rollicking, seductive, "pal" relationship which was much more significant.

In this connection, it is often useful to inquire as to "pet names" or "nicknames" by which the patient has been called throughout his life. These often characterize the interpersonal relationships which obtained at the time. Patients occasionally have a special name by which they refer to the analyst, either with others, or in fantasied conversations. Such names may also clarify the transference.

e) To patients with severe problems of identity the use of their names may be surrounded with powerful emotion in a very concrete fashion. A college freshman had refused to affix his name in the required place on the door of his room in the student dormitory. When asked about it, he explained, "I can't put my name on the door because it would mean facing myself every time I enter. I wouldn't like what I see. Inside, the room is a mess. That door has been opened and closed and slammed by everybody. This is me, no name that's mine. To be honest I should put all the names of my relatives on the door."

f) Use of the patient's first name may foster generally positive and dependency feelings due to similarity to the forms used by parents and friends. It is also reminiscent of the mode of address used by teachers in school. This latter type of transference is marked in early group therapy meetings, where patients' first names are used by convention. They may develop a conflict over the reciprocal mode of address which elicits new information about the doctor-patient relationship. One patient became panicky, warning me that he could not continue to call me "Doctor" if I used this first name in the group because, "It would be too humiliating, like being a child." Feelings revolving about mode of addressing patients are also fruitful areas for countertransference analysis. My preferences for certain forms with specific patients have revealed aspects of the relationship of which I was unaware.

g) Honorifics and euphemisms are formal verbal defense mechanisms that should be included in this general category. Honorifics are terms designed to honor or pay respect but may also be used sarcastically.[15] Thus "realtor" is substituted for "real estate agent," and "custodial engineer" for "janitor." A gentle reversal of these substitutions will uncover the warded-off emotions.

2. Idiomatic Language Patterns

a) Change of national tongue in multilingual patients has been perceptively studied by Krapf.[16] He describes the spontaneous, and often compulsive "switch" to another tongue when the patient speaks of certain subjects, "to avoid anxiety, the individual uses the language that in a particular situation is least likely to provoke a feeling of anxiety, or conversely, most likely to give him a feeling of security." This is a clear and dramatic example of the control of subjective experience by formal language patterns.

b) However, idiomatic changes within a single national tongue may serve the same function. An Italian-American used English translations of Yiddish colloquialisms to feel close to me without exposing his conflicts. I suggested that some of the equivalent expressions of his own group be used. This necessitated much explanatory translation and specifying of subtle connotations so that I would understand the "private" idiom. The process was accompanied by intense anxiety, the discussion of intimate feelings for me, and by a flood of "primal scene" dreams. In one of these he was discovered while observing parental intercourse. The common denominator of both the interpersonal anxiety and the frightening dream experiences seemed to be the fear of "knowing and being known." Following this period the patient was able to use both cultural idioms comfortably, reflecting a greater acceptance of his origins.

c) In contrast, I recall a Jewish patient who carefully avoided all Yiddish colloquialisms. This pattern ended, without interpretation, coincident with the beginning discussion of homosexual feelings. The avoidance seems to have been a defense against feelings of intimacy and identification with me, which would have been heightened by acknowledgment of a common background.

d) Observations on colloquialisms of speech by T. Reik have led him to the conclusion that "men and women speak different languages."[17] For instance, women may refer to menstruation as "the curse," among themselves. There are parallel male idioms. Their adaptive significance only becomes apparent when a male tries to speak to a female in the male idiom, or vice versa. Analogous phenomena occur when one tries to speak to persons of higher or lower status in peer language forms.

We all have many languages, perhaps as many as the social situations in which we participate. These forms help to limit our experience of the situation to what we believe to be appropriate.

3. Person and Number

Changes in the person of pronouns are related to intimacy, commitment and social distance. First and second person are more direct than third person. Changes in number (singular, plural) may serve similar functions.

a) A patient was discussing an imminent test of strength and popularity within an organization. As the head of one contending faction, he was obsessionally involved in a spurious question, i.e., his own importance relative to that of the group he represented. This question was essentially unanswerable. In the session preceding the test he voiced the fear, "I will fail." His first words in the session following the test were, "Well, we won." When his attention was drawn to the change from "I" to the "we," he was at first embarrassed. The statement "I will fail", part of his self-castigating pattern, served to deny his own ambition and aggression, and to guard against disappointment. The verbal prediction of failure also meant magically to insure success. He could be committed to such a position since it epitomized a life-long adaptation, hence the first person pronoun. The statement, "We won," was to ward off the jealousy and resentment he expected from me, by giving the group the credit. It also served to elicit compliments from others, such as remarks about his modesty. Later in the session he realized that a consistent grammatical pattern, i.e., "I fail, I win," or "We fail, we win," would entail a gross change in his orientation towards responsibility and relatedness. Total responsibility for failure implies undivided glory in success, and is lonesome. Sharing of blame implies sharing of rewards.

b) Patients whom I treat in both group and individual therapy will often verbalize feelings differently in the two settings. In group therapy sessions the group support constitutes the necessary defense. Thus, a patient said, in individual sessions, "Psychiatrists annoy me." She was clearly identified, but I was made part of a professional group. When she began concurrent group sessions she was relieved to find that other patients freely expressed similar feelings. In this setting she could say, "You annoy her." The two defenses were equivalent; both indirect. When she finally was able to say, "You annoy me," therapeutic progress had occurred. The protection of the group (plural, us) was supplanted by the "you-me" (singular, one-to-one) relationship.[18]

c) A patient referred vaguely to fantasies about my family for several years, always using the expression "your wife" (second person). However, she was reluctant to become more specific. When she finally began to analyze them, she consistently used the expression, "Mrs. Jaffe." The change from second to third person seems to have rendered the fantasy more distant and impersonal.

4. Tense

The defensive function of tense has long been recognized in the psychoanalytic rule of technique which says, in effect, "When the patient speaks of the past the analyst should speak in the present, and when the patient speaks in the present the analyst should speak of the past." This rule may apply to individual sentences [19] as well as to the larger divisions of lifetime, as follows:

An obsessional patient consistently reported his dreams in the past tense. The themes were generally hostile and aggressive, whereas his relationship to me was ingratiating and bland. Following the report of a dream I asked him to repeat the dream in the present tense. The following inter-change occurred:

Patient: "That would make it much more immediate . . . In the past tense it's not me, I can preserve some detachment from it. (one minute silence) I feel a definite resistance against doing this, I will in a few minutes, but I'm stalling for time before beginning, to insure control."

Doctor: "What makes it dangerous?"

Patient: "It would be doing what is so difficult for me . . . free associating . . . I have a feeling that in the present tense I might begin to act it out in reality . . . I can't be critical of the content and therefore am more vulnerable to attack."

In finally telling the dream there was a tendency to lapse into the past tense repeatedly.

Conversely, a primarily hysterial patient, with gross amnesia for childhood, consistently reported dramatic dreams in the present tense. Requiring this patient to relate her dreams in the past tense decreased their vividness and increased their psychological distance. The patient then experienced the dramatic dream events in the appropriate context of the forgotten past.

Lowenstein describes patients who speak in psychoanalytic cliches. They demonstrate a "paucity in the choice of verbs . . . without placing them in a temporal context, as for instance: '. . . this is homosexuality; this is a father fatigue, etc. . . .' Describing events in static, rather than in temporal or process terms, produces objectivity. This prevents experience of the event as an ongoing subjective process." [20]

In relation to this example, the emotional effects of the progressive present participle and participial adjectives should be noted. "He was smiling" evokes the actual experience to a greater extent than "He smiled." A patient who could comfortably describe "feelings of love" for her husband experienced anxiety when she tried to say "loving feelings." Her associations were that, ". . . Loving feels very private, participating, . . . feminine . . ."

5. Passive Constructions

These are grammatical distinctions which indicate the relation of the speaker to the action expressed. The interpersonal relationship which exists is often clarified, as follows:

a) A patient reported a visit to her family. "It was very warm and friendly. I was dancing with my uncle and brother. My mother came in and I ran to her and hugged her. My father entered and I hugged him and then there was a kiss." The impersonality of this final remark surprised the patient as she said it. Occurring in the second week of analysis, it immediately focused attention on a central problem.

b) Another patient stated that a man at a recent party had been "attracted by her" and quickly changed it to "attracted to her." Analysis of the slip revealed her fear of her seductiveness, necessitating the substitution of the less active preposition.

c) Another patient describing a visit, quickly changed the statement, "I went there," to "I found myself there." His reasons for disclaiming responsibility for the visit later became apparent.

d) Two female patients have spoken of putting their contraceptive diaphragms "on." When asked why they said "on" instead of "in," the first merely reported some feeling of discomfort leading to the choice of the word. The second said, "Putting it in is too literal, it would be like inserting it here, exposing myself. I'd rather refer to it as a garment."

e) A patient reported a long dream in which she told a man, "I don't want you to marry me." In summarizing the dream I rephrased the remark as, "I don't want to marry you." She clenched her fists and corrected me, repeating the original form of the statement. When asked what the difference was she said that in her version she had less to do with the rejection of the proposal. This summarized one of her problems with men.

6. Exaggeration and Lack of Commitment

These are placed in the same category because they are characteristic overall language patterns in hysterical and obsessive patients respectively.

a) A hysterical man, prone to subtle exaggeration, described driving 65 miles per hour on a road which I knew to have a maximum conceivable speed of 40 to 50. In retelling the story at the proper velocity, this patient had a definite feeling that he would not be understood, believed or responded to. This simple statement of actual events had never been an adequate stimulus to evoke parental interest in childhood. His attempts to communicate by exaggeration now result in people actually disbelieving him.

b) An obsessional patient would habitually say, "It seems to be so. I guess that is what happened. That might perhaps have occurred." He was describing events he knew to be true. He experienced anxiety when saying "I know," or "That did happen."

c) The uncommitted language pattern as an adaptation to illness has been studied by Weinstein and Kahn.[21] Taking as a prototype the sentence, "I am sick,"[22] they term various formal departures from it the "language of denial." Other investigations have shown that degree of committment or qualification can be reliably quantified in verbal materials.[23]

DISCUSSION

Psychoanalytic investigations of language have generally been concerned with the meaning of specific symbols. The advent of character analysis, and the current emphasis upon ego psychology have focused attention upon formal patterns or styles[24,25] of symbolic behavior. As a consequence, psycholinguistics and psychoanalytic research have developed an area of common interest.

The new discipline of psycholinguistics attempts to relate structure of a language to the psychological states of people who use it. Current theory posits a continuous interplay between language and experience. Thus language can be said to "express" that which is already formulated non-linguistically.[11] But conversely it can be shown that the structure of the language habitually used influences the way in which the environment is apprehended.[26] This may be illustrated by contrasting two hypothetical English-speaking persons stereotyped for purposes of exposition.

The first has been reared in a language environment characterized by decision, commitment, and absolutes. His voice is assertive, and his speech abounds in clear-cut "either-or" constructions. He speaks in absolutes, and uses few qualifying adverbs such as "perhaps" and "maybe." The latter make him uneasy because they seem vague and indefinite. He is intolerant of ambiguity, non-introspective, a man of action. His verbal structure may be said to "express" his mode of experience of himself and the world. In his logical structure any assertion implies the negation of its alternatives. However this person lacks the verbal, and presumably the conceptual tools to make subtle discriminations. A whole dimension of phenomenal experience is beyond him.

The second person has always been forced to be aware of shades of meaning, and of inconsistencies. His voice is hesitant and he prefers to speak in the third person, with subjunctives and qualifiers as in the sentence, "One might perhaps consider that." He is overintellectualized and introspective. Clear-cut alternatives distress him for they never seem to do justice to the complexity of the facts. His language is said to "express" a more tentative inner state. His linguistic and conceptual structure do not admit the possibility of commitment. He cannot give an unequivocal "yes" or "no." A firm stand is impossible since he can always identify to some extent with the opposition. His is a relative world, devoid of strong beliefs. He is indecisive and action-inhibited. He cannot experience powerful, uncomplicated emotion welded to action.

Thus language, thought and experience are intimately related in a formal sense. The psychoanalyst who interprets his patient's linguistic patterns is made dramatically aware of their function in maintaining psychological equilibrium. It is for this reason that a primarily verbal therapy is able to effect basic alteration of the patient's mode of experience of himself and the environment. But the change of his patient's language is not the psychoanalyst's goal. Speech is merely his instrument, a most easily available stream of behavior from which psychological processes may be inferred. What of therapies whose goal is specifically the modification of the patient's speech? To what extent can speech patterns be altered without specific attention to the language structures which play a key part in the psychological economy of an individual, and thus are necessary to his mental health? These and many other questions are raised by this paper.

REFERENCES

1 Eldred, S. H., and Price, D. B.: A linguistic evaluation of feeling states in psychotherapy. *Psychiatry,* 21:115-121, 1958.

2 Eldred, S. H.; Hamburg, D. A.; Inwood, E. R.; Salzman, L.; Myersburg, H. A. and Goodrich, G.: A procedure for the systematic analysis of psychotherapeutic interviews. *Psychiatry,* 17:337-345, 1954.

3 Whitehorn, J. C., and Zipf, G. K.: Schizophrenic language. *Arch. Neurol.* and *Psychiat.,* 49:831-51; 1943.

4 Jaffe, J.: Language of the Dyad: A method of interaction analysis in psychiatric interviews. *Psychiatry,* 21:249-258, 1958.

5 ——. An objective study of communication in psychiatric interviews. *Jour. Hillside Hosp.,* 6:207-215, 1957.

6 Mahl, G. F.: Disturbances and silences in the patient's speech in psychotherapy. *Jour. Abnor. and Social Psychol.,* 53:1-15, 1956.

7 Saslow, G.; Matarozzo, J. D., and Guze, S. B.: The stability of interaction chronograph patterns in psychiatric interviews. *Jour. Consult. Psychol.,* 19:417-430, 1955.

8 Balken, E. R., and Masserman, J. H.: The language of phantasy III: The language of phantasies of patients with conversion hysteria, anxiety state, and obsessive-compulsive neurosis. *Jour. Psychol.,* 10:75-86, 1940.

9 Goldman-Eisler, F.: A study of individual differences and of interaction in the behavior of some aspects of language interviews. *Jour. Ment. Sci.,* 100:177-197, 1954.

10 Gottschalk, L. A.; Gleser, G. C., and Hambridge, G.: Verbal behavior analysis. *Arch. Neurol. and Psychiat.,* 77:300-311, 1957.

11 Lorenz, M.: Expressive behavior and language patterns. *Psychiatry,* 18:353-366, 1955.

12 ——and Cobb, S.: Language patterns in psychotic and psychoneurotic subjects. *Arch. Neurol,* and *Psychiat.,* 72:665-673, 1954.

[13] BREUER, J. and FREUD, S.: *Studies in Hysteria,* New York, Nerv. & Ment. Dis. Monographs, 1950, pp. 210-211.

[14] FERENCZI, S.: On Obscene Words. In: *Sex in Psychoanalysis,* New York, Brunner, 1950, pp. 132-153.

[15] WEBSTER'S NEW COLLEGIATE DICTIONARY, Springfield, Mass., G. & C. Merriam & Co., 1956.

[16] KRAPF, E. E.: The choice of language in polyglot psychoanalysis. *Psychoan. Quart.,* 24:343-357, 1955.

[17] REIK, T.: Men and women speak different languages. *Psychoanalysis,* 2:3-15, 1954.

[18] JAFFE, J.: Communication networks in Freud's interview technique. *Psychiat. Quart.,* 32:456-473, 1958.

[19] STEIN, M. H.: The Cliche: A phenomenon of resistance. *Jour. Amer. Psychoanal. Assoc.,* 6:263-277, 1958.

[20] LOWENSTEIN, R. M.: Some thoughts on interpretation in the theory of practice of psychoanalysis. *Psychoanalytic Study of the Child,* 12:127-150, see pp. 128-129, 1957.

[21] WEINSTEIN, E. A., and KAHN, R. L.: *Denial of Illness: Symbolic and Physiologic Aspects,* Springfield, Ill., Charles C. Thomas, 1955.

[22] KAHN, R. L and FINK, M.: Changes in language during electroshock therapy. In: *Psychopathology of Communication.* New York, Grune and Stratton, 1957.

[23] JAFFE, J. and SLOTE, W. H.: Interpersonal factors in denial of illness. *Arch. of Neurol. and Psychiat.,* 30:653-656, 1958.

[24] THOMPSON, C.: *Psychoanalysis: Evolution and Development.* New York, Hermitage House, 1950.

[25] REICH, W.: *On character analysis.* In: R. Fleiss, (Ed.), *The Psychoanalytic Reader,* New York, International Universities Press, 1948.

[26] WHORF, B. L.: Language, Thought and Reality: *Selected Writings of Benjamin Lee Whorf,* New York, Wiley, 1956.

Stage Fright in a Musician: A Segment of an Analysis

by Samuel L. Safirstein, M.D.
American Institute for Psychoanalysis

Samuel L. Safirstein, M.D.

The author teaches psychiatry to non-psychiatric physicians at the American Institute of Psychoanalysis, and is Associate Attending Psychiatrist at Mount Sinai Hospital in New York City, where he is in charge of aftercare services in the Department of Psychiatry and Institute of Psychiatry. He is also engaged in private practice in psychoanalysis and psychotherapy.

HISTORY

MARY was thirty-four when she came to the Karen Horney Clinic. Her chief symptom was an intense fear of auditioning or performing in public despite six years of professional experience. Occasionally she would play for a small group of friends who knew and understood music. She could not practice for any length of time, but refused to give up music entirely.

Mary impressed her interviewers as desiring help. She was an attractive woman, well and neatly dressed, responsive to questioning but unspontaneous. She cried easily and indicated a great deal of internal turmoil. She felt desperate and lost. There was something tenacious and colorful in her to which I responded with a desire to help and treat her.

Mary, the eldest of three children, was born in the Southwest where she lived until the age of twenty-three. Her Protestant parents were from different economic and cultural backgrounds, and differed sharply in their personalities. She blamed them equally for her unhappy life. The father came from a poor family. He was now in the building-supply business and Mary saw him as deeply involved with the acquisition of money and worldly possessions. She also believed him to be crass, money mad, concerned with practicalities and financial success, insensitive to aesthetics, beauty, feelings, art, and spiritual qualities.

The mother came from a wealthy family. She was artistically inclined and had studied piano and ballet, all of which she gave up for the marriage that would take her away from her parents and home. While outwardly repudiating her own values and embracing those of her husband, she never lost an opportunity to remind him that she was better than he. She was very sensitive to status, prestige, and any external manifestations of wealth. She regretted that she had not pursued her study of piano and encouraged Mary in her musical career. Mary saw her mother as a severe, strict, rigid, rejecting, uninterested woman, mindful only of social status. No expression of angry feelings was tolerated, and when Mary used improper words she was made to wash her mouth with soap. She resented her mother's insistence on good manners. She felt that the only way she could express her anger was through her music, and it was then that she played her best.

Constant conflict between her parents and the internal conflict of the mother instilled rather early in Mary the feeling that she was unwanted. This fact her mother confirmed when Mary was twenty-two by saying that she came earlier than planned. Mary also experienced feelings of isolation and of not belonging.

Very early in life Mary rebelled. She was a stubborn child and recalls refusing to move her bowels or to urinate for days. On a few occasions she had to be catheterized.

She longed for someone strong on whom she could rely. Mary recalls a dream which she had at the age of three in which she was given an Indian chief's suit by an Indian chief. In the morning she ran to the dresser drawer expecting to find it. Her mother bought her one and for a long time Mary and her Indian suit were inseparable.

The poignancy of longing was such that she did not take it as a dream but as reality, a characteristic she experienced in most of the dreams in her later life.

When she did not find the suit in her dresser drawer she learned she could get it through crying. Crying became a lifelong pattern to which her father and mother responded by giving her what she wanted.

But what she wanted most was affection. This expressed itself in preoccupation with dolls. She spent most of the day playing with them and took them to bed with her at night. The parents were too busy quarreling and fighting to notice this need.

When she was five, her parents separated, and Mary stayed with her mother. After one year of separation the family reunited "on mother's terms," with her mother established as the dominant person in the household. From this time on, Mary began to spend a great deal of time in her Uncle Sam's house. He was a physician, a mild and considerate man whom she recalls with tenderness and affection. She began to take piano lessons, which both he and her mother encouraged. A short period of calm followed. The parents found a basis for living together after their reunion, and Mary had her uncle and her piano.

The birth of Mary's brother occurred when she was six and a half and was another disturbing influence in her life. Immediately he became the mother's favorite, and Mary's attitude toward him has continued to be one of intense hostility. The brother's birth coincided with the beginning of Mary's school life. Her rebellion found expression in a refusal to say a word in school for as long as two weeks at a time.

At the age of eight, Mary's sister was born. Mary was more accepting of her. About that time frequent moving began and changes in schools and music teachers followed. This period of instability continued over several years. She responded to it by disturbed body rhythm in the form of insomnia. At twelve she had her first menstrual period. She responded to this with severe pains and vomiting. These symptoms of insomnia and dysmenorrhea were forms of rebellion which stayed with her later in life.

At the age of twelve she also saw her brother struck by a car. He sustained a broken hip. She felt as though she were paralyzed, but she picked him up and carried him in to the house. He was in traction for one year. Moved partly by guilt for her hostility toward him and a desire to be good and incur favor and affection from her parents, she became his custodian. The brother was the center of attention and no one ever noticed her, despite all the work she put into caring for him. She again felt let down. Her hostility toward her brother became more intense. It found expression later on in dreams in which he molested her sexually. In one she smashed his picture. Her disparagement of her sister was more subtle, but not less real. Mary saw her as spineless, doing what she was told by her father, and interested only in saving money.

Mary found refuge in fantasy life. While practicing ballet and piano she saw herself as a fictitious character, usually someone with fame and success in the field of art. She became interested in the life of Chopin. In one fantasy she saw herself as a struggling pianist who lived in Paris. One day she fainted of hunger on the street and was picked up by Chopin, who nursed her back to health and became her patron. In this fantasy the solution of helplessness emerges. What she cannot get by crying she might get by being hungry, sick, helpless, suffering, and self-obliterating.

In the meantime, the piano became her whole life. She was completely absorbed by it. She played with abandon and practiced most of the time. She won prizes and several scholarships. She gave recitals and played as soloist with several orchestras. This all-out involvement with music, besides being a convenient way of submersion through activity, was also a way of obtaining recognition and affection through achieving success in the field of art. She could succeed where her mother failed, yet compete with her brother and sister for mother's affection.

But as she became a better pianist fears appeared. There were other good pianists. What if she could not keep up with them? What if she could not live up to what was expected of her? What if she were criticized? She had to be the only successful one. She began to resent her teacher's criticism and his corrective attempts.

She changed teachers several times. Her practicing began to lag. One day she gave a performance on a stage separated from the audience by a moat. At one point the piano stool tilted and she caught hold of the keyboard for fear of falling into the muddy water. She rebelled against the piano and expressed her fury and vengeance by abandoning the piano completely. Success meant performing in a field of limited competition where she was the best, the only one to get recognition, love and affection.

Mary was then nineteen. She could not give up her piano playing for long. Whatever recognition had come to her in life so far was through an instrument. She first took up the viola, then the cello. She was a beginner all over again. There were fewer cello players and the competition was minimal. She soon became promising as a cellist.

She met Luigi, a noted cellist, during one of his concerts. He suggested that she come to New York to study with him. She interrupted college, came to New York and worked with him for nine months. He encouraged her to take training leading to a master's degree. She returned home, completed her undergraduate degree in two years and enrolled in the school of music. She was then twenty-six. Luigi was her teacher in the music school. One year later she began to experience the same fears with the cello that she had with the piano. She was a good cellist among other good cellists, and not as outstanding as she had been in the West. She shrank from competition.

At the same time, Mary's relationship with Luigi became intimate and she had her first love affair with him. Her hopes for love and marriage were aroused. Luigi was married, but his wife was ill. He said he intended to divorce his wife and marry Mary. One year later he left his teaching position at the school of music and moved to New York. Mary interrupted her studies to follow him. During the next year she continued to study with Luigi, occasionally teaching and performing. Musically she was going downhill. She experienced more and more fear while performing and practicing. Luigi refused to divorce his wife and broke off with Mary.

She was again rejected and frustrated in her attempts to obtain love and affection. Recognition from music was meaningful only inasmuch as it led to love and affection. Her strivings in music contained her neurotic ambitions, the pursuit of glory, and her vengeful feelings, as well as the desperate struggle to come through as a person in her own right.

With the loss of Luigi's love she withdrew from music. Yet she could not give up completely. She stayed on in New York. She worked as a typist and played less and less. Her relations with people were difficult. She had frequent changes of jobs, many disappointing friendships. She felt helpless.

Her parents begged her to stay home but her rage and bitterness were at an all-time high. She openly defied them by refusing to return home, but bombarded them with letters and phone calls asking for financial assistance. She teased them by going home each summer and returning to New York in the fall. Returning home meant complete failure at being a person on her own and submitting to a loveless life.

She never gave up hope of continuing with her musical career. Yet her musical activities dwindled to a minimum. She developed a relationship with a musician, a pianist. She hoped to marry him. When he was indecisive about marriage for four years, she broke off with him. She was tired of struggling. Thoughts of suicide appeared. She was about to give up yet she could not. It was then that she came for treatment.

PROCESS: FIRST YEAR

The course of therapy was stormy and difficult. Mary was seen for a total of 200 hours, initially once a week, then twice weekly. She was a most willing patient, was almost always on time, and missed only two sessions.

During the first phase of analysis (one year; thirty-six sessions), I learned a good deal about her and a working relationship was established. She used dreams as a predominant way of expression. She promptly experienced her deep conflict between her needs for love and for grandiose achievements. She moved between extreme ups of hope and downs of despair. She began to use me as a stabilizer. What stood out in the foreground were her attempts to attach herself to me in a possessive way, by way of helplessness.

Her first therapist had left the Clinic after six sessions. She again felt deserted. She cried every night for several weeks. She called his office several times. In the six weeks she had attached herself completely to her therapist. She felt he was a savior, someone to hold on to for dear life. Through this quick and complete reliance on her therapist she experienced new hope and new motivation. When her therapist left this was one more "evidence" that one must not trust people.

In the second session with me she had a dream to report: "I was in an elevator which got stuck between floors. I pushed the emergency switch and began to float. With all my energy I pushed it down and my feet touched the floor. The elevator went down. The door opened and a man wanted to come in. I said, 'Don't, you'll be killed.' He came in anyway, and as the elevator moved he wanted out. He pushed the door, which was of rubber, and walked out."

Besides being a symbolic condensation of her relationship with her first therapist, the dream blue-printed her interpersonal conflict. Without another person to attach herself to she could only float aimlessly in life. The need to attach herself, to merge, was so strong, so all-encompassing, the grip on the other person so complete, that it amounted to a possessing and devouring. The symbolic killing of the other person could have two sources: the sheer violence of the hold, and the resentment for needing the other person so desperately. My response to this dream was one of anxiety.

The first reference to music came in the sixth session in the form of another dream: "I was on the bus with my cello and Civil Defense files. As I was leaving the bus, I took the files and left the cello." The warning was clear. She was not ready for any assertive expression, like music. She needed the defensive aspects (Civil Defense files) of her dependency and helplessness.

In the eighth session she expressed the other side of her conflict in the form of another dream: "I was a dancer and observer. Maria Tallchief was dancing 'The Firebird.' I was alone in the audience. She was in a red costume with red feathers. I yelled: 'Fire!' I located the fire and called the Fire Department." Here the expansive image of Mary as the great artist and flashy performer emerges. It is experienced as a dreadful threat, and it has to be extinguished.

In these last dreams Mary painted her internal conflict very quickly. Having failed to obtain love, she rebelled by resigning from music. Love and music are intertwined. She cannot play unless she can feel she is loved. Love means to her merging with another person, a man. She will reenact it with men as she did with others in the past. This is exactly what she proceeded to do. She did it compulsively, through helplessness and misery. She expressed discouragement about music and played the cello. She bitterly complained about her stage fright and how this stood in her way. She felt abused by the slightest criticism from people. She felt people did not understand her and that men deserted her as soon as she needed help from them.

Next, she began to voice complaints about me. I was being too clinical; she could not influence my facial expression; was I strong enough for her to trust me; would I reject her as the others had?

In her dreams the merger was effected: "I was married to you or was your housekeeper. Dozens of children were asking me to play with them. Here I looked up and you were standing calm. When I saw you I calmed down, too, and the rest didn't matter." The rest did matter because she expected the same in return. In other dreams I was making love to her, giving her food, candy, gifts. I was taking her with me in cars, planes, rockets. During sessions she wanted to know more about me personally, my age, country of origin, marital status, and so forth.

When her fantastic expectations did not materialize, she felt rejected and reacted with rage. "Either you make love to me or I try to kill you," she exclaimed after a dream in which she was having a love affair with Marlon Brando. Following this she became depressed.

Death and suicide appeared in her dreams and/or associations. She feared insanity. She had abdominal cramps and headaches. She bombarded me with her difficulties at work, the indifference of her boss. She even changed jobs. She complained about poverty and feared eviction from her apartment. She reenacted the Chopin fantasy with me, as if to say that if she were desperate enough a man would rescue her. She believed that if she made a suicidal attempt and someone called me, I could come and pull her out of it.

Slowly her mood improved to allow for emergence of an expansive, glorified self. She began taking dancing lessons. In one dream she was Margaret Truman, covered with diamonds, the queen of the ball. The allusion to music was there, but distant. A roundabout way through dancing was less threatening. She stated that she feared playing the cello because there she had to excel.

Her attempts to attach herself to me continued unabated. She left her job and decided to work for a doctor, preferably a psychiatrist. With the coming of the summer she decided to go home and stay temporarily attached to her family until the resumption of therapy in the fall. Her hopes were high, grandiose. She expressed them in a dream prior to the summer vacation, in which she and her family entered a white building, took the elevator, and went up to the top, the sixteenth floor. While on top she wondered how such a feeble foundation could support such a tall building. I thought she was on the verge of making another attempt to obtain love from her parents, the kind of exclusive, possessive, and all-encompassing love which she had begun to sense had little reality, little likelihood of achievement.

THE SECOND YEAR

In the second phase of therapy (one year; forty-two sessions), there was a desire to achieve success through musical performing. It was wrought with the same compulsivity to be the most accomplished performer. However, each attempt at assertive performing clashed head-on with her strong, clinging, dependent needs. She felt a pull in the opposite direction, the expression of which was self-contempt, depression, and accident-proneness. She experienced it in the externalized form; that is, outside people, mostly men, would not permit her to succeed and tried to destroy her achievements. Mary handled this head-on collision by resignation inertia, and depression of her living processes. In essence, she repeated her withdrawal from the piano and later from the cello, when she became proficient at it. Her needs for ease and uninvolvement came through. This time all these events took place in the therapeutic setting and relationship. Her need for me continued to be great.

The summer at home was revealing to her. She met with acceptance and warmth. For the first time it occurred to her that she might have been too critical of her father. "I was behind with some bills and he helped. I never asked him for help. I screamed at him. Mother yells at him. I never could talk to him. I considered him a red-painted Indian." She felt uplifted and immediately upon her return to New York, she found a job as typist for an orthopedic surgeon. She also ventured, for the first time in seven years, to play the cello and performed in a trio at a hotel. She was surprised at how easily it all came back to her.

These positive and assertive moves were too much for her and her reaction was instantaneous. She brought in two dreams in which a man was trying to shoot her, and she followed them by another dream in which Basil Rathbone held her captive and tried to take away her cello. She began having serious difficulties with her new employer. Next, her anger toward me found expression. I was asking too many questions, was not giving her enough time, and I looked bored with her. It was clear that she experienced men as frustrating her self-assertive aspirations and as robbing her of her desire to play, perform, work, and develop. Her anxiety markedly increased. She had a dream in which a little girl committed suicide while others looked on. The foundation of the solution of being the helpless, suffering child was shaking. She needed more closeness with me. She asked for an extra session in my office for which she paid. Although she felt better after the session, she was full of hatred because she had to pay despite financial difficulties. She also saw money as a restricting element in her music because she had to depend on father to pay for her musical instruction and instruments, another way in which men wielded power over her. She asked for another private session, on credit, and I agreed. She decided to write to her father for a "loan." She was sure she needed a man, the kind of man who gave, but had no power over her. She began to look around for a possible candidate.

She fell back on her solution of helplessness and of possessing a man.

She had another dream about me, "I was going to your office; it was raining. I was wearing slacks and took along clothes to wear when I got there. I went to your bedroom. There were twin beds with pink spreads. I was naked when I heard footsteps. I made a dash to close the door. You walked by. I thought, now he saw everything there is to see. When I walked into your office you said 'There is nothing like having a twenty-five minute session. The other half you spend undressing.'" She wondered whether it might be that she was wasting half of her time in sessions.

This was an important dream indicating change. Although she still wanted me on the primitive, sensual level, the only way she felt a man could relate to her, the door was opened to a different kind of relationship, the therapeutic relationship. She sensed she could perhaps better utilize her time with me and perhaps uncover herself further.

The door was opened also in relation to her musical performing. She began to practice in preparation for a solo appearance. The desire to perform was great, but the opposing forces were equally great. She experienced anxiety in its free-floating form and in the form of palpitations and other somatic symptoms. But she gave her concert. Here is how she experienced it: "The only time I had fear was when I sat down to play. Later I played with abandon and enjoyment. I plan to play quartets and look for a job with an orchestra."

That night she had two dreams. First "I was sleeping with my sister in a double bed. There were cockroaches crawling in the sheets. I hit a big one and it spat out a number of small roaches. I woke her up to help me get rid of the bugs. She was sleepy. I was all set to kill the bugs. I woke up." And second: "I was at the Academy of Music with this singer I know. I said to him we must do the Villa Lobos number for eight cellos. He said we could do it in Town Hall. I said, no, we will do it at Carnegie Hall. I want to do the solo part."

In these dreams there was an open clash between her glorified and despised selves. She tried to solve her conflict by killing her despicable dependency and helplessness. She tried to put forward her glorified musical expansiveness. She wanted to reach the heights as a solo performer.

The self-punitive process for such daring strivings followed immediately. Right after the concert she sprained an ankle and came down with several consecutive colds. She went into a depression and did not touch the cello for ten weeks.

The experience of the acute clash between her opposing trends threatened her with disintegration. She had to depress her daring aspirations and seek refuge in inertia. In the classical literature, this is known as the negative therapeutic reaction.

While depressed, she continued to struggle with her conflict and made attempts at solving it in dreams and fantasy. She had several dreams about planes, missiles, saucers; she planned to devote all her time to a musical career (expansive solution). She talked about how good it would be to have a man, be loved and cared for by him; she had several unsuccessful dates (self-effacing solution). She remained inert and resigned.

She then reported two dreams. In the first she was floating in a bathtub twice as long as she. She was reading a book and felt good. She decided to practice floating. Suddenly her face went under water. She became panicky. In the second dream she was with her family, about to move from one house to another. The old house contained an upright piano and two books of music, one old and the other a Schirmer edition of Chopin. It came to her that they could move but that she would stay put. In her associations she compared life to water and swimming. She identified me with Chopin. We were both born in Poland and lived in France. To move to new surroundings was fearful. The old and familiar felt more secure. To float inertly was easier than to swim. To "stay put" with minimum exertion seemed more appealing than to move actively toward music. She felt like staying with me, to reenact her Chopin fantasy. She did not want to struggle. "I think I became depressed at the prospect of doing something with my music. If I do, I don't want to struggle with it. Music to me is a big struggle." All she could tolerate was a minimum of activity, but even this met with self-criticism and self-derogation.

She practiced on and off. She was asked to join an orchestra in the process of being formed. She accepted. In connection with rehearsals several accidents happened to her. Her bow "disintegrated," the peg broke, she got lost and could not find the place of rehearsal, she had migraine headaches, neuralgia, broke out in hives and feared insanity. She missed phone calls with offers of musical jobs. The difficulties with her boss became unbearable. She wanted the kind of recognition which he apparently refused to give. Mary quit her job and piled up all these obstructions to movement to convince me and herself that she did not want to struggle. She had to remain uninvolved, inert, resigned. Her dependency needs supported the inertia. She then decided to become a model, a doll.

When she tried to go to modeling school to become a model she was told she was not modeling material. She liked the idea of parading in front of people in different apparel. She had a few dreams in which she was trying on different hats and multicolored dresses with all kinds of jewelry. In another dream she was a Japanese doll modeling a long silk dress. In discussing the dream, she brought out her ideas of femininity. Women are dolls, taken care of, have no brains, are careless. She juxtaposed her dream about the Indian chief, the man, who does the taking care of, is the head of the tribe, and has everyone answering to him. He is the boss and the master. In another dream she was lying naked in bed with a jewelry box. A faceless man was draping her all over with jewels.

These dreams demonstrated the rigidity of her concepts of men and women and the gulf that separated them. She could not tolerate her symbol of the woman who is all doll, helpless, taken care of, covered with jewels, and delegated to the bed and the kitchen.

She began to fear that she wanted to be a doll, a kept

woman, a prostitute. She tried to do something about it. After four weeks without a job she began to work for two opthalmologists.

She gave a solo concert in a hospital. "It was formal. I played well. I was looking at the audience. Ha, ha. They didn't know I will tell my analyst about it tomorrow. I wasn't scared until I walked out on the stage. I was a little shaky, my pulse was rapid. It lasted but wasn't paralyzing. I didn't miss, no lapse of memory. When I was bowing I was glad these people were there and I was playing. I had less of a feeling of playing a role. I still felt dressed up like a doll. I want to play before a real audience."

The opening sentence of the following session was: "I feel like hell, hell, hell! Oh God, what am I going to do about money! I feel like going home for the whole summer and being fed by father." She wanted it easy. She was making plans to go home. She externalized her own obstruction to movement. She felt her father would not permit her to come back to New York in the fall and that I would refuse to resume treatment.

Father sent her money. She paid off some of her debts and bought her plane ticket. Now she was sure he would reproach her for the money. She wanted ease, but her self-critical attitude did not permit her to accept it. Her next dream documented this. In it she used up her last money to buy popcorn and had none left to go home. She asked father for more. He had a pained expression, but gave her his key chain with a dime and a nickel on it. She felt she took his last penny. Upon arriving home she was greeted by her Uncle Sam. She told him that he was not her uncle and turned away from him.

She played a concert with the new orchestra. Her dependent needs, as well as her desire for ease, found expression in a feeling that she was falling in love with the conductor.

In her next dream she came to her session late, but I came even later. I then threw her on the couch and tried to rape her. At first she liked it, but then she thought I could not continue being her analyst. She pushed me away. She told me she felt it was "lewd and disgraceful." She felt it was an attempt to downgrade me. My reflections on this dream led me to believe that Mary did not experience me as supportive of her inertia, resignation, and desire for ease. This was another externalization to me of her own self-derogatory attitude toward this way of life. Could she be seeing me as attempting to "rape" her into active living?

Whether this was so or not, she had made up her mind to take it easy, to be passive and inert, and to let someone else do the work for her.

Before leaving she was able to report, "All's quiet on the western front." In the last session she brought her camera and took my picture. She reported a dream in which I was in Montmartre Cathedral and she was coming toward me. She expressed the feeling that I was going to lead her out of the mess she had been in. "I can breathe easy now."

At the end of the second year of therapy, Mary again settled for a rest in the shadow of her parents. I welcomed the rest myself. I felt she had moved a good deal in the past year. Although her relationship with me was still predominantly expressed in erotic symbols, she felt more secure in it and was able to venture out much more.

She feared being dependent and was terrified of standing alone. It was to her an either/or situation. She craved a relationship with a man, but could not enter into it, as it could only be that she was dominated or dominating. She was able to take steps in the direction of resuming her music. With each successful step her expansiveness and grandiosity became apparent. But this contradicted the symbol of dependent doll.

As her dependency was probed, uncovered and undermined, her solution of resignation became more apparent.

I was much more comfortable with her as I came to understand her better. I felt her well anchored in therapy.

THE THIRD YEAR

In the course of the third year (fifty-three hours), Mary made several important moves. Although she desired resigned living, she found it unacceptable. This was exactly what her parents wanted for her. She wanted their love and affection and also to be herself. Being herself was connected with being assertive and being a musician. Being a musician was symbolized by being a man and this, in turn, rigidly opposed her symbol of femininity, the woman-doll who is loved and cared for. She made serious attempts to work through the polarity of these symbolic representations. In this process she came closer to herself and me. She used her sexual feelings toward me as symbolic moves toward an attempt at solution. She made strides in loosening and softening up the powerful father symbol in her.

She was in deep conflict when we resumed our sessions. Resigned living in the shadow of her parents held more appeal in her fantasy than in real life. While home she experienced her wish for inertia as an oppressive attitude imposed on her by her parents. She could not practice the cello and had one session with a local psychiatrist. "Mother was jealous of my music and father tried to give me advice to settle down, not to change jobs so often, and to save money. I have the same old feeling of a machine that is jammed." Once more she held her parents responsible for her not being able to play and perform. Mother resented her for achieving what she herself could never achieve and father hated her for not espousing his own standards of money making. Both parents in her mind stood for her own resigned trends.

All Mary could realize after her visit home was how utterly dependent she was on her parents and how they did not approve of her. She decided she must counteract these dependency needs by putting more value on her own thoughts and looking less to authorities. She was offered a permanent job in an orchestra in the West which she refused. This was too close to her parents. Yet as soon as she returned to New York she felt homesick. She again wanted someone to take care of her, a man to marry her, and give her love and affection. She followed it up with a dream which illustrated the horror of such eventuality. "I was in the living room of a big house, in front of a fireplace. To the left was a picture window. Outside there was a girl with a bridal gown. I knew she was a ghost. She beckoned me to come with her. Then she came into the room through the window. I still knew she was a ghost but I was no longer afraid of her. We all followed her to a grave with an open casket. We watched her get into it and lower the lid. Father opened the lid and out came a seven-year-old girl, a real girl." To resign herself to marriage was tantamount to dying. This is what she felt father had in mind for her.

In order not to be resigned to marriage and inert living, she had to be assertive and aggressive. But only men can be assertive and aggressive. In order to play the cello she had to be assertive and aggressive. This was being like a man. "One cannot be a cellist and a woman. When I am doing well in music I am not interested in men and vice versa." She admitted having had frequent dreams in the past in which she turned into a man. Her parents wanted a boy when she was born and were partial to her brother. "When brother was born I died. I am the girl in the coffin. It's the bride who gets all the attention. I have this man-woman conflict. I don't know what or where I am."

Mary was experiencing not only the leaden weight of her resignation reinforced by dependency; she also reactivated her deep, frustrated longings for love and affection which she was unable to get from her parents. If she had been a boy, like her brother, love would have come easily. Her next chance at obtaining parental love was through compliance with her parents' wishes for her to marry. Perhaps as a bride she would obtain what had been unobtainable so far. Brother-man symbolized being loved and accepted. Doll-woman stood for rejection and self-contempt.

A period of marked turbulence followed.

At that time a girl friend of Mary's who was in psychiatric treatment made a suicidal attempt. She was institutionalized. Mary took it very hard. It further activated her self-contempt through identification, and she expressed feelings of guilt and responsibility for her girl friend's action. She made weekly visits to her girl friend in the hospital, but was afraid of retaliation once her friend was released. That is when I began to see Mary twice weekly. Several months later she severed their relationship on the basis that her friend was too sick.

During these turbulent times Mary expressed her self-contempt in the form of self-frustration, self-destructiveness, and self-mutilation. She kept practicing in preparation for a concert.

However, one day before the concert date she cut her finger and could not play. She also bumped her head against a cabinet in her apartment and passed out for a couple of minutes. She saw these events as the expression of her fear of performing in public.

She reacted to all this with a period of expansiveness and elation. She tried to do more about her music, and also go out with men. She felt she was in love with her boss and had the urge to go to bed with the orchestra conductor. She was taking flamenco lessons.

She played two more concerts. She came out with more evidence that being a woman meant resignation and death. "Playing the cello means expressing strong feelings. I can't stand it. This is not feminine. I fear my feelings are running away with me. Getting close to feelings means getting close to people. They are going to clutch me and I won't be able to get away. If I express and examine feelings, this means taking a chance on you. I can't stand success. I am playing with an orchestra. It may be a success. I am scared. I feel no damn good as a person. How can I feel good as a musician?" She also restated that coming to life is connected with getting involved with people who are experienced by her as "swallowing" and destructive of her selfness.

A dream followed which indicated a very important move in therapy. Mother called her to have lunch with father right away. She could not. Mother insisted. Mary hung up on her in tears. Next she was on the lawn playing with her cat. She let me pick him up and play with him. I had my arm around her reassuringly. She was sad. We came to the Clinic where I told her I would be away for two weeks. She said in association: "I feel I had to make the choice between you and father. His love depended upon what he wanted me to do. You gave me the feeling I can do what I want to do and your feelings will not depend on what I'll do. My cat never goes for men. I am leaving father for you. But you don't act like a father."

In this dream Mary indicated the beginning of a breaking up of her solutions, a rearrangement of her symbols, and a movement toward herself. Could she dare to be sufficiently busy with herself as to oppose a relatively trivial wish of her mother's? Could she substitute the father symbol, which stood for resignation, for the therapist symbol, which stood for movement? In the past she had felt she did not need to commit herself to anything, but could restrict her activity to fantasy, either dreaming of glory or feeling abused. Now, was there perhaps a possibility of becoming involved more actively with people and living, of which her therapist was the expression? I felt that Mary hesitatingly and tentatively answered "yes" to these questions. In the reassuring climate of our relationship she might permit me to play with her. She used for herself the symbol of a cat, popularly charged with sexual overtones. She might try to find out to what purpose I would use our "play."

She began to experience the division between the masculine and feminine in her. She tried to utilize the sexual feelings as symbolic moves toward another attempt at solution of her conflicts. She was dating several men. She saw her need to fight them and win.

"The crevice is widening. I have one foot on one side and the other foot on the other side." She saw sex as cruel and giving the man the upper hand. The man was wielding power over the woman. During sexual intercourse she had the feeling of being forced into something; a person's intellect goes during intercourse. "The result of lovemaking is sinking, floating, and having no ground." Masturbation was much easier. This was more like being a child. She wondered if she might not have sexual feelings toward her father. She became frightened, expressed fears of dying, and bcame depressed. I did not think that the idea of seducing her father was novel to her. She more than once exploited her father and felt guilty about it (the popcorn dream). This time she experienced it. Seduction of father was unacceptable to her, anyway.

In the next session she came all dressed up, smelling of perfume, and decided to use the couch. This was the only time she used the couch. In the following session she had hoped to seduce me this way. She again expressed fear that I would not return to the Clinic in the fall. I passed the test successfully. Now she felt that I would retaliate by refusing to see her in treatment.

The direct approach having failed, she tried an externalized version of it. She expressed it in a dream. "I went to the Clinic and instead of going upstairs we went to the garden. I sat on a bench next to you. I couldn't sit still and began to walk. I came back to you and you said you couldn't see me because you were in love with me. I asked, 'Can't you forget it?' You said, 'You'll get another therapist.' I said I didn't want another therapist and you grabbed me in a passionate embrace." She could remotely sense that in her testing of whether I would be like her father her therapy was at stake. If she could not bring me down to her father's size, could she perhaps bring father to my size? To put it in intrapsychic terms, was she on her way toward deglorifying the symbol of man and elevating the symbol of woman?

Mary played another concert well. "Playing and the Indian chief seemed to be the key to the whole business of the conflict between man and woman. When I play well I am a show-off, a man. Then I can no longer be attractive as a woman. A woman is a fragile little flower. She cannot be in control. If I show off they'll find out I am aggressive and will refuse to know me socially. I wonder if I see all men as I see my father, on Mt. Olympus, and whom I want to slay. Oh, I feel like twenty pounds lifted off my chest." I felt that her great feeling of relief stemmed from a loosening up of the rigidity of her masculine and feminine symbolism.

In the last session before summer vacation she brought in her sister, who was visiting New York. She wanted me to meet her. Mary did not go home that summer.

At the end of three years of treatment (131 hours), Mary was well on her way in experiencing her conflict as symbolized by the Indian chief and the Japanese doll. The addition of another session weekly was most valuable. She could reveal more, since she was not left a whole week alone with her anxieties. She could now tolerate anxiety better.

THE FOURTH YEAR

Upon resumption of therapy, it became apparent what Mary was attempting to do, once her symbol of masculinity had weakened and softened. She tried to move in and take over. It permitted her aggressive tendencies to have freer play.

She stayed that summer in New York City. She greeted me in the fall with the statement that she now could play without anxiety and therefore did not miss me. She had met many men, but "nothing happened." She was thinking of going to live in Mexico, where men were plentiful. She reported a dream in which I beat her to make her go away. She felt negative about continuing therapy, saying that there was a point in involvement with me beyond which she could not go. I looked strange to her and she felt she was just beginning therapy. Her boss had announced plans to marry. Where did this leave her? "There are stupid fish it's easy to catch. These I don't want. It's those that are hard to catch that I want." In the next dream she tried to unzip her boss' pants.

After she played her next concert she received compliments about being soft and feminine. She felt she did not deserve them. She saw herself as aggressive, domineering. She now identified herself with the male. She could be as aggressive and self-sufficient as he. She could now conquer men if she so chose. She could play the cello without fear and felt self-sufficient. She could do without me and treatment. She wanted to cohabit with me, but on a "mutual basis." She discussed love with me. "The only love I know is sexual. You try to give me the kind of love I don't understand. Maybe I fear that if I let my feelings come out everyone would run from me, including you. Yet it's I who run."

She portrayed aggressive and rebellious behavior. She had fights with her boss, the nurse in charge of the office, and accused me of trying to rape her.

I sensed a feeling of power in her sexual feelings toward me and that she was trying to get power over me.

Two weeks later: "Help! A man is after me. He is a cellist, reminds me of you. He has the same complexion. He is interested in me. I want to run." That night she had a dream: "Someone broke into my apartment and stole a chair slipcover, the telephone books, and half of my music." Of the chair, she said it was the one she used most often, in which she rests, listens to music, and watches TV. About the phone books she said that now she could not go to people as much, and of the music, this was her creativeness. Another dream followed: "I was going to sing Carmen. I told my mother I couldn't do it. I can't act the part. I called the voice teacher, a woman, and told her I can't sing. She said, 'We will get someone else.'" She said that Carmen was a girl who did not know what she wanted. She threw herself at everyone.

What she portrayed in these two dreams was how she experienced involvement with a man. He might rob her of her newly acquired cover of aggressiveness, self-sufficiency, and musicianship. He might again reduce her to the helpless, dependent, resigned, and inert doll-woman. She could not and would not be the kind of Carmen who does not know what she wants and who needs men in order to live and function. Mary wanted to be in control, in charge, to possess and own the man. Short of that, she would have to fall back into the resigned and dependent girl.

A stormy courtship followed. Mary was discovering that a man can be tender, considerate, and loving. She was able to enjoy lovemaking and sexual intercourse. She still was far from relaxed. "What if he does not ask to marry me. I am not in control. I feel helpless. I want to own him; I want a showdown. Till I have a wedding ring I cannot put all my eggs in one basket. What if he does want to marry me. In marriage you can't run. Either I depend on him or he depends on me. Either I am the mother or the child, either the man or the woman."

The man, George, was leaving on tour. When she brought up marriage he told her he felt married to her already but would make arrangements for a formal wedding in June. More doubts set in. Was she marrying George or me? Now she would have to choose between him and me. There was no room for the two of us together. She still felt she wanted to go to bed with me, so how could she be in love with George and marry him? She wanted to leave therapy.

She had to control and overpower not just one man. She had the compulsive need to control me as well—all men. Her fear, her terror of involvement was so great that she had to keep her allegiances in compartments. She could not "put all her eggs in one basket," yet she had to choose between George and me; she experienced us as mutually exclusive. She had to do something about it.

She brought in a dream: "I was happy, singing, and I was trying to seduce you. You were in a chair. A woman was standing behind you, your wife. I had to vie with her. I embraced you and at the same time looked for an erection. I and the woman tried, but I won. I woke up." In association she said: "still want to go to bed with you, but it can't be done. We have had many lessons in the past four years. I never could get a rise out of you. For four years you said nothing. There is no room for two men. I have a headache."

She solved the situation by vying for me and winning me away from my wife. Only after having conquered me could she begin to entertain the idea of letting go of me for George. After this dream she gave up her active attempts to seduce me. Her fear of involvement with George was still great.

She auditioned for an orchestra that was going on tour and was accepted. She was leaving for eight weeks. She said, "This is the beginning of my life. I am driven to be absolutely perfect as a musician. I now have all the eggs in one basket. At rehearsals I feel surrounded by enemy camps. I feel they are better." That night she had this dream: "I was with the orchestra ready to go on stage. Mother was dress mistress, but my dress was not ready. When it finally came it was very tight. My right arm was glued to my side. How can I play if it is glued to my side?" In her associations she said: "The conductor implied I might be the first cello on the tour and I am scared of the responsibility. I feel musicians are critical. This distracts me from playing. I say I am afraid of failing. How about being afraid of succeeding? With my music I defy father out and out. People and George say I am a better cellist than he. A friend told me not to get too good. I might end in divorce."

This castration dream can be seen as an expression of her fear of involvement with music. She was accepted as a competent musician and felt she must successfully compete with other musicians around her. She must slay all the men whom she placed on Mt. Olympus, including her father. Such complete involvement with her aims and goals could only bring retaliation, mostly from father, in terms of reducing her to impotence, because she was taking on his, a man's, prerogatives. But it could also bring retaliation from mother, who could not permit Mary to become what she herself never could be.

Before leaving on tour she made sure that she could come back to continue in therapy.

At the beginning of the tour she discovered she was pregnant and arranged with George for a wedding between concerts. Four days before the wedding she spontaneously aborted and had to have a dilation and curettage of the uterus. George substituted for her for the rest of the tour. Her parents arrived for the wedding, which took place in New York.

Mary had no problems with stage fright during her tour. She was the best of the three cellists, made many contacts and felt "things looked good." She did not need treatment, and did not feel the need to call me when all these difficult events took place. When I indicated doubts, she again repeated that there was no room for George and me, that she felt like saying, "Who needs you?" and walked out on me. She said I was like the evil eye. She did not want to put up with me but would not leave loose ends to bother her later.

This apparently nonchalant attitude toward treatment soon changed into a cry for help when difficulties with George appeared. Her unresolved competitive and perfectionistic strivings came to the foreground in terms of George. She not only compared him with me, but also with Luigi. George came out second best. She knew she was a better cellist than he, yet he got most of the jobs. At times she saw him as a dictator trying to change her into a helpless child. At other times she saw him as a helpless baby whom she had to mother. All along I had the feeling that she was interested in her marriage and wanted to preserve it. She took a temporary job as a typist again, but practiced the cello very actively. There were financial difficulties.

She decided to consult the minister who married them. She thought highly of him and felt he could help her better with problems of everyday living. The minister was sympathetic, listened to her story, and counselled that since the man is the head of the household, it would help the marriage if he were in charge of all money matters. He then proceeded to talk to her about religion.

God is a person of infinite kindness, with infinite resources; it is good to unload one's troubles onto Him. This was the essence of the lengthy talk he gave her. When she left him she was floating on air. "Everything was lifted away from me. I felt guilty no more. I felt an accepted member of the human race." That night she had a dream in which she was going to her appointment with the minister. As she was entering the church, he was leaving. He did not recognize her and when she reminded him of the appointment he told her he had no time and left. She could not understand the discrepancy between the dream and the reality.

The following night she had another dream: "I was in a taxi with George's cello, driving on a snow-covered road. We came to a fork. The driver took the wrong, muddy road. I knew it was the wrong road, but let him do it. We came to a dead end. He sat there doing nothing. At first I sat there, too. Then I went in for help to a farmhouse. I told them that the idiot driver is not going to get me where I want to go. I went back to the taxi and there he was casually smoking a cigarette. The cello was upside down. I was horror stricken. I turned over the cello and walked off with it, back to the fork. I stood there trying to get a ride. I woke up."

Her associations and feelings were that she was eager to take the easy way out and permit herself to be driven. This could only lead to a dead-end street. She had to commit herself, do something on her own, with her cello and George.

The two dreams vividly illustrate Mary's intrapsychic conflict. She was ready to respond once more to the Almighty Father, throw herself into His arms, and lead a carefree life ever after. The first dream repudiated this solution. In the externalized form she gave a cold shoulder to father. The second dream gave symbolic expression to both arms of her conflict. She had to retrace her road in the course of therapy. She regained her music. The main obstacles to overcome were deep involvement and commitment to both music and George.

Then she and George auditioned for a six-months' tour and both were accepted. A dream followed in which she was playing in a huge auditorium, the Taj Mahal. During her associations an emotional crisis took place. She cried bitterly about the fact that if she were to play in a big auditorium she could never get through the performance, that she had no right to have a good marriage or good things happen to her. That night she had a dream in which her father died. Again with great emotion and tears she realized how her father did help her, always did. She again must not succeed for fear she will be hated for it, especially by George.

In the Taj Mahal dream Mary synthesized her conflict. The Taj Mahal symbol stood for love and grandiosity. Shah Jehan built this, one of the most beautiful structures in the world, for his beloved wife and himself. In one stroke Mary achieved love and fame. This is what she hoped for and expected from her marriage with George. Prior to embarking on this journey, she had to rid herself of the symbolic father who stood in her way as the exponent of resignation. Perhaps this could help her to put all her eggs in one basket, the basket which would take her and George to the Taj Mahal.

After the summer, Mary and George were preparing to leave on tour at the end of October. The question of continuation of therapy was discussed. She was confronted with my inability to keep her hours open for more than six months. In a letter the director of the Clinic told her that she could return to the Clinic if she needed further help, but that I might not have any free hours.

She missed the following session. She had the feeling that I had died and she was in mourning. She was depressed during the last session, but looked forward to her tour. She declared that when she returned from tour she would want private treatment with me or "someone else."

At Christmastime, I received a card with a long note. Musically and financially things were fine. She had had some violent fights with George, but most of the time they were getting along well. She hoped she would be able to continue with therapy at "some future date."

Two months after she returned from her tour she called me and I saw her privately. George had been accepted as a member of an orchestra in the South. She had applied for a teaching scholarship and was going to teach in the same city. Her stage fright had been completely absent throughout the tour. She felt completely satisfied as a musician. She was having some difficulties with her husband. She came to see me mainly because she wanted some advice on how to get George interested in therapy or counseling. She did not mention any interest in further therapy for herself.

PSYCHODYNAMICS

Psychodynamically, diagnosis concerns itself with conflict. Usually it is conflict between compulsive, deeply imbedded, and incompatible character trends. Harold Kelman emphasizes the process of continued changing in the course of therapy, and the need to discern the subtle changes taking place in the personality make-up.[1] Grossly speaking, the conflict in Mary was between her self-effacing, morbidly dependent, and aggressive-expansive trends. She is basically a feminine woman who, in the course of her early life, decided she must not be so. A reactive masculine-aggressive trend developed which brought her into irreconcilable conflict. The important characteristic of her conflict was that it had been acute and alive, and that she had kept fighting. Despite pain and disappointment, she had not given up and episodes of resignation were rare and short-lived. This offered better than average therapeutic opportunities. She was able to experience her conflict in the therapeutic relationship until certain changes in the conflict and her character structure became apparent.

Resigned trends emerged as an important factor in the therapeutic process. They did not permit involvement with and commitment to either her self-effacing, feminine solution, or with her expansive, masculine solution. Neither did they allow her to come close to love, music, people, and therapy. At first, resignation as a solution was not apparent. It was masked by and merged with her self-effacing and dependent trends. She not only craved love and affection, but used it as a means to justify inertia, inactivity, shallow living, and being cared for. Resignation developed when her reactive expansiveness came in strong conflict with her basic, unfulfilled need for love. She had to resort to resignation in order not to experience the acuteness of these incompatible, powerful feelings. It is therefore more accurate to state that her main conflict consisted of the opposition of dependency-resignation with expansion-aggression.

Most of her hopes, strivings, and ambitions had to do with playing an instrument. All the dynamisms of her personality reverberated in her musical activities. She was willing and eager to work and to develop musically. The piano was her mother's choice. As Mary became more proficient at it, a threat to her dependence on mother set in. She must not be better than mother, as this was tantamount to being independent and isolated from mother and eventually being alone. This is a frequent characteristic of the morbidly dependent personality. There are few people in our culture who are satisfied with being dependent and self-effacing. The next step is a compensatory drive for independence and success. This includes elements of healthy, self-assertive behavior and the desire to be oneself. Mary feared her success as a pianist, or anything that would put her on her own. A change of instruments seemed a possible solution. The piano had the connotations of femininity, someone akin to her mother. The viola and then the cello were the symbols of masculinity, strength, the Indian chief, assertiveness and rebellion against the existing order of things. It worked fine until again it looked as though she were going to be successful. She had to shrink and withdraw before she became successful. Success meant becoming involved with her music. What stands out is fear of involvement and commitment.

Mary was not aware of this. What she constantly repeated was that she might not play well enough, that she would be criticized. Another fear was that if she gave a good performance she would be in the limelight and more would be expected of her. With each expectation, mostly her own, to be better and closer to perfect, she would move farther and farther away from her basic dependent needs. Being dependent on another person was, in her mind, not only being weak, vulnerable, open to exploitation, being the underdog, raped, violated, and taken advantage of, but also being feminine, delegated to the kitchen, doing menial jobs, being the servant of a man.

Submission to a composer, a director, to practicing, or to any directive put her in the despised position of femininity.

"I get a practice jag for a week, then something happens that turns the switch off for months." Since practicing and playing were connected with expression of feelings, her solution of resignation was threatened. Mary was aware that when she was able to play she was able to express angry feelings. She put it in these terms, that no expression of angry feelings was otherwise tolerated by her parents. What she was not aware of was that she had to keep in check the expression of feelings, as this would invariably bring her into the experiencing of her conflict. On a few occasions Mary compared her playing to sexual intercourse. It was difficult for her to let go during the act of intercourse. She had the feeling of losing ground, losing control, floating in space—and this was extremely frightening to her. She was also aware she could not let go of feelings during the sessions.

She had to maintain rigid control of her feelings as another way of dealing with her conflict. Her strivings for love, as well as for assertion, were over-determined, compulsive, idealized, and invested with pride and grandiosity. Whenever she dreamed of love it was an all-encompassing and possessive one. Whenever she dreamed of easy living she was lying in the depths of inertia showered with a deluge of devotion, and the utmost attention. Whenever she dreamed of musical accomplishment she was the virtuoso. With such push and drive behind her feelings, she had to keep them in check through constant control, which restricted not only the idealized and grandiose aspects of the feelings, but the normal legitimate aspects of them as well.

The amounts of energy required for such purpose are enormous. She needed additional ways and means to maintain some unity of psychic functioning. She used suppression. She suppressed one side of her conflict, as temporary as this might be. At times she seemed to be giving up the natural, as well as the idealized, notions of her musicianship. At times like those, she wanted marriage, a home, children, nice clothes, and a husband to take care of her.

At other times, nothing but music mattered. She planned to go back to school, get her degree, play professionally in an orchestra, become a soloist, practice, and teach.

At still other times she tried to suppress her entire conflict. She would become listless, resigned, depressed, suicidal. Fortunately, her periods of giving up never lasted too long. She was able to respond to the appeal of either her femininity or music to come out of her self-contempt. However, the striving to be the most appealing woman or the most accomplished musician soon took over and she was again divided and torn.

Mary also used externalization. People, her parents, particularly her father, were held responsible for her difficulties. An important change took place when she was able to realize in the course of therapy that some of her resentment toward them came from the frustrations of her incompatible wishes and needs, rather than from parental negative attitudes toward her. This was symbolically represented by the dream in which her father died. Besides the quite obvious therapeutic implications, it also marked an important step in the process of lessening the alienation from her actual and real self, a decrease of her guilt feelings toward her parents, and a step in the direction of assuming more responsibility for herself, and her own living.

These additional means of keeping conflict in check were all insufficient. The threat of conflict breaking through was omnipresent. When this was taking place she was helpless to deal with it, and on the verge of disintegrating. Reintegration on a different lower level of functioning became a necessity. The phobic symptom fulfilled this role.

THE THERAPEUTIC RELATIONSHIP

Mary had been in need of a meaningful relationship throughout her life. This does not mean that she could accept one. I realized the therapeutic opportunities this offered, as well as the responsibility that came with it. She had a great fear of being alone and all her relationships so far had been disappointing and led to more aloneness. She could not accept her dependent needs and the solution of love.

How did these considerations come to life in our relationship? Attempts at seduction stand out. In her dreams and fantasies I made passionate love to her, she was married to me, and we flew in planes and rockets. In her dreams she waged battles with my wife and always came out victorious. She was frightened I might seduce her and yet she had to test me. She included her employers as targets of her seductive attempts, particularly when they were single. At no time did she act out her seductive attempts nor, to my knowledge, did she act out sexually with anyone after she began therapy.

Her attempts at seduction stand out. The seducer says in essence, "I have something I am sure you like and want. It is yours for the taking. It would please me if you did." There is something she wants in return. She might have wanted importance and power. This could be important to a person who feels as worthless as Mary.

Had Mary succeeded in her attempted seduction, it would have meant the end of her therapy. To simply state that she was destructive and self-destructive may be true, but would not take into account her active attempts at wanting to be helped and treated.

We often talk about the support a patient finds in the therapeutic relationship. What is insufficiently stressed is the anxiety and tension generated in the same relationship by its very structure and its implications. The patient falls back on his usual ways of alleviating anxiety, ways he had used most of his life with varying degrees of success. The anxiety is further increased by the incorruptibility of the therapist, who withstands the repeated attempts at seduction until the patient becomes aware of them and is sufficiently strong to no longer need them.

DREAMS AND THEIR UTILIZATION

Mary was the most prolific dreamer I have ever met. Every occurrence in her life was followed by dreams relating directly or indirectly to it.

At first she felt no connection between herself and her dreams. Yet the fact she brought them in at session after session indicates that she attached importance to them.

Since her early life Mary had made great use of fantasy and dreaming. It is not my intention to put fantasy on the same level as dreams. What they both have in common, however, is that they provide an outlet for frustrations in reality, and more importantly, afford a temporary solution to what is insoluble in reality.

Since her emotional responses pertained to the manifest content of dreams and the symbolic representation depended on the analytic work in therapy, she concerned herself only with the ego-syntonic dreams for a long time.

Through a process of selection she paid attention only to those dreams or fragments of dreams which were uplifting to her. She was too weak to be able to tolerate the ego-alien dreams. This sort of attitude toward dreams is a frequent occurrence. But Mary went a step further. She made it a way of life. She developed a pattern of transforming events in life into fantasies and dreams which would fit the idealized notions of herself. This was an active process during her sleep which her excellent memory kept alive and her compulsiveness drove her to bring into the sessions.

The changing of the dream character was an important aspect in the diagnosis of her progress in therapy. It preceded changes in her behavior and everyday living which continued rather tempestuously, full of ups and downs. It denoted a change from within, creating a basis for changing from without which followed later. Since my focus was more on inner events, I was able to discern a favorable prognosis before the patient, whose focus was on outer events, concerned with externals and externalizations.

I have been wondering about this massive recourse to dreams. To see it as a form of resistance to therapy alone would be, to my mind, insufficient. The acting roles, daydreaming, the living in fantasy, the make believe, self-expression through night dreaming, have all been outstanding characteristics of Mary. In my opinion, her dreams have the dual role of expressing her alienation, a process which began early and continued through her life, and they are also an attempt at keeping alive feelings, attitudes, values, strivings, and hopes in a sort of repository, away from the actual self which is unable to handle them. At the same time, as her dreams are the expression of her grandiosity and self-idealization, they are also a treasury in which most of the constructive elements of her real self are kept.

THE PHOBIC SYMPTOM

The history of psychiatry can be viewed from the evolution of the attitude toward symptoms. It is the symptom that is the most readily recognized factor of the illness for which the patient seeks help from the physician. In this respect, psychiatry does not differ from any other medical discipline where the first approach to a patient had been symptom-oriented. Progress came when symptoms became understood in terms of underlying anatomical physiological factors and their dynamic interplay. In order to understand Mary's stage fright, one must draw on the psychodynamics of her character structure and the underlying conflicts. "The neurotic symptoms, such as phobias, depressions, and alcoholism, ultimately result from these conflicts. The more thoroughly we recognize this fact the less will we be tempted to interpret the symptom directly. If they are a result of conflicting trends it is as good as useless to try to understand them without having previously gained an understanding of the underlying structure." [2]

I have indicated how her conflict found expression in a condensed form in her music. Stage fright was a symbolic representation of her acute conflicting trends with which she was unable to cope. Playing an instrument proficiently was an acutely experienced threat to her basic dependent needs. It was also experienced as interfering with resignation and inertia, and as bringing her closer to herself, closer to her conflicting feelings. In the same way, not playing was felt as a threat to her expansive and self-assertive needs.

Prior to therapy, the only way she could handle this acute conflict was by maintaining it in a capsule in the form of a symptom, delegating it to a specially built compartment, and eliminating it from herself. It became a self-alien or ego-alien product. Some "face saving" devices were necessary. One of them was that she was not good enough. Another, that others were critical and cruel. Still another was that she had to work for a living, which was directly related to resentment toward her parents for not helping her. She denied responsibility and put all the blame on her father. With this precarious defensive construct, Mary was able to function on some level. She was only aware of the annoying aspects of her symptom. She was totally unaware how the symptom fitted her solution of resignation, how it blended with her needs for inactivity, inertia, uninvolvement, and noncommitment. Yet the symptom was an important "way out" and in many respects life saving.

Sheiner sees a phobia as an expression of a major restricting influence resulting from inner conflicts. "The phobic mechanism makes it possible for them (the phobics) to avoid living situations which require choice, planning and decision, and thus to avoid test." [3] The person torn by conflicts restricts his functioning in certain important areas of living. The avoidance of these areas, as expressed symbolically in the phobic symptoms, is also life saving.

In the therapeutic relationship, Mary was able to bring out more and more aspects of her conflicting trends. Some working through and experiencing of conflict took place. However, before this could happen she had to feel sufficiently secure and accepted, so as to be able to give up her pretenses and "face saving" devices. Two hundred hours of therapy are too short a time for deep inner changes to take place. Much longer therapy is necessary for a more thorough working-out of a conflict. However, certain changes did take place. These were sufficient to enable Mary to function on a somewhat different plane. This, in turn, permitted her to give up the symptom of stage fright.

As indicated before, my emphasis was on character structure and conflict. However, as far as the patient was concerned, the symptom was of paramount importance. This is what brought her to therapy and kept her interested in therapy. An important therapeutic endeavor was to de-emphasize the symptom and elicit interest, concern and involvement in her conflict.[4] Until her interest shifted, her interest in the symptom was respected, but not supported by me. In practice, this meant attending her occasional performances. In her mind this was a sure way to overcome her stage fright. Actually, she was able to perform to some extent from the beginning of therapy. This did not mean an improvement. It only meant that she could feel somewhat stronger through the therapeutic relationship.

Painfully and laboriously, the process of taking more responsibility for herself and her actions was taking place. It culminated in the dream of the death of her father, who for a long time had been the symbol of Mary's conscience and responsibility, and who was blamed for everything undesirable that happened in her life. She became more committed to life, an expression she used after the two dreams which followed the consultation with the minister.

The expression "commit myself" had a multidimensional sound to me. The direction was toward herself as a person, musician, wife, daughter, patient. As appealing as the idea of an Almighty Father was to her, and despite the feeling of elation which followed her visit to the minister, the deeper commitment was to the slow and difficult process of therapy in which she had been engaged for several years. The growing, deeper awareness that her future was not in the realm of wishful thinking, but in the more difficult process of living was another slow change which took place.

Concomitantly, the process of accepting her dependent needs was taking place. This was extremely difficult, as she tended to see everything in terms of the "either/or" phenomenon.[5] This connotes rigidity, absoluteness, and dividedness. It is yet another way of avoiding conflict by keeping feelings, needs, and symbols in separate compartments. Things must be either white or black. Shadings are excluded. Mary was either good or bad, either a prostitute or a perfect musician, either working extremely hard or completely idle. Although she made some strides in the direction of lessening her rigid compartmentalization, it still remained strongly operative at the end of therapy.

Some of her desires for marriage were constructive and reflected a real human need. Others were of the same nature as her expectations of therapy and the therapist, predominantly magical. She could not reconcile George and her therapist. It had to be either one or the other.

It is my contention that Mary's dependency needs and their ramifications have not been worked through sufficiently. She made a transition from the support she obtained from her therapist to support from her husband. Following the cessation of treatment, Mary has continued symptom-free. Marital difficulties continue to exist. When I last saw her, nine months after interruption of therapy, she was very involved in her marriage and determined to preserve it. She was regretful that George could not accept professional help, either for her or for himself. Despite occasional disagreements and fights, she felt she was infinitely better off married to George and that she would do her utmost to make the marriage successful.

TERMINATION OF THERAPY

It happens frequently that marriage in the course of therapy brings about interruption of treatment. This was the case with Mary. At times marriage can be the expression of a resistance of deeper involvement in therapy. I see some validity to the prerequisite of classical analysts that no important decisions, including marriage, be made in the course of treatment. On the other hand, this kind of intransigent attitude tends to postpone and, at times, exclude a very important experience in living. Mary was thirty-eight and wanted children, as well as marriage. From her productions it was clear that she had decided to marry and leave on tour with the desire to resume therapy in the future. I was confronted with the problem of interfering or not interfering with this decision. Upon due consideration I decided in favor of the latter. The factors involved in my decisions were satisfaction with partial results of therapy; a respect for certain of the patient's aspirations, such as marriage, musical career, children; trust in the curative value of involvement in meaningful living; and the knowledge that her mind was made up and that interference on my part would be fruitless. It could only impair our relationship and lessen the possibility of further therapy in the future.

There is awareness of what might have been done but was not. There is hope that some of it might be done in the future, with or without further therapy.

REFERENCES

1. Kelman, H.: Diagnosing and Prognosing in Psychoanalysis, *Amer. J. Psychoan.*, Vol. XV, No. 1, 1955, 49.
2. Horney, K.: *Self Analysis,* New York, W. W. Norton & Co., 1942, 69.
3. Sheiner, S.: The Dynamics of Phobias, *Amer. J. Psychoan.*, Vol. XI, No. 1, 1951, 82.
4. Kelman, N.: Fundamentals of Psychoanalytic Technique. Course given at the American Institute for Psychoanalysis, 1956-1957.
5. Kelman, H.: The Psychoanalytic Process. Course given at the American Institute for Psychoanalysis, 1956.

Techniques Effecting Change In Analytically Oriented Psychotherapy

by Daniel Kaplowitz, M.D.
Postgraduate Center
for Psychotherapy

Daniel Kaplowitz, M.D.

In addition to his private practice, the author teaches at the Postgraduate Center for Mental Health, where he is especially concerned with the supervisory process in training students of psychotherapy and analysis.

THIS paper refers to change in its broadest sense. This means any change, no matter how infinitesimal, which will eventually lead the patient toward health. The ultimate goal is to achieve in the patient changes with real shifts in motivations that will be reflected in the growth and maturation of his personality. In order to accomplish this difficult task, it is essential that we understand the patient thoroughly. The therapist has to enter the very special world of the patient and see him from the inside of this world, as it were. Only then can we truly feel what the patient is experiencing: his anxieties and needs; his goals and values, and the real meaning of his existence. This necessitates a thorough knowledge of the patient's nuclear emotional constellation and the psychodynamics of his personality.

Once this is accomplished there comes the most difficult task of getting the patient to understand himself, not only on an intellectual level but also on an emotional one.

We have come to realize that patients are benefited by most of the known methods of analytically oriented psychotherapies;[1] but it is the therapist and his personality in relationship to the patient that are decisive in these procedures.

To produce change, anxieties must be released and we must help the patient tolerate them. In addition, we must help the patient substitute more gratifying and constructive forces which he will appreciate, as his self-realization and potential as a human being becomes possible.

SPECIFIC TECHNIQUES

Understanding the nuclear psychodynamics of the patient is of primary importance. One male patient, treated by the therapist, had a passive-dependent personality and was unable to assert himself in any way. The patient's anxiety was allowed to mount to such a degree that it helped overcome his strong initial resistance to psychotherapy. He did well as long as he was protected by the symbolic mothers in the form of the civil service or the Army. However as a school teacher without backing he found he was unable to assert himself in front of his pupils because this meant exposing the repressed rage and hostility he felt toward them. His inability to control his pupils was directly related to his unconscious feelings about his family. The more dependent he felt upon them the greater his rage.

The therapist felt that in order to get the patient into therapy, he would have to stop all superficial reassurance. He told the patient that the best solution for his difficulties was to undergo psychotherapy so that he could understand the reasons for his symptoms. The patient pleaded for pills. The therapist refused the patient any medication and firmly stated that there were no magical formulas for solving his difficulties except to investigate them. As could be anticipated, the patient's anxieties mounted at first but gradually he was able to overcome his resistance and to enter psychotherapy.

Early in treatment, no attempt is generally made to probe the innermost feelings of the patient. It is known that unless there is a basic trust in the relationship, the patient is not going to reveal himself. This is especially noticeable in patients who manifest overt anxiety reactions. If questioning early in therapy is broad and general, the patient is able to gain insight gradually. For example, one patient associated as follows:

"Changing my job bothers me. I feel guilty toward my boss. Same was true in the army. I got a transfer to New York and it felt like I deserted my friends. I recall failing in school. While worrying about it I was extremely harsh to my mother, so she wouldn't expect too much from me. Before I moved out of town I'd act terribly so she'd be glad to get rid of me."

By reading between the lines one can see that the patient has a fear of closeness and dependency. He uses hostility as a defensive maneuver.

To express this to the patient would be fruitless at this time. However, a broad question such as, "Do you think you're concerned about what others think of you?" will introduce to the patient a large area of insight. As he begins to think about this, he will open up a new vista involving his way of relating to people. We can then guide him by leading questions and well-timed interpretations, peeling them off, as it were, until we lead him to understand the core of his emotional difficulties.

At the beginning of therapy it is best to avoid "why" questions because patients are especially sensitive to criticism and blame, and they easily feel challenged. The use of the third person is helpful. For example: "One might be curious about . . ." or "What could the reason be for . . ." This will prevent the patient from becoming involved before the dynamics are better understood.

Emotional understanding is the "royal roadway" to reconstructive change. Leon Saul states, "An ounce of feeling is worth many pounds of cold external fact." [2] Empathy on the part of the therapist is a prime factor in helping the patient to feel accepted. He must feel a basic trust in the therapist before he "lets himself go." No one can talk a patient into trusting or feeling accepted. He must sense this in the relationship.[3] Once the patient does, he will then be willing to reveal what he considers the worst aspects of himself. He will be willing to tolerate the anxiety and conflicts connected with them. We must keep in mind that this is the hidden part of himself which he has repressed in order to be loved by the significant people in his life. We wholeheartedly approve his innermost revelations by our encouragement, acceptance of the patient, and our unceasing sympathetic understanding.

Getting to these emotional areas is accomplished by noticing at what points tonal variations, shifts in communications, somatic reactions, inappropriate behavior or feeling, and obscurities or confusions arise in the patient.

The direct expression of feelings toward the therapist can, at times, be difficult for a patient.

One female patient illustrated this difficulty when she was kept waiting forty five minutes one Saturday morning due to a mix-up in appointments.

Therapist: I guess we were both confused. In mix-ups like this, both people are responsible. Yet I slept 45 minutes longer this morning; and you must have been sitting here, fuming because you felt taken advantage of. Is that right?

Patient: It is an old story with me. I'm not definite, and people do take advantage of me. I wind up being hurt. I called my boy friend and told him all about it.

Therapist: What did you say to him?

Patient (hesitating): You can imagine . . . (avoids the question)

Therapist: Please don't hold back. It's so important to get to your innermost feelings. What did you say to him?

Patient (anxiously): I told him you're a stupid doctor.

Therapist: Why shouldn't you? You must have felt annoyed, sitting and waiting.

Patient: Yes, I do resent you. You know I was hoping you'd feel bad when you saw me waiting. I usually do this, I realize. I wind up being the hurt one; and now you will feel sorry for me. I could have called you easily, because there is a phone on my desk.

Therapist: That could have cleared the confusion. There must be a reason that you allow this to happen.

Patient: That's how I express my resentment. I often did that with my mother to make her feel sorry for me.

Our own emotional reactions can be employed as a tool and used favorably as long as we are aware of them and know what they mean. At times, they can also be a reflection in others of the reaction patterns set off by the patient.

When the therapist revealed his frustrations over a patient's use of long periods of silence to "control" the session the patient replied, after a pause: "I also try to manipulate my supervisor at work and I know I make him uncomfortable. I can get what I want by manipulating people. I can tell you all to go to hell. I can defy my father this way also. I'm a good actor and I can put people into impossible situations."

The remainder of the session was spent in discussing the patient's relationship to his father so that he could gradually grasp more clearly the origins of his severe authority problem.

It has been very useful to work with such patients "on the periphery," as it were, until they begin to understand the dynamics involved. Then we can slowly involve ourselves in the patient's transference reactions.

In the transference, the patient has the opportunity of learning and understanding his own irrational behavior over and over again as he gradually becomes aware of his unconscious patterns and impulses in action. We can then help him change his reactions, with constant practice and working through. This is the so-called "corrective emotional experience" which is essential for real change. Deconditioning and reconditioning processes begin in the transference situation and continue on the outside where they really count.

As the process of change takes place, like anything that is new and different, a feeling of apprehension will develop in the patient. This new anxiety is more tolerable to the patient as compared to the old. We must work toward keeping the patient on the road toward growth and maturity. We must build up incentives in the patient. We must inspire him and constantly remind him how his neurotic pursuits and values have made his life miserable. In fact, the therapist must literally increase in the patient some of his fears regarding the destructive ways of life. At the same time, as in all learning, we give the patient his reward in his success.

Many of us have had experience with some patients who absolutely refuse to change their compulsive behavior or their phobic reactions. No matter how much insight and understanding is conveyed to them, nothing happens. The patient may make minor changes here and there, but he continues in the same rut: ready to come to therapy and talk about his problems for years and years. In such cases, the therapist has to resort to his own devices in order to outwit the patient's neurosis. The following example will illustrate this point:

A 24-year-old man came into therapy in 1956 because of an acute depression, uncontrollable scratching of his body, insomnia, and explosive hate reactions toward his wife. He had been working in his father's candy store since the age of thirteen and knew no other trade. The business was failing because his father was drinking excessively, and literally chasing the customers out of the store. The patient was helpless at the hands of this man who, in addition, ridiculed him constantly and blamed him for the deterioration of the business.

The patient's marriage was failing because, strange as it may sound, his loyalties were to his father and the candy store. His mother had died a few years ago, but when she was alive, she lived in fear of her husband's brutality. She also felt that the store came first. Thus, the patient's only moral and economic support was crumbling and, not being equipped for anything else in life, he developed his current neurosis.

Because of the patient's feelings of guilt, the early analysis was directed at uncovering the patient's repressed rage against his father, in addition to removing his self-blame for the deterioration of the business. As the doctor-patient relationship improved, so did his hopes. He felt there could be a way out. Soon his acute symptoms practically disappeared. Fortunately for him, the father, during one of his alcoholic bouts, was taken away and admitted to the psychiatric division of a hospital. He was, however, soon signed out. The patient and a friendly lawyer convinced the father that it would be best if he retired, on a weekly income. The father, having barely escaped being committed to a mental hospital, accepted and signed the store over to the patient.

Without the hampering effects of his father, business began to thrive. The patient worked indefatigably, averaging 14 hours a day in order to make the business prosper. As his success increased, so did his ego strength. He devoted little time to his family. Being endowed with tremendous energy, he became a financial success in one year. At this point, the patient felt that he would like to stop therapy, but he changed his mind when he realized that without the store he was lost.

Much effort was extended to help the patient understand the symbolic meaning the store had for him. He began to understand many of his irrational fears involving his interpersonal relationships. He made some minor changes so that he got along better with his wife and children. Yet he would not go away on vacations with them or take a Saturday off. In fact, even though he had two very fine workers, he would have his lunch in the store. This obvious masochism was thoroughly investigated but he continued working as hard as ever. The store which had given him newly-found success and worth, had become a boomerang from a social point of view. He was now entrenched, more than ever, in a cocoon-like existence.

The therapist was seeing the patient twice a week during late evening hours. The following are fragments of sessions demonstrating what happened:

Therapist: I'm tired these days and working too hard. I've stayed late with you over two years. I would appreciate seeing you during the day. What a blessing it would be for you, too.

Patient: You mean, during the day? You're kidding.

Therapist: No, I mean it. I think we both deserve a break. I have an opening on Tuesday at 9:45 A.M.

Patient: Demands like this make me angry, but if I have to get angry to do it, I'll do it. Gee, suppose the store works smoothly without me? What will I do?

Therapist: What will you do?

Patient: I can take it easy and not kill myself with overwork. You know it probably won't be so bad. I am such a fool. Yet I bitch and complain. I like luxury and I am entitled to it. Why should I kill myself by working so hard?

Therapist: You're on the verge of something. I can feel it.

Patient: I'm beginning to feel good about that morning appointment. I want friends, and if I make a gain in one thing, it will spread to other things. I'll come . . . I think. You know, you're tough on me; but I can take it.

The patient arrived 15 minutes late for his first Tuesday morning appointment. He had emerged from that store during the day for the first time in years. The following is a fragment of the session:

Patient: I was more interested in taking in all the money I could get than coming today.

Therapist: How do you feel?

Patient: I was as nervous as hell last night. I even scratched a little. That's when I fight and curse; but I told you I'd come.

Therapist: You kept your word. You deserve a great deal of respect for what you accomplished. Tell me, how do you feel right now on the couch?

Patient: It feels like an evening session. I don't have any anxiety.

Therapist: There's your proof. It isn't as frightening as you expected. Can you see that?

Patient: There is no question about that. It does seem strange though, walking through the streets. It's a bit frightening. Everything is so different during the day.

Therapist: I am very happy for you. In fact, I am reminded of the Russians who shot a rocket to the moon and the thrust was so great, it went beyond that, to the sun. I believe you have the thrust.

Patient: You have more confidence in me than I have in myself. Yet it's true. Here I am, away from the store, and I feel no pain.

Therapist: I'll see you Thursday morning at 9:45 A.M.

Patient: You're kidding! Once a week is enough! Please, Doc, you can't do this to me.

Therapist: I'm sorry. I have to insist and I will. You've got the thrust.

The patient continued to come during the day and has done so ever since. A new world has opened up for him. He takes Saturdays off from the store and recently he went on a weekend holiday with his family. He is making arrangements to work an eight-hour day.

It is interesting to note that, at a later date, the patient admitted the following reasons for the change: He felt that the therapist was saying, "Look my friend, there is nothing more to learn. You must do something, otherwise you're wasting my time." He had also identified with the therapist and wanted to help him out because the therapist was also overworked. Finally the therapist had confidence in him and said he had the thrust.

SUMMARY AND CONCLUSION

It is important to have a thorough knowledge and understanding of the patient. This process can be accomplished by diagnosing the nuclear psychodynamics of the patient, preferably before the transference fully develops with its ensuing complications and ramifications.

The next essential step is to help the patient understand himself on an emotional level. This is contingent upon the doctor-patient relationship which must be more than a transference countertransference phenomenon. Unless there is a warm, trusting, mutual human relationship, no real, lasting change can take place.

This is where the therapist's skill and sensitivity is in optimal operation. He must be in tune with the patient's needs, existing capacities and anxieties; and he must be able to reach the patient wherever he is.[4] At the same time, the therapist must use care, consideration, and tact in his dealings with the patient, always keeping in mind that no harm must come to him. No one will deny that this is a difficult task.

Specific techniques effecting change in analytically oriented psychotherapy have been presented. We shall enumerate those factors which have been found to contribute decisively to the changes described above:

A. Releasing the patient's anxiety and allowing it to mount to the degree where it becomes useful as a motivating factor in overcoming resistance to psychotherapy.

B. Getting to emotional areas by noticing at what points there are tonal variations or shifts in the patient's communications.

C. Helping the patient express his feelings toward the therapist by using peripheral approaches.

D. Employing our own reactions to the patient as a helpful psychotherapeutic tool, since they can be a reflection of the reaction patterns set off by the patient in others.

E. Using the transference as practice sessions for the repeated working through of the patient's irrational behavior patterns in order to achieve the "corrective emotional experience".

F. Maintaining change in the patient by comparing the old anxiety related to destructive patterns, with the new anxiety related to constructive living.

G. Using active measures by the therapist in order to outwit the patient's neurosis.

Harry Stack Sullivan has often said in relation to ourselves and our patients, "We are all much more simply human than otherwise." [5] The more our self-understanding and our skills as therapists increase, the more successful will our techniques be for effecting change.

REFERENCES

1. Wolberg, Lewis R.: *Technique of Psychotherapy.* Grune & Stratton, New York, 1954.
2. Saul, Leon J.: *Technic and Practice of Psychoanalysis.* J. B. Lippincott Co., Philadelphia, 1958.
3. Fromm-Reichmann, Freida: *Principles of Intensive Psychotherapy.* University of Chicago Press, 1950.
4. Kilpatrick, Elizabeth: What is Effective in the Therapeutic Process? *Am. J. Psychoanal.,* 17: 3, 1957.
5. Mullaby, Patrick, Ed.: *Contributions of Harry Stack Sullivan.* Hermitage House, New York, 1952.

The Psychoanalytic Treatment of the Elder Person Via Group Psychotherapy

by Jack D. Krasner, Ph.D.
Postgraduate Center
for Psychotherapy

Jack D. Krasner, Ph.D.

Dr. Krasner is presently Supervisor of the Department of Group Psychotherapy at the Postgraduate Center for Mental Health, and Adjunct Associate Professor in the Department of Psychology at Fairleigh-Dickinson University in New Jersey. He has been associated with Englewood and Bergen Pines Hospitals in New Jersey, and the New Jersey Center for Psychotherapy. He is a member of the Board of Directors of the American Psychological Association, the American Group Psychotherapy Association, and the Group Psychotherapy Foundation. He has been a contributor to several books and journals, including the American Journal of Psychotherapy, and the International Journal of Group Psychotherapy.

IT is the purpose of this paper to show that in older persons, 50-70, personality reconstruction can be brought about through group psychotherapy that is analytic in orientation in a group specifically confined to this age range. This contention is strikingly at variance with commonly held (and certainly less optimistic) views regarding psychotherapy of these older persons.

In the past, the chronological age of a prospective patient too often was a deciding factor in determining prognosis and acceptance for reconstructive psychotherapy. Some psychotherapists and out-patient clinics accept a very select group of persons beyond the age of 50 for reconstructive therapy. These select patients, although possessing psychopathology, usually manifest relatively intact and strong ego boundaries. The others in this advancing age group are rejected due to the erroneous concept of irreversibility of characterological patterns in older persons. The recommendations accompanying rejection for reconstructive psychotherapy are re-repression of early conflictual material and guidance in acceptance of and adjustment to his experienced frustrations.

Experience with the older person (over 50) has shown that transference problems arise which are time-consuming and difficult to work through. In individual psychotherapy, the initial transference is usually negative. The patient experiences the therapist as "child" upon whom he is forced to depend. In psychotherapy groups with younger persons, most of these patients assume a role of parental figure, and need to prove themselves a "good" parent. This rigid role thwarts the development of other transferential relationships, as well as placing the patient in a defensive position. Any critical response is experienced as rejection and results in *hostile aggression and/or withdrawal.* Other patients in this age range attempt to *deny their age,* assuming a facade of youngness. They attempt to participate in activities identified with the young, but actually display the strong needs and drives unsatisfied in childhood or adolescence. *Grotjahn*[1] also reports similar experiences. He theorizes that the neuroses of old age are defenses against castration anxiety, that advancing age tends to shatter the illusion of eternal youth. He also stresses the importance of having to work through the parent-patient relationship to the child-therapist.

Interest in the psychological problems that afflict the aged is mounting. Many people have begun to report investigations of these problems with an emphasis on the origins of such disturbances and methods of aiding these previously neglected people.[2, 3] The method of treatment has essentially been based on environmental manipulation to help the elderly person overcome his feeling of complete helplessness and to activate him toward following some pursuit.[4] There is also a beginning effort to utilize psychotherapeutic techniques in helping this age group resolve its emotional problems.[5] The psychotherapeutic approach has been tried in both individual[6] and group settings.[7] Many of these groups are socially oriented, in an effort to make available participation in group activities, e.g., Golden Age Clubs. The group process has also been utilized in institutional settings,[8] with the reported application of psychotherapeutic techniques. However, a scrutiny of the literature and verbal communications suggests that psychotherapy plays a small part in the total therapeutic endeavor. *Linden*[9] has described various transferential relationships and their use in determining diagnosis and treatment progress. *Goldfarb*[10] has recommended a course of treatment which closely resembles guidance and counselling. Rosen (in an Eastern Group Psychotherapy Society panel discussion) has referred to the "Smith Remotivation Technique" which is being tried in a Pennsylvania hospital for the aged. Again, this technique appears to be another form of group participation in some activity. There is no evidence that the use of the group process in a confined age range has been adopted for personality reconstruction. The writer wishes to present his observations of the progress of the first twelve months of an experimental project which utilized analytic group psychotherapy as a means of personality reconstruction for the older person.

SETTING

The setting for this study was the Postgraduate Center for Psychotherapy, New York City. The candidates completed a personal information form and were seen for an initial diagnostic and evaluation interview by an intake psychiatrist. The writer then processed each patient's personal information and initial interview reports. The intake department had "rejected" (as had other agencies and/or private psychotherapists) most of the patients for treatment at the Center because of the severity of pathology combined with the age. Although rejected as poor prognostic risks, these applicants were interviewed by the therapist and motivated to accept group as the choice of psychotherapy. The selection of patients for the group was limited only by the minimum age of 50 and the patient's acceptance of group therapy as a means of help with his psychological problems. The first two patients were seen in individual sessions once a week for several weeks to maintain their motivation until the group could be formed. All subsequent patients were seen only once individually to prepare them for the group. Of all patients interviewed by the writer, only two did not enter the group. One man could not join the group because of a time conflict with his job. A second man (paranoid) insisted that his former government position would prevent his being able to talk in a group. Each patient was referred for psychological tests and complete physical examination before entering the group.

TECHNIQUE

In originally planning the group, the therapist believed that psychoanalytic procedures would be utilized. From the beginning of the treatment, a non-authoritarian approach was taken. There was no attempt to manipulate the environment, or to place restrictions upon the patient's reaction in the group session. The therapist fostered an accepting, psychotherapeutic attitude towards the group members' needs and conflicts as an individual within the group constellation. The treatment plan and direction of therapy were as follows:

(1) Establishment of psychotherapeutic relationships within the group setting by means of an accepting attitude of the therapist and transmission of this attitude to the group.

(2) Ego support and strengthening by offering understanding to present difficulties and focusing on the positive.

(3) Activation of transference relationships and the relating of feelings and associations.

(4) Focusing and analysis of resistances.

(5) Focusing and analysis of acting out.

(6) Surfacing, analyzing and working through of early conflictual material by analysis and interpretation of dreams and transferential relationships.

(7) The establishment and experiencing of new values and like experiences within the group, which might be utilized in outside life situations.

METHOD

Following the plan of treatment originally formulated (as described above), each patient was seen in individual sessions. The individual sessions were utilized to "get acquainted" and establish a therapeutic relationship with the patient. The patient was encouraged to discuss the major problems that precipitated his seeking treatment: familial, social and professional constellations and relationships; life patterns from early childhood to present. The informal setting fostered a therapeutic relationship and the patient was motivated for psychoanalytic group therapy. After acceptance of group therapy as the choice of treatment, the patient was assigned and asked to attend the group sessions. The group met for 1½ hours once a week. There were no scheduled pre-, post- or alternate sessions without the presence of the therapist. (This procedure was a clinic policy rather than the therapist's preference.) However, on two occasions when the therapist was unable to attend the weekly session, the group met without a leader. The group started with four patients, two men, two women and the therapist. During the first year, four new members joined and two left the group. At the time of writing (one year of group activity), the group was composed of two male, four female patients, and the therapist. A non-verbally participating observer (group therapy trainee) attended group sessions for a period of over five months. The observer joined the group therapy team during the seventh and left after the twelfth month of the group's existence.

DYNAMICS

In the initial therapist-centered stage, the therapist was able to offer support as well as present a figure with whom patients could identify. The therapist was also able to focus on individual, as well as group resistance. Taking their cue from the therapist, patients initially imitated and then spontaneously began to interact with one another. As this occurred, the group's intellectual facade began to drop off. Although they were consciously unaware of this, effects of emotional involvement became manifest in the patients' interaction.

Following the departure of one male patient and the arrival of three new patients the therapist became more aware of each individual's behavior. Each patient in his own way was acting out life-long neurotic reaction patterns. The therapist, although not condoning, accepted each member's own right to his feelings and desires. As a consequence, rigidity began to diminish and the patients began to accept themselves as well as one another. They started to relate more intimate details of their lives, and to offer emotional rather than intellectual support.

The most outstanding defenses observed were passivity, denial of dependency needs, emotional detachment and depression. As the patients began to interact with one another, the therapist focused on the meaning and effect of these mechanisms. With the working through of one woman's suicidal attempt, the group for the first time became fully aware that behavior might result from unconscious needs and drives and that these unconscious forces might be made conscious. They continued to pick up cues from the therapist and although offering ego support, began to probe and analyze their own, as well as interaction and dreams of the others. This ego-support and accompanying strength resulted in the development of group cohesiveness. The sessions no longer took on a classroom atmosphere and the therapist became a parental figure rather than teacher. Emotional interaction became more spontaneous and multi-transferences were manifested in the patients' inter-relations.

The patients' acting-out of life-long patterns of neurotic behavior showed how each of these people had previously attempted to deny their strong dependency needs. One patient's attempt at self-sufficiency (offering, but never asking or accepting anything from anyone else) was a reaction formation. Her life was filled with activity and responsibilities, yet she could never experience any feelings of closeness or emotional satisfaction. Another patient sought to deny her dependent needs on the powerful mother figure by constantly placing herself as "the mistress of the house." She had no wants, yet felt completely frustrated that her own efforts were not properly and graciously accepted and utilized by others, especially her husband and sons. Her early anxiety related to fears of hurting her children with a knife may have been related to feelings of distorted power which she held over these young humans. When her eldest son, after two previous marriages, was to be married for the third time, her strong sexual drives were reactivated. She experienced the son's behavior as a reflection of her own "controlled" sexual needs. Jack, another patient, although denying any needs, used passivity as a means of manipulating others into doing for him. A third female patient had selected a profession and early life of "bohemianism" to display and constantly reassure herself of her independence. However, when a male friend threatened suicide, she married him in order not to lose this object of dependency. One male patient's feelings of complete inadequacy at the time of seeking treatment may also be seen as a reaction to the loss of his children's dependency on him. These children were the only ones over whom he had any power. The others' reactions may also be attributed to like deterioration and failure of previous defense mechanisms.

Depression was the most frequent common feeling expressed by all the patients. The question arises as to why a depressive reaction. If one looks at the earlier life patterns among these patients, it becomes clear that the depressive element had always been present. Although each patient may have been involved in various activities, to a lesser or greater degree, there appear to have been no experiences of lasting emotional satisfaction. None of these patients appears to have realized his dependency, or to have been aware of the means taken to gratify these needs. The initial childhood dependency fostered, with or without outside encouragement, the illusion that the parent was a source of unlimited gratification. Frustration of needs during the ongoing years of childhood may then have been experienced as rejection by the all-powerful figure, rather than limitations of the parent. The child, unable to begin developing self-initiative to exploit potential sources and, in turn, experience satisfaction, perpetuated the distortion that the parental figure was the only source of gratification. The need for continued dependency intensified, and in an effort to regain and/or retain the flow of gratification, the child assumed a compliant, submissive role. Further frustration led to resentment, and, in turn, may have resulted in the introjection of this all-powerful figure, in an effort to provide self-gratification. Any failure in this new role results in inwardly directed resentment and hostility to the introjected parental figure. The individual experiences a loss of self confidence and a rejection of self. Dependency is seen and felt to be a sign of weakness, something which an "adult" should not have. Thus, weakness, symbolized by dependency, was rejected, and would be rejected by others. These dependency needs had to be repressed by means of reaction formations or other defense mechanisms.

As the person grows older, the reduction of physical activity resulting from biological changes, as well as cultural attitudes toward the aged, tends to force reality upon them. They can no longer conceal their dependency needs by activity, and thus they begin to re-experience the early weak ego. The depression [1] and accompanying tendency toward withdrawal by means of impotence, and decreased professional and social activities [1] appears to be another defensive move to encapsulate and protect this weak ego from experiencing outside destructive forces. The older person is no longer able to battle the threat which is experienced as coming from the outside and must seek new ways of protection. Stripped of previous defense mechanisms, his only recourse is to withdraw within a shell of depression.

The major force and advantage of the group process is to confront the patient with reality. The advantage of the group confined to age 50-70 is that each person is able to experience himself as being amongst peers rather than as a "good" or "bad" parental figure in a group with younger persons. The acceptance of himself by others permits the acceptance of his own needs as something other than weakness. He is able to express his need to take as well as give help to others. This giving, taking and sharing result in his development of ego strength and the experiencing of himself as an individual. This experiencing of himself as an entity appears to be a completely new experience for the older person in reconstructive psychotherapy. With this gaining of ego strength, the patient is also able to express his needs and seek satisfaction outside of the therapeutic situation. This latter may be exemplified by one patient's change from complete compliance and submission to a position where he was able to attend a fraternal organization meeting and demand his rights as a member.

The one questionable failure was Bob, who left the group after only a few sessions. The question arises whether Bob's failure to benefit from group psychotherapy was due to faulty selectivity or the therapist's emotional reaction to him. It is the therapist's belief that both of these factors may have been involved. The therapist permitted, and in so doing perhaps condoned, the group's demand that Bob relinquish his dependency upon his sons. The therapist also did nothing to prevent the son from withdrawing Bob from treatment. Also, the fact that Bob did not participate in any outside activity may have made him feel different from others, and therefore an isolate in the group. If so, it may be advisable that such patients be placed in activity groups such as "Golden Age" groups or a day center for the aged such as the "Hudson Center" in New York City. Through daily activities in participation with others, this isolated patient may begin to experience feelings of acceptance, encouragement and recognition for his efforts. With this continued activity, he may begin to experience the feeling of accomplishment, eliminating or diminishing the feeling of complete uselessness and frustration.

CONCLUSIONS

A year's experience with group psychotherapy of individuals in the age range of 50-70 years has resulted in these conclusions:

(1) There is significant evidence of the usefulness of psychoanalytically oriented treatment for this age group.

(2) An effective psychotherapeutic relationship can be established in a relatively short time.

(3) Confinement of the age range, 50-70, avoided emotionally obstructive relationships due to presence of younger ("child") persons. It gave members of the group additional identification with one another and facilitated awareness of individual and mutual reactions and transference situations.

(4) Initial reactions by isolated individuals were supplanted by emotional interactions with others and eventual formation of a cohesive functioning group. These changes, initiated by imitation of the therapist, thereafter proceeded spontaneously.

(5) Ego strengthening and beginning reconstructive psychotherapy were demonstrated in the overt behavior, interactions and dreams of the patients described. In individual participation varying between 3-12 months, progress was evident in every patient.

(6) Group psychotherapy, as described, activates the production in members of the group of awareness of the dynamics of their disturbances, thus allowing healthful modifications of some long-standing attitudes and modes of reaction.

The results of this experimental project present significant evidence of the value of this technique in aiding individuals over 50, whose emotional conflicts result in debilitating psychosomatic and/or psychological handicaps. The major emotional problem of the elder person appears to be a perpetuation of early conflicts. The exacerbation of these conflicts may result from the decomposating of early defense mechanisms, e.g., reaction formation, compensation et al. The initial findings warrant continuation of this project to determine the extent of personality reconstruction which may be produced in this age group. The writer also hopes that the primary success in this experiment may encourage others to utilize psychoanalytic-oriented group psychotherapy as a means of aiding these "forgotten people."

Further experimentation may be set up to determine the value of utilizing activity group participation such as may be experienced in day centers as a preliminary to, and in conjunction with, group psychotherapy. Control studies may be established in relationship to patients who have continued active participation in some activity and those who have become isolates.

REFERENCES

1. Grotjahn, M.: Analytic psychotherapy with the elderly. *Psychoan. Rev.* 24: 419-427 (1955).
2. Gronewald, T. W.: Involutional psychotic reactions. J. Lancet 76: 8-10 (1956).
3. Ebaugh, F. G.: Age introduces stress into the family. *Geriatrics* 11: 146-150 (1956).
4. Busse, E. W.: Treatment of the non-hospitalized, emotionally disturbed person. *Geriatrics* 11: 173-179 (1955).
5. Stern, K.; Smith, J. M. and Frank, M.: Mechanisms of transference and countertransference in psychotherapeutic and social work with the aged. *J. Geront.* 8: 328-332 (1953).
6. Wayne, G. J.: Modified psychoanalytic therapy in senescence. *Psychoan. Rev.* 42: 419-427 (1955).
7. Linden, M. E.: Geriatrics; In Slavson, S. R.: *The Fields of Group Psychotherapy*, p. 129-152. New York: Int'l U. Press (1956.)
8. ——. Group psychotherapy with institutionalized senile women. Study in gerontologic human relations. *Int. J. Group Psychother.* 3: 150-170 (1953).
9. ——. Transference in gerontologic group psychotherapy. *Int. J. Group Psychother.* 5: 61-80 (1955).
10. Goldfarb, A. I.: Psychotherapy with aged persons; patterns of adjustment in a home for the aged. *Ment. Hyg.*, 39: 609-621 (1955).

Techniques of Group Psychotherapy With Children

by Malcolm J. Marks, Ed.D.
Postgraduate Center
for Psychotherapy

Malcolm J. Marks, Ed. D.

Certified by the National Psychological Association for Psychoanalysis, and by the Postgraduate Center for Psychotherapy, in analytical group psychotherapy, he has continued to concentrate in group psychotherapy, and holds the position of Supervisor at the Middlesex County (New Jersey) Clinic for Mental Health, in addition to being in private practice. He has been president of the New Jersey Group Psychotherapy Society, and recently presented three papers at the annual meeting of the American Group Psychotherapy Association.

THE most basic tool in psychotherapy is the therapist. This maxim obtains even more essentially in treating children than adults. The "activity" of the therapist, in working with children, is analogous to the need for greater activity in the form of a more active, less mask-like role in the treatment of borderline schizophrenics in the adult population. The group therapist is more exposed than the individual therapist and this is, once again, more true in the practice of group therapy with children. The therapist in this position should have a genuine liking for children, and sufficient personal analysis in individual and group psychotherapy because of the extent to which he will have to interact with the children in his group. There is little use in making a conscious or contrived effort to be nice, loving and understanding with children. If you are able to feel empathic with them and respect their persons, without "accepting" their personality disorders, you can probably treat them effectively. In saying this, I am presupposing the possession of knowledge and training from one or another of the major social scientific disciplines. The additional help of supervision for the group therapist is vital for his growth and development. Particularly in group therapy with children, where the therapist's defenses are often threatened and invaded, supervision is vital. If experienced supervisors are not available, the possibility of peer supervision, via one-way screen observation, and a group session among peers, where errors and counter-transference reactions may be freely expressed, may help to bridge the gap.

However well-analyzed or trained the therapist may be, blind spots will be encountered. I remember my own reactions when, after practicing group therapy for several years on a very intensive basis, a colleague pointed out that one of the boys, in an activity group I was working with, was openly bullying the others

MALCOLM J. MARKS, Ed.D.

and controlling the group. I felt humiliated and inadequate, to state it mildly. My deep aversion to bullying was related to early experiences with an older brother. To have this occur, where I was in the position of the parent, was unforgivable on my part. I was unable to see what was going on, just as my parents did not see what was being done to me. The tendency (in treating children, or any group, for that matter) to resolve early conflicts in the family group or to repeat them, is one of which we must beware. The group therapist is in the parental position and may quite unconsciously recreate an old situation and be unable to handle it objectively as the therapist. One analyst, working with adult groups, for example, worked most effectively with a group of three which is the least likely number for treatment of a group. But this number was found to be identical with the number of siblings the analyst had, in a situation where there was only one parent in the home. When this analyst left a training center, in which she had successfully kept these three members in a group for four years, the "group" could not be transferred to another group therapist. The reason: the members said "they could not stand each other," and refused to be in the same group together.

A central tool which any therapist must have is a basic feeling of respect for his patients. With children, this does not mean total acceptance and understanding of anti-social behavior, but an understanding that, beneath his acting-out behavior, the child has a need for control. That the therapist may have to supply a super-ego function more actively and openly in treating children in play groups and activity groups is unquestionable.

For example, one day the therapist arrived at the play room with a group of five children and found that the person who had used the room the day before had left a tempting array of materials on one of the tables. The children saw the materials immediately, grabbed them, tore through the containers, opened packages of food and "claimed" various models of ships and planes. The therapist told the boys to return the models as well as the food. They complied while protesting and complaining. Later in the session several boys returned to the food and continued to take things out of the boxes. The therapist first acted by making the boys sit down and getting them quiet. Then he said to them: "I understand how tempting it is for you to take these things and that you are angry with me for stopping you. I want you to know that I am not stopping you in order to protect the toys from you. I am doing this because I think it is important for us to learn to respect the possessions of others and because I think we will have more respect for ourselves if we can." Some boys continued to take, in a furtive manner, packages of jello and custard and pour them onto the table. The still unopened packages were put in the cupboard and the boys were asked to stop taking them but, for some, the temptation was too great, and they continued. A few weeks later, the situation recurred and, this time, all the boys in the group responded cooperatively to the request that the materials should not be taken and tampered with. The therapist voiced his approval of their ability to control their impulses. He agreed with the boys that it was unfair to tempt them in this way, and that while the person who left them there might deserve to lose them, we were more concerned with growing up and meeting this situation in a way in which we would feel better about ourselves.

The above example may be more striking if we are aware that the members of the group consisted of three hyper-active, aggressive boys and two passive-aggressive boys. Much of the early behavior in this group consisted of violent destruction of materials, escapes from the playroom via the window, throwing objects about the room and at each other, attacks on peers, shouting, pounding and screaming. The controls established were largely effected through the medium of discussions within the play therapy sessions. The focus of these discussions was an exploration of existing behavioral patterns and defenses with an attempt to substitute introspection for impulsivity. The attacks on peers were related to anger at having to share the therapist, to the lack of a basic, good experience in growing up with peers, and to the basic use of motor activity as an aggressive defense against internal feelings of emptiness, aloneness and depression. The interspersing of discussion into play therapy sessions served an educational purpose, the goal of which was to teach the child that individual feelings of rage and isolation were not confined to the individual children; that they could learn something and even get understanding from one another; that it was better to verbalize feelings than to defend against them by violent motor activity; that understanding (love) was not confined to a symbolic relationship; that the therapist's attention to the most needy (sometimes the most overtly violent or most passive) member of the group was not, in reality, a separation from the other members of the group. In one session with this same play therapy group, one member was acutely disturbed and actively destructive. He had to be held and physically restrained by the therapist. He threatened to hurt the other boys and to destroy the room. He was told he needed to be helped at that moment, by not being "free" to do just as he felt. Other boys made demands and asked for help with tools, woodwork or to play a game with the therapist. They were asked to help John too, and to talk about how John must feel just now.

Some children and adults are less threatened in a group than in a dyadic (one to one) experience. For some children in their early teens (thirteen to fifteen), this is particularly true. I feel strongly that the use of the group is more effective with children and adolescents than is the focus on individual treatment since it is closer to a natural setting for them and less threatening. Children are more inclined to action than to introspection and feel more at ease in a play or activity setting. The group is seen by some theorists as more effective in exposing defenses and characteristic behavior patterns. It is simpler and more efficacious to deal with a concrete situation with children than to deal with a narrative account as in individual therapy. The child who has no friends and sees his peers as enemies soon learns how he contributes to this by his behaviour patterns in a group. There are many accounts in the literature of how this is manifested and dealt with in group therapy. Exposure is, however, not the purpose of using the group as a therapeutic medium any more than is catharsis. There is, I believe, for children, a developmental and educational potential in the use of group therapy.

One sequence which I have found effective with children is to begin with some individual contact, and then proceed to a play therapy situation which is something like a pre-school three-to-five-year-old experience. Thus, with a positive transference, provided sometimes by a relatively brief period of individual therapy, the child, unless severely regressed or autistic, might be placed in a play therapy group. Here, there may be games, clay, toys, blocks, etc., and the children may play side by side, some together, some in an isolated corner, and gradually come to some feeling of safety about being in contact with each other. The therapist is active in helping the children individually and collectively, playing with them, moving in and out, sensitive to the timing for this in terms of an individual child and the group. Wherever there is an opening, he encourages verbalization. Sometimes he may start with one child who is having difficulty or sometimes with two who are quarreling. Then an opportunity to move toward group discussion may arise; others may be asked how they feel about Bob and Jack fighting over a piece of wood, etc.

In a clinic setting, in the metropolitan area, an activity group could not be held within the confines of the clinic. The possibility of trips to museums, to the parks and zoos can be utilized in terms of expanding the cultural horizons of the children as well as in terms of the developmental concept of more mature behavior. In working with a play group in an institutional setting, there was a request for play on the grounds outside, and for hikes, cook-outs and trips. The first outing on the grounds was a "disaster." The boys got out of control, ran into forbidden areas, made noise through the hallways on the way out, and disturbed a classroom. One climbed a tree and refused to come down, and the therapist no longer had a group. The transfer of the freedom of the playroom to the freedom outside the playroom, in terms of greater space and less control, did not work. The therapist ended the session and managed to get the children back to their cottages. At the next meeting, he spoke with the boys about their request for outside activities and said, in effect, "to have this freedom you must have more self-control. I cannot control you outside of the room in the same way that I can inside the room." The therapist focused on this for many sessions, within the group, and worked towards the goal of doing something together outside of the playroom with some assurance that they would remain together as a group and respect the rights of others in the community. Gradually, in the spring they had ball games outside the playroom, or would walk together as a group to the carpenter's shop to get wood for making things at a small workbench in the playroom. The big event of the year was a trip some ten miles away from the institution where they had a cook-out and some outdoor play. There were tense moments on this outing when some of the boys wandered away, but they managed to remain together and to return intact to the institution.

Within the play and activity group sessions, discussion is interjected at every opportunity. This is used to develop insight, to work towards greater maturation, and to substitute words and thoughts for deeds. I have worked with girls groups and mixed groups, but boys are the ones who object most to talking. When they would ask "What's the use of talking; words don't mean anything," it was possible to point out how they used words to taunt one another and to show how they were often more sensitive to, and more hurt by, words than by physical abuse. It was stated that words could be used in a positive way, too, to understand our feelings and help us feel better inside.

The work of Slavson in activity group therapy and the film on this approach, present the therapist as passive and non-verbal. One of his disciples cited an instance where two boys were about to get into a fist fight and the therapist interrupted by walking between them and dropping a glass he was carrying. This is, in my opinion, an extension of primary process as a mode of life, of acting out rather than the use of words to express thoughts and feelings. The trained, sensitive therapist may come close to what the child is feeling and saying in his play or activities, but he does not really *know* unless he explores this verbally with the child and the members of the group. In our work with adults we often find our interpretations inaccurate or ill-timed. This must also happen in group therapy with children, and it is only by verbal communication that we can come closer to what is at work internally in the child, and what a particular situation in the group, at a specific moment, may mean. Two boys may be wrestling on the floor in sport, or for physical contact with each other, or in the hope, for one, that it will bring the therapist into contact with him. It may have highly specific meaning for one child in terms of his history. For one who may have been over-protected and isolated it may be a growth experience, another may be "murdering" his parent. Our knowledge of the history of the individual child is essential, and can enhance our more knowledgeable exploration of his behavior in the group. While play and activities are a natural media for children and may be utilized as protective and expressive tools, words are perhaps our most helpful tools in arriving at an understanding of what is going on internally in a particular child in interaction with another. To think and feel with the child on a verbal level is to respond to the more mature component in him and to reverse the regressive, infantilizing process which would appear to be inherent in a play therapy group.

The techniques which may be utilized with childrens and adolescents groups may be as varied and creative as the therapist's talents allow. Psychotherapy is essentially a creative process and there are no hard fixed rules, except as the ego strength or weakness of the patients may indicate. One child may have to be restricted in the use of tools or darts or games, while others are given more freedom. This must be determined by the therapist. Among useful variations with younger children, say eight to eleven, I have found puppetry, hand puppets and marionettes effective. A form of psychodrama may be enacted. In a group which met weekly, each child had his turn in staging a drama. He selected the puppet he wished to play, and he sometimes soliloquized initially or immediately brought another puppet into play, designating which puppet and which boy should take the role. Then, as others were needed in the play, he would bring in other children. Weddings, primal scenes, births, killings, etc., were enacted. The Oepidal scene was often dramatized; the boy killed the adult father, became a man and married the mother. Following a fifteen- or twenty-minute play, a discussion would be held on what the play was about. This served as an effective projection medium and as a helpful approach toward discussion. Groups using this mode of treatment were restricted to four or five members.

Another approach with larger groups was the use of stories from fiction, and short stories written about incidents which happened to the children in their institutional setting. Stories of conflicts with peers, teachers, parents, etc., were read or told to the children. The stories ended at a moment of crisis for the child. The group was asked what they would do if they were in the child's position or role in the story. As they projected themselves into the situation, they were asked to take the part of the boy or the teacher, parent, social worker, etc. Others might be asked to represent the classroom group. Dramas were held, discussed, and other dramatizations were then made on the same situation. The possibility of alternative modes of behavior were thereby presented in an emotionally charged situation in which there was an opportunity for gains in insight and a broader perspective. Another approach was to get the group members talking about incidents which had occurred that day or during the week in which they had gotten into trouble. The incident was then dramatized with group members taking roles. Discussion followed and the group members portrayed different ways of behaving in a similar situation. Through this, the possibility of learning that "what happened" had to do with the problems and feelings of the boy involved, not with the situation per se, was enhanced.

The danger in the use of projective techniques such as this is in starting too early, before the children have a feeling that they can trust you as a therapist. In a school system where this technique was used, a boy came out freely with a story about losing his bike, and getting into a fight with another boy and his parents. The role playing of this incident and subsequent discussion made this adolescent feel exposed and inadequate. He felt he had been made fun of, although this was not the feeling of the therapist. He did lose face with his peers as a rebel and tough guy opposing authorities. This interfered with the therapeutic relationship since it occurred too early in treatment.

There is a shift in the balance of permissiveness and limitations which points up the developmental focus of the group therapy experience. The therapist demonstrates respect for the group initially by accepting them where they are, with their symptoms (infantile, dependent, submissive, aggressive, impulsive) however they are expressed. As the individual members move toward self-acceptance and social acceptability by their peers, there is a gradual shift in the direction of higher expectations by the therapist. Here, belief in the child is manifested by belief in his capacity to develop controls and to relate to peers and the adult in a more mature manner. This is demonstrated by expectations of greater controls, of the group's ability to develop its own norms for co-living, and the individual's increased capacity for satisfactory and satisfying relationships.

As the group is gradually able to build in its own controls, it needs less and less the support of the therapist. It becomes freer and more independent. There is less insistence on help and/or attention from the therapist. Boys turn more and more to each other for help and for the emotional satisfaction of a close relationship. They learn the satisfaction of relating in a way which is not designed to meet neurotic or unhealthy drives: to submit, to be dependent on another, either for dominance needs and aggressive drives, or for dependency needs and needs to punish one's self and reduce tension thereby. They are free to savor the joy of relating for its own sake.

The Integration of Group Therapy With Individual Psychoanalysis

by David E. Schechter, M.D.
William Alanson White Institute

David E. Schechter, M.D.

The author is Assistant Clinical Professor at the Albert Einstein College of Medicine, and is affiliated with the William Alanson White Institute of Psychoanalysis. In addition to his private practice with adults and children, he has been engaged in research on personality development and its relation to emotional disorder.

THE purpose of this study is to investigate the therapeutic possibilities of group process and the effect of the group upon the course and structure of the individual analysis, with special emphasis on changes in the analyst-patient relationship. With Sullivan's scheme of personality development as a frame of reference, it was suggested from a preliminary clinical study that too early introduction of group therapy in an individual psychoanalysis obstructs the development and resolution of certain kinds of infantile and childhood transferences. On the other hand, it was noted that with optimal application of group therapy as an adjunct to individual analysis there were several important contributions that could be made, especially in clarifying and resolving certain transference and countertransference problems.

THE GROUP

To investigate the optimal conditions for the application of group therapy to individual psychoanalysis I found a group of three men and four women who fitted the prognostically hopeful criteria for group therapy and who were in individual analysis with me, so that there could be a meaningful control, in accordance with my one-to-one individual psychoanalytic orientation, in the study of what effect the group was having on the lives and analyses of the group members.

Aside from some of the useful criteria postulated by Powdermaker and Frank as well as by Slavson,[1] I assumed that the group would be of particular value for patients who tended to relate chiefly in a rather exclusive or "incestuous" manner and/or with great difficulty in peer and sibling types of situations. Five of the patients were seen three times weekly in individual sessions; the other two were seen twice weekly. At the time of the group's first meeting all the patients, with the exception of one, had been in analysis for a period of at least one and a half to three years. At the time of this writing the group had met every week for two years.

The techniques for study included the presence of a psychologist who took shorthand notes of both the verbal and nonverbal events. As suggested in the research of Powdermaker and Frank, the recorder acted as a nonparticipant observer who could give his impressions not only of patients' reactions but also of the therapist's behavior, his tone of voice, gestures, emotional attitudes, and other nonverbal communications.[2] The therapist processed these records weekly, together with records from the individual analyses, to formulate dynamically what was going on between the group, the patient, and the therapist. Every third week, these findings were discussed in a research seminar group.

THE POTENTIAL CONFLICT OF GROUP THERAPY WITH THE ANALYTIC PROCESS

From observations of the group studied here, the first hypothesis that presents itself is that from the point of view of Sullivan's developmental scheme the group situation tends to evoke and revive past attitudes and feelings that are chiefly related to the juvenile and preadolescent eras.[3] In connection with the juvenile era, one finds competition, conformity, cooperation, banding together of peers against authority, and sibling rivalry for parental approval. Among attitudes associated with preadolescence are the emergence of leadership, collaboration, and compassion. The "we" becomes as important as the "I." There is a feeling for the other person which approaches an importance equal to the feeling the person holds for himself; there is a striving for relatedness to avoid the pain of loneliness; there is the opportunity for consensual validation of both one's worth and one's warps, as Sullivan put it.

A second hypothesis I would like to present is that these group-provoked juvenile and preadolescent attitudes may inhibit behavior and feelings which are characteristic of, and derived from, the infantile and childhood eras.

Both of these hypotheses are clinically testable, and some data will be offered to substantiate them. Assuming their validity for the moment, I would then suggest that the optimal time to introduce group therapy in an individual analysis would be after the major infantile and childhood cravings have emerged for analysis. Another way of saying this is that for patients with whom one has analytic goals, the optimal time to introduce group therapy is after the most dependent and infantile transference have been established and worked out to the extent of some insight into this transference. This inference, as well as the second hypothesis presented here, is based upon a specific view of the structure, stages, and goals of analysis which will be described. One of the corollaries that follows from these statements is that group therapy alone cannot achieve analytic goals as here defined.

Unlike some of the exclusively "here-and-now" oriented therapies, I would stress the importance of working through unresolved feelings and conflicts of the past which determine present attitudes and behavior. Working through, as I see it, is characterized by a sequence of chiefly feeling experiences, including:

(1) The development of a positive dependent transference to the analyst, implying that the patient will irrationally expect rather magical solutions and extremely special, benevolent, and exclusive treatment from the analyst.

The analyst should realize that the patient would never open up his most repressed hurts and wishes unless there were hopes for some kind of resolution and fulfillment of these from the analyst. This hope is most often on irrational and neurotic grounds, for if the patient had other workable solutions immediately available to him he would probably not be consulting the analyst.

(2) An awareness of the traumata and the unsatisfied cravings, as well as various other positive forces of the personality that had to be repressed at some time in the past.

(3) A re-experiencing of feelings of certain crucial, repressed events and attitudes in as close to the original form as the chronological age of the patient will permit, without resulting in excessive anxiety or loss of self-esteem.

(4) The last stage of working-through, characterized by a growth of the personality beyond its typical former anxieties, conflicts, and defenses. This expansion is achieved with the help of transference resolutions and, probably even more important, by real life experience and experiment.

To be sure, the early analytic work must also include a confrontation and investigation of the patient's defensive operations and neurotic character traits. A direct, massive confrontation of the defensive structure, which often occurs in a group, without working out how the defense was born, may lead the patient to feel that he as a person is being attacked since, at this point, his defenses are still ego-syntonic. He may thus feel even more evil and unacceptable than before and attempt to reform to please the analyst, the group, and his own ideal image. As J. C. Maloney put it in *The Magic Cloak*, "The acting-out of the adult role congeals his union with his mother. It does not cut the cord." [4]

One of the big problems in analysis is overcoming the shame about having certain infantile cravings which are experienced as evil. Indeed, needing of any kind is often felt by such patients as evil, or as a sign of weak character. Patients then act out or substitute for such cravings by means of character traits or behavior such as demandingness, petulance, whining, or rage. Underneath this behavior there is usually a profound hopelessness about ever fulfilling their needs. Their manifest behavior is a defense, either obsessional or acting-out, against feeling their need and frustration. It is one of the most difficult of tasks to get a chronically obsessive or depressed patient to feel his hurt in a really acute way. If this can be done, the patient can then go through an adequate mourning period for what he would now feel as his acute loss, instead of continuing the whining complaints about his terrible childhood with obsessive repetition of the same stories, as if his very talk protects him from feeling the hurt.

The boundary between the classical professional role of mirror and that of human, interacting participator probably has to vary with each analyst, each patient, and often even with each situation that confronts them. However, I believe that the analyst does offer the patient an active gift of love by dint of the elaborate, patient, careful, and detailed work he does in the collaboration of analysis. For this reason I think on relatively rare and selected occasions such as described by Sechehaye that the analyst has to give materially, physically, or by active intervention, and counseling.[5]

The point of this digression on some of the goals of analysis was to demonstrate the importance of establishing the analytic conditions necessary to the working through of, among other things, the most shameful infantile feelings before embarking on group therapy, which, I believe, can subvert this aim. I stress this particular aspect of the analysis because I feel it is the most difficult to resolve and the one with which the group could potentially most interfere. This is not because the group will reject a patient's shameful feelings; but rather because often the patient at first will not present them in the "public" of a group without a feeling of confessional self-humiliation—that is, at a price to his self-esteem. Patients may use self-humiliation in a group to protect themselves against feeling the very thing they are confessing. They indulge in this moral self-flagellation to avoid the hurt, the anxiety, and the deeper guilts. On the other hand, in order to protect itself from being excessively stirred up, the group may overidentify with one member and prematurely "absolve" him or his guilty feelings. This promotes a short-circuiting and disassociation of the guilt, which then cannot get worked through to its origin. As will soon be discussed, the group can also have a very positive function in this regard. It helps the patient accept himself by accepting his problems, sharing them, and showing him that his problems are of the same human variety as theirs, rather than monstrous in nature.

THE CONTRIBUTION OF GROUP THERAPY TO THE ANALYTIC PROCESS

In the preceding section I pointed out the obstacles which the group might pose, at certain stages in the analysis, to the development of the transference and hence to the experiencing of the more unconscious wishes and fears. This section will explore the positive functions that a group may have at an appropriate stage of analysis, including its relation to the final development and resolution of the transference.

A third hypothesis I would now like to offer can be stated and explored in three parts:

(a) Group therapy tends to increase awareness of the analyst-patient relationship and intensifies certain kinds of transference to the analyst, while diluting others.

(b) The very group characteristics described as typical of the juvenile and pre-adolescent eras, and as at times hindering the development of an infantile and dependent transference, can, after this transference has been well established, be of value in gaining dramatic awareness of it and in resolving it.

Such a transference may be considered well established when the patient has not only verbally shared with the analyst these infantile wishes and fantasies but also transferred them in the sense of expecting the analyst to fulfill them, even if in disguised "adult" equivalents.

(c) Some of these group characteristics are experienced by the patient as sibling-peer pressures and may be referred to as such. They accentuate the competitive, rivalrous, and hostile features of the transference as well as the struggle for equality and self-assertion in relation to the analyst and group. The working-through of this stage is necessary before the patient can be free to express feelings of compassion, sharing, tenderness, and love.

No matter what is said or done in an individual analysis, it can still represent for the patient, at least in fantasy, an exclusive, possessive, symbiotic parent-child relationship. The group introduces into this relationship some crucial features of social reality. The patient, often with a shock, finds that the analyst is not his exclusive parent whom he can possess for himself. To be sure, he discovers this only after desperate attempts at re-establishing his dependency upon the analyst, which follow upon his starting in the group. Ackerman has experienced the function of the group quite similarly and has expressed it in this way:

> The group, composed of multiple relationships personifying the presence of both male and female parents, siblings, etc., brings rivals into the picture, counteracts the infantile urge for the exclusive possession of the parent figure, and dilutes the degree of reliance on omnipotent fantasy.[6]

Because of the group sibling-peer pressures, the patient becomes painfully aware of his dependency strivings, but cannot easily dissociate them now, as he might have done if this self-awareness occurred early in the establishment of such a transference. He finds that he must share the analyst and assert himself, often in a competitive way, in order to be heard. The rivalrous, resentful, and envious feelings of sibling relationships become exposed and acted out. The group member learns that his relationships not only survive but may even flourish after he has expressed these feelings. As will be illustrated later, when there is an open clash of hostility, the patient can dramatically discover that his world does not collapse and that he is not annihilated. In fact, he discovers that the reality of a direct and even angry encounter is not nearly so bad as his fearful fantasies in which he expected to be humiliated and defeated. In finally making direct emotional contact in the group with an opponent whom he has been avoiding in his real and fantasy life, the patient tests out and discovers his reserve strengths and can correct the impotent little-boy image of himself. I believe that this whole experiment can take place because of the basically safe therapeutic atmosphere in the group, where it becomes clear that the over-all desire to help is stronger than the desire to defeat and destroy. However, once the anxiety of the encounter is overcome by the real experience, and the self-image is corrected, the patient then feels ready to deal more directly with his inferior, competitive, or hostile feelings in the outside world. This is not to imply that he then must act them out where it would be inappropriate but, on the contrary, that he would be able to face and deal with such feelings *rather* than escape from them, compensate for them, or act them out.

The group's continual, vivid confrontation of his repetitive character patterns often seems to provoke a more genuine curiosity in the patient than does individual confrontation. He discovers that he is not unique in feeling inferior, "queer," anxious, or lonely. This creates in the group members a bond of mutuality which can probably never be quite achieved during an individual analysis between patient and analyst. The peer relationship allows for really mutual criticism, validation, and openness. The patient thus finds that there is more than rivalry to be derived from a sibling or peer relationship. He does not have to depend exclusively on the analyst or parent figure for the understanding and fulfillment of his needs. Someone like him—that is, a peer—is capable of this.

As to the problem of authority, the patient received support in evaluating and criticizing the analyst. Certainly group rebellion against the analyst's authority will in itself not solve the individual's problem with authority. However, those patients who have never before experienced the peer group adequately find that there is a way of relating other than in the parent-child, authoritarian-submissive way. Like the play group or gang in earlier life, the group may be the medium through which the patient gains encouragement to face up to the analyst—or parent—with an eye of critical evaluation. In the end the patient has to work this problem through with the analyst as an adult on his own, and the concurrent individual sessions afford this opportunity.

There is always the danger that the patient may conform to the pressures and the authority of the group, just as in individual analysis he may submit to the authority of the analyst and his interpretations. To the extent that this happens in either situation, it becomes a problem for analysis. Hopefully, such conformity or submission is not a necessary condition of either the group or the individual situation.

The group relationship has several features which are more or less unique to it as a therapeutic instrument. Reference has been made to the new kind of social reality it affords the patient. Unlike psychodrama, the expression of feeling has more than a play-acting, "as-if," cathartic quality. Similarly, with proper guidance by the therapist, group behavior need not be limited to compulsive acting out. The principal difference from both psychodrama and from simple acting-out behavior is that each member is under the pressure of group responsibility, so that he has, in effect, to account for his behavior, even though he is encouraged to be as free and open as possible. The particular group under study has become most sensitive as to when superfluous distractions and unfelt pronouncements are confronted and analyzed.

Another means by which the patient's social reality becomes clarified is through his experimentation with the group as a miniscule reproduction of his society, where he can rehearse, or test out before living out, new insights, values, or self-evaluations. The group occupies a sort of halfway station between the relative social isolation of individual analysis and the reality of the outside world. It seems to be a familiar experience in analysis that a patient has apparently worked through some of his major problems, yet his behavior is slow to change. The group situation can provide the safe intermediate ground where the patient learns that neither he nor the group members are devastated by an exchange of angry or tender feelings. He discovers that he is still accepted and respected by the analyst when he rebels against him and challenges either the irrational authority which the analyst has really assumed, or which the patient has granted him earlier in the analysis. This is the price and condition presumed necessary for the analyst's fulfilling the patient's infantile and childhood desires.

Among the many other therapeutic functions which could be described, I would like to stress two more: one is the group as an ideal setting for multiple and "family" transferences to emerge; another is the fertile field it offers for separating parataxic distortions, because situations of social reality are available for checking on the spot during the group session. The clinical illustrations will attempt to clarify in more detail these and other contributions that group therapy offers to the analytic process.

CLINICAL ILLUSTRATIONS

To illustrate how the group functions to clarify distortions, one of the most fascinating episodes for some members was to experience themselves as the object of someone else's transference or parataxis. One patient, Rod, addressed another patient, Ann, in derogatory tones, as if she, like all women, including his sisters, were out to dominate and exploit men. Ann saw how Rod was distorting her into a witchlike image and said firmly and calmly, "There's no chance for a woman with you." This, more than any previous interpretation, struck home with Rod. On her part, Ann, who was particularly prone to explosively transfer attitudes in lump sums, was able to see herself as the object of a transference distortion without getting embroiled in a countertransference. She was shocked to experience how it felt from a vantage point of one of the victims of such distortion.

It was noticed in the groups of two other therapists as well as in my own that the meetings of the first few months tended to be competitive for the attention and approval of the therapist. I also noticed in this period a much keener sensitivity and preoccupation among the patients with the nature of the therapist's role and authority. One clinical incident may demonstrate the way members of the group act out their feelings toward the analyst and each other and what effect this has on the patient-analyst relationship. One day, in the second month of group therapy, when I walked into the office I found one patient, Jerry, seated in the chair I always use in both group and individual sessions. I showed my surprise with raised eyebrows, a smile, and the question, "Not enough chairs?" The patient offered the chair to me, and I took it. In the ensuing discussion of this incident it emerged that this was a "put-up job," to use the vernacular; that is, another patient, Mary, had provoked Jerry to sit in my chair, and she viewed the incident with a look of gleeful satisfaction. Mary had been very silent in the group and had used silence as an expression of her anger toward the analyst in individual session. Transferring from her relationship to an overbearing mother, she ascribed excessive power to any authority with whom she came in contact. She would then find herself afraid as well as secretly resentful and contemptuous of such a person—all of which she was with the analyst. In this acting-out incident, she attempted to "dethrone" the analyst and to humiliate Jerry, whom she regarded as boyish and ineffectual. This was somewhat of a replica of her family situation, with which she associated this incident. She had always wanted to provoke her ineffectual father into action against her tyrannical mother. However, at the same time she identified with her mother and would often manipulate and humiliate her husband, just as her mother had done to her father, and as she herself did to Jerry in the group. One factor that emerged clearly from this incident was that Mary could not express her anger directly to the analyst and was still venting her rage against her mother by way of hapless male victims. In the ensuing months she was able to be more and more direct with the analyst and, for the first time in over two years of individual work, began to look him straight in the eye when expressing either a strong positive or strong negative feeling toward him.

From the same experience, Jerry became aware of how competitive he was with the analyst; how he envied his success and would actually like to be an analyst, which role he frequently played in the group. At the same time he became painfully conscious of how dependent he had been on the analyst; how he had wanted to curl up in his lap, as he actually did with his first girl friend when he was sixteen. From the beginning of his group therapy this patient was most active and assertive in the group and shortly afterward began to be in his private life. For him the group was a place where he could clearly see the special precocious-little-boy role he had always held with women, as well as a place where he could finally and successfully try out his masculine assertiveness in a peer setting, which he had never known in his sickly, female-protected childhood.

For three patients in the group both the above chair incident and the very sharing of the analyst with the other patients proved quite threatening. However, in one of these patients, who had distorted the analyst into a "Jehovah with a booming voice," the group's open critical appraisal of the analyst helped to dissipate this image, with therapeutic effect, and gave the patient further courage to conceive of himself as at least of the same species as the analyst. Two previous analysts had reigned in superior climes, and the patient had pictured himself as a "dirty little immigrant," even though quite successful in his career. To be sure, the more realistic appraisal of his self-esteem had begun before the group sessions, but it was my impression that the group was a most important catalyst for him.

With another patient, Ed, who had been in analysis for under a year, the group was most anxiety-provoking. He could not bear to see the analyst in a vulnerable position and resented him for getting into any situation from which he came out less than perfect. His need to transfer on to the analyst the image of the ideal parent was thwarted by group pressures. For some months he remained more or less silent in the group and resentful in his individual sessions. He suppressed the shameful infantile fantasies that he had been sharing with the analyst before the group started. This patient almost left the group but stayed after several patients made clear their desire to help him, stressing, however, his responsibility to use the group more productively by greater participation in it. Ed explicitly stated that such expressions of either tenderness or firmness on a man-to-man peer basis frightened him. He would much have preferred being treated as a child by the group. Although the patient survived the initial few months in the group and has subsequently done much better, I have the impression he was assaulted with group tension too early in his analysis and probably at the price of some limitations in the transference that could subsequently develop.

Reference has been made to the therapeutic function in the group of an open clash between one patient and a representative of the type of person he most fears. Two patients were fortunate enough to discover in each other the archetype of their most feared enemy. One saw in the other the epitome of crude aggressiveness and masculine brutality, similar to his experience of a long series of men, from his older brother to most of his bosses at work. After he dared to stand up to the "enemy" he was not only amazed at his own lack of fear but could subsequently feel compassion for the problems of the other man, who he previously felt was as strong and insensitive as a lowly but dangerous beast. The second patient, with his problem of crude and often unsuccessful manipulation, looked upon the first as a member of a sophisticated, suave, superior breed. After their encounter of anger, accusation, and envy, the second patient saw the worth of his own effusive, social, if somewhat crude, temperament and no longer regarded his "opponent" as superior and untouchable in his gentility and suavity.

There were similar instances in relation to the open and direct expression of tender and intimate feelings in the group. At first there was much embarrassment and suspiciousness about such positive feeling, and several members learned quite dramatically that it was much easier for them to express hostile rather than tender and affectionate sentiments. The group was most valuable not only as a place to discover this in *vivo,* but also as a setting in which there could be experimentation in such direct and frank self-expression with the world, as represented by the group, looking on. Patients also discovered how various family figures and attitudes, as represented by different members in the group, followed them into their adult life with feelings of inhibition, shame and embarrassment. With the help of the group to express their feelings more directly, and with concomitant working-through they could overcome much of the shame and embarrassment connected with their previously secret yearnings for tender and direct contact. For several members this opened up a whole new way of relating to their friends and spouses, and even to relative strangers.

COUNTERTRANSFERENCE

The group very definitely changes the equilibrium of the doctor-patient relationship as well as the nature of the countertransference. Just as the group is a different social situation with properties and dynamics of its own, so there is a somewhat different social self that emerges when the analyst is with a group of his patients. Moreover, the analyst is now subject to multiple transferences impinging upon him simultaneously. In these new frames of reference certain covert forms of the analyst's relatedness to his patients, as individuals and as a group, are unmasked. For example, in the sudden acting out by the patients in the chair incident, the analyst was abruptly brought to an awareness of his chair as a symbol of his role and authority in the group. The analyst's rational and irrational authority, as well as his problems and defenses connected with these, come under sharp focus in a real, immediate social situation rather than the more leisurely scrutiny usually possible in individual work. Thus the group is apt to reveal to the analyst any encrusted, ritualistic role-playing that he may have been using in his individual sessions; which is not to say that a group therapist does not erect a new role and set of defenses in the group.

If group therapy is started later in the analysis, as suggested, there is less strain on the analyst, since he is freer to express both his social self and his countertransference of the patient's irrational feelings to him. At this later stage of analysis, it is by means of this very comparison of the patient's projections on to the analyst with the analyst's real personality that the patient is freed to get in touch with his most unconscious strivings, and to separate the irrational aspects of the transference—in short, to resolve the transference.

REFERENCES

1. Powdermaker, F. B. & Frank, J. D.; *Group Psychotherapy; Studies in Methodology of Research and Therapy:* Cambridge, Mass., Harvard University Press for the Commonwealth Fund, 1953: p. 66, and Slavson, S. R.: *Analytic Group Psychotherapy with Children, Adolescents, and Adults:* New York, Columbia University Press, 1950; p. 228.
2. ibid.
3. Sullivan, Harry Stack, *The Interpersonal Theory of Psychiatry;* edited by Helen Swick Perry and Mary Ladd Gawel; New York, Norton, 1953.
4. Maloney, J. C., *The Magic Cloak;* Wakefield, Mass., Montrose Press, 1955; Ch. 9.
5. Sechehaye, M. A., *Symbolic Realization;* New York, International Univ. Press, 1951.
6. Ackerman, Nathan W., "Some Structural Problems in the Relations of Psychoanalysis and Group Therapy," *Internat. J. Group Psycotherapy* (1954) 4:131-135; p. 134.

Intertransference: Transference Relationships Between Members of the Psychotherapy Team

by Gerald Sabath, Ph.D.
Postgraduate Center
for Psychotherapy

Gerald Sabath, Ph.D.

In addition to his private practice, the author is a member of the faculty at the New School for Social Research, New York City, and an associate psychologist at the Postgraduate Center for Mental Health. He recently presented a paper on family dynamics before the Sixth International Congress on Psychotherapy, in London, and served as a delegate to the White House Conference on Narcotic Addiction and Drug Abuse.

THE PROBLEM OF INTERTRANSFERENCE

TRANSFERENCE and the acting-out of patients in group therapy have received considerable systematic attention. The same manifestations occur among cooperating therapists engaged in conducting treatment, but these are seldom studied systematically. Intertransference, the transference relationships between members of the therapy team, does receive some attention in supervision and, at times, in staff conferences and casual conversations. Despite the lack of effectively focused concern about intertransference, it can be as important a problem as the transference of patients.

This paper considers a few aspects of intertransference as it relates to a recent experience with a therapy team, all of whose members did individual and group therapy in a child guidance setting. The group discussed here is the therapy team, not the patients.

EXPECTATIONS PRIOR TO THERAPY

The team's reason for beginning group therapy and the therapists' lack of experience with it seemed to be related to the expectations and attitudes of the team members prior to the organization of groups. Group therapy was attempted largely as a practical measure to provide service for more patients than could be treated with individual therapy alone. Therapists' initial attitudes toward group therapy ranged from open interest to strong doubt. As a whole, the team had no particular belief in the efficacy of group therapy, nor much initial eagerness to attempt it.

The first therapist to start a group had a favorable attitude toward group therapy. The staff consensus was that this group went well from the beginning and continued to be more productive than any of the other groups, thereby resolving much of the initial resistance to group therapy. Discussion then shifted from details about treating groups to material derived from on-going groups. The pressure to share group experiences was great. Anxiety of the therapy group diminished and rapport improved as common challenges and experiences were shared.

INTERTRANSFERENCE DURING EXPERIENCE WITH GROUPS

Various types of intertransference networks might be expected: one, based largely on competitiveness between therapists from different disciplines, another revolving around advocates of different theoretical positions, and another between experienced practitioners and neophytes. None of these became important in the setting under discussion. The occasional cleavage that occurred seemed to take the form of an authority system similar to that of a neurotic family.

"Family" position or status in this network was based largely on staff hierarchy, age, and tenure. In general, there was some tendency for therapists in lower positions (the offspring or sibling surrogates), to be rebellious, while those higher up (the parent figures) were, at times, arbitrary.

The parent figures among therapists tended to discharge their hostility on those of offspring positions. They tended to avoid or to refuse discussing their patients with offspring figures among the therapists when both were treating members of the same family. Parental figures tended to make greater claims for their personal mental health and to insist that their personal analyses were more complete than those of sibling surrogates. Parental figures tended to interfere with the therapy of offspring figures by insisting on the use of specific techniques which they favored, often without regard for reasonable differences of other staff members. On a few occasions, they insisted on abrupt reversals of treatment strategy. Generally, parental figures supported one another while attacking siblings. On occasion, parental figures were threatened. However, only sibling figures suffered sustained attacks.

Intertransference distortions of sibling surrogates seemed to be less varied, though they were no less frequent. They tended to have extremely high work out-put to which they called attention and used as means of expressing hostility to parental figures on the staff.

Sibling surrogates expressed their hostility both directly and circuitously. They were far more aware of and interested in the shortcomings of parental figures than their own. Parental figures on the staff engaged in relatively little conflict with one another, although sibling figures were caught up in periodic rivalries.

The fact that various staff members worked with different persons from the same families intensified intertransference reactions and the involvement of team members with one another. Countertransference also became a problem, as therapists tended to protect their own patients and attack the patients of other therapists. Some therapists tended to regard patients of co-therapists as more disturbed than their own, and at times, insisted that a co-therapist discipline his patient.

There was, during the course of the group experience, an encouraging increase in goodwill among the team members. Notwithstanding the greater attention given in this report to the distortions and difficulties of the team, interaction was quite rewarding and overbalanced the negative aspects which are not completely avoidable. On the simplest level, team members profited from the increased exchange of information, attitude, and opinion.

On a deeper level, team members became more understanding of differences in technique and approach, and began to integrate elements learned from others in their own modes of operation. Thus, it was not only the patients who derived personal benefit from the experience with group therapy; team members as well, did so.

CONSENSUS AND INCIDENCE OF INTERTRANSFERENCE

Two questions are especially relevant to the present discussion: First, what is the consensus of team members as to their own participation and that of other team members? Second, how common are intertransference phenomena including, especially, intertransference distortions in various therapy teams?

Regarding the first question, it was a surprise to find there was considerable agreement between various team members as to which therapists manifested specific behavior patterns. Thus, it seems that the study of intertransference does not rest entirely on the quicksand of subjectivity. Quite the contrary, a good deal of consensus is apparently possible.

The second question was: How common are intertransference reactions in various team settings? A survey of colleagues in other settings indicated that intertransference is a universal occurrence in team settings. There are broad differences in the degree to which conflict and cooperation characterize the intertransference, but its existence, as such, and the inclusion of intertransference distortions to at least some degree, is universal. In addition, there are differences from one setting to the next as to the form and content of the intertransference network. There is probably greater intertransference difficulty when the therapists work with associated patients than when the patients are not associated. Better trained therapists appear to manifest less intertransference difficulty than do neophytes. However, specific training and experience in team settings seem to be of greater value than general experience which does not involve team work. There are numerous exceptions to these generalizations, particularly with regard to the effects of training and experience. Much intertransference appears to occur as a result of previous experience rather than being eliminated by it.

The answers to these two questions would seem to be in doubt only prior to their consideration. Upon reflection, it seems axiomatic that trained professionals would be human enough to have intertransference difficulties and, at the same time, expert enough to arrive at a consensus of their nature.

SUMMARY

When therapists cooperate in the conduct of psychotherapy—working together with different members of the same family, with patients who are associated with one another in other ways, or with the same patient—they tend to become more intimately involved with one another. The intertransference relationships that are then developed among the members of the therapy team appear to affect the quality of the work that is done.

Intertransference networks include a formal structure which may be characterized by the polarization of team members according to different disciplines, different theoretical positions, different family surrogate positions, and so forth.

Intertransference networks include specific manifestations. There may be various forms of conflict including, for example, misunderstanding of and intolerance for techniques that are used by others which are different from one's own. On the other hand, positive interstaff feelings may develop subsequent to the intense expression of frankly hostile feelings. Thus, intertransference includes compatibility and combatability, to use an expression coined by Hyman Spotnitz (1961).*

More attention should certainly be given to systematically dealing with intertransference. The analysis of this phenomenon has, in the present instance, proved to be far less painful in actuality than in fantasy. The benefits, for the patient and therapist alike, have been gratifying. This discussion has highlighted a few aspects of the overall problem of intertransference in relation to clinical experiences. Hopefully, there will be more focused interest in this problem.

REFERENCE

* SPOTNITZ, HYMAN. Comments during the Plenary Session of the American Group Psychotherapy Association Institute, January, 1961.

Infertility and Amenorrhea In the Hysterical Character

by Warren J. Gadpaille, M.D.

Warren J. Gadpaille, M.D.

Since 1958 Dr. Gadpaille has been a psychoanalyst in private practice in Denver, Colorado. He was the Director of the Delinquency Study Project, Research Division, Louisiana State Department of Institutions, an instructor in the Department of Psychiatry and Neurology, Tulane University School of Medicine, and lecturer at the Denver University Department of Psychology. He has published papers on delinquency and has filmed programs for television on this subject and on both exceptional children and retarded children. His television work is a natural outgrowth of a separate theatrical career he has followed since the age of ten when he began to travel with an orchestra.

THE interrelationships between emotional conflicts and disorders of the reproductive apparatus in the female are being recognized with increasing frequency and clarity. Emotional conflicts centering about the sexual functions can be manifested in altered humoral and autonomic responses; these altered responses can, in turn, be reflected in functional, physiological, and anatomical disorders of the reproductive apparatus; and these reproductive disorders may be amenable to alleviation through the resolution of the basic emotional conflicts.

I

Selye,[61] Mazer, and Israel [44] summarize the evidence that the gonadotrophic hormones of the anterior hypophysis are necessary for the maturation of the primary and secondary sexual organs. In humans, anterior hypophyseal hypofunction before puberty results in failure of development of the gonads and secondary sex organs; similar hypofunction after puberty results in atrophy of the gonads and secondary sex organs, with amenorrhea in the female, and sterility in both sexes. There is evidence [61] that gonadotrophic stimulation is important to the development of ovarian structure well before puberty. The gonadotrophins, however, do not seem directly to effect the maturation of the secondary sex organs. Allen and Doisy [2] demonstrated that ovarian hormone produced uterine growth, and Selye [61] points out that prepubertal ovariectomy results in failure of the uterus and breasts to develop, in spite of normal gonadotrophin levels. Reynolds [57] indicates that uterine growth begins well before puberty, and proceeds concurrently with the development of the breasts and secondary sexual characteristics. This points to ovarian activity long before menarche. Late menarche is considered [44] a sign of a definite endocrine disturbance which often leaves some residual maldevelopment in the genital tract. The developmental sequence seems to be the stimulation of ovarian development by gonadotrophins, as early as the seventh or eighth year; this in turn produces sufficient elaboration of ovarian estrogen, long before cyclic ovarian hormonal activity, to initiate uterine and breast growth, and the development of the secondary sex characteristics.

In considering uterine maldevelopment, a distinction must be made between the terms "infantile" and "hypoplastic." The infantile uterus retains the cervico-uterine ratio of 1 : 1, characteristic of the uterus in infancy; the hypoplastic uterus is a miniature uterus with an adult cervico-uterine ratio of 1 : 2.

The system of delicate checks and balances between ovarian and pituitary hormones can be disturbed or interrupted at any point, and disturbances in the occurrence or nature of the menstrual cycle will result. There appears to be no clear distinction between the underlying pathological processes producing the symptom of amenorrhea, and those producing infrequent and/or scanty menstruation.

The classification of hormone patterns by Reifenstein [56] describe, in addition to those resulting from primary pathology of the pituitary, ovary, or endometrium, one which he calls hypothalamic amenorrhea. In this type, there is no production of ovarian estrogen, the endometrium is capable of response, and there is normal production of pituitary FSH, in spite of the lack of estrogenic inhibition. He states that even with normal levels of FSH, there is no production of estrogen by the follicle in the absence of LH.

The role of the hypothalamus in the regulation of the pituitary hormones has been intensively investigated in the last two decades. Selye [61] considers that FSH plus LH in the proper amounts and time relationship will produce ovulation, and Klinefelter et. al.[31] describes amenorrhea with no estrogen and normal FSH, suggesting that it is probably due to a lack of LH because of a disturbance of hypothalmic impulses. Reifenstein [56] suggested that the primary disturbance was a loss of nerve impulses from the hypothalamus so that there was no LH produced in the anterior hypothysis. He noted that this type of amenorrhea usually has complicating psychogenic factors.

Various investigators [19,21,26,27,48] have studied the mechanism of anterior hypophyseal control by the hypothalmus. Other studies [5,21,29] have concerned themselves specifically with hypothalamic-pituitary control of ovulation in rabbits. These studies make it clear that the control is not neuronal, but humoral. All indicate that stimulation of the hypothalamus effects the release of a vasopressin from secretory neuronal cells, which is carried to the anterior pituitary via a venous portal system, and which there controls the elaboration of the pituitary gonadotrophins. In rabbits, copulation provides the stimulus to thalamus and hypothalamus which, following the same sequence and path, results in the elaboration of LH, so as to produce ovulation in about one hour.

Experiments regarding and utilizing the effects of histamine in the central nervous system [20,59] provide evidence of an intimate relationship between the hypothalamus and the rhinencephalic or limbic portions of the brain, and suggest that impulses from the limbic system are integral to the function of the hypothalamus in integrating and regulating neurohormonal reactions.

Marsh and Vollmer [43] suggest another neurogenic inhibition of ovulation: vascular changes, controlled by the autonomic nervous system, may lead to genital and gonadal congestion, with impairment of circulation, inadequate nutrition of the ovum, follicular atresia before maturation of the ovum, and irregular and continuous follicular growth from excessive pituitary gonadotrophins due to a lack of the inhibiting effect of hormone from *corpora lutei*.

Neurohumoral mechanisms influencing fertility in the presence of normal ovulation have been less extensively studied. Conclusive evidence has been produced [15,43,63] that tubal spasm and decreased tubal peristalsis, produced by autonomic imbalance, are important causes of infertility in the female, and Fischer [15] suggests that similar autonomic effects upon the male reproductive apparatus can cause infertility in the male.

Scharrer and Scharrer [60] have demonstrated that oxytocin is produced by neuro-secretory cells in the hypothalamus, then transported along the nerve cell axons through the hypophyseal stalk to the nerve terminals in the neurohypophysis, where it is stored and released. This work and its corroboration supplants the previous belief that oxytocin is produced by the neurohypophysis. Heiman [24] has carefully reviewed the experimental evidence of the effect of oxytocin upon fertility. Oxytocin is produced and/or released during coitus, parturition, suckling, certain emotional stimulation, and, experimentally, by tactile stimulation of the genitalia. Oxytocin has been shown to have differing effects upon the smooth muscle of the reproductive system depending upon the phase of reproductive activity during which it is produced and becomes effective. During parturition, it produces contractions and peristaltic movements which aid in the expulsion of the fetus. During and immediately following coitus, however, the peristaltic waves move in the opposite direction, and have been shown to be of vital importance in sperm transport up into the fundus of the uterus and into and along the tubes. Interference with this mechanism results in decreased fertility.

II

Emotional turmoil and conflict is capable of disturbing so delicately balanced a system. Cannon [7] first documented the control of humorol and autonomic functions exercised by the emotions. It is also currently held that the hypothalamus is intimately related both to the expression of primitive emotions and to the autonomic nervous system, and serves to engender and integrate viscero-somatic expressions of instinctual drives.

The somatic expressions of emotion with which this paper is concerned are the "vegetative organ neuroses," following Alexander's classification [1] and not the conversion reactions. His definitions are:

Conversion reactions: symbolic resolutions of emotional conflicts occurring in structures supplied by the voluntary nervous system.
Vegetative organ neuroses: physiological concomitants of prolonged, unresolved tensions, from excessively stimulated organs innervated by the autonomic nervous system.

To the latter classification could be added:

Organs under hormonal control.

The bulk of studies have indicated the pituitary-adrenal axis as the effector organs in body response to emotional stress, and work cited in the previous section identifies the hypothalamus as a major brain site for the control of stress responses. Evidence is accumulating for the inclusion of the limbic system as vital to the integrating and effecting of stress response, as in Sawyer's work.[59] Another group of investigators [22,23,36,37,38] has done extensive experimentation with electrode implantation and the stimulation, recording and destruction of this area in cats, monkeys and humans. Their results provide strong evidence that the limbic system is specifically involved in the response to psychological stress, and in the initiating and mediating of the complex neurohumoral adaptive responses to stress, involving the hypothalamus, anterior and posterior pituitary, and adrenals.

Selye's work [62] is the most extensive in this general area of the relationship between emotional stress and bodily disease. It is perhaps his principal thesis, which he documents with overwhelming detail, that emotional stress is an effective "Alarm Reaction," and produces the "General Adaptation Syndrome"; emotional stress can produce physiological responses which, if prolonged, result in somatic disease and damage. The principal endocrine response to stress is a shift in anterior hypophyseal hormone production, giving increased ACTH, and decreased GH, FSH, LTH, and TTH. The characteristic response of the female sex organs to systemic stress is ovarian atrophy and amenorrhea, as illustrated in war amenorrhea from emotional stress. Selye relates some types of delayed puberty to the General Adaptation Syndrome, and finds amenorrhea and diminished fertility to be a result of stress occurring after puberty.

Exploring this relationship from another direction, Benedek and Rubenstein [4] have demonstrated consistent correlations between unconscious emotions and thought processes, and changes in the metabolic gradient of specific gonadal hormones.

Of the specific reproductive system dysfunctions, amenorrhea has perhaps been most convincingly demonstrated to have frequent psychogenic roots. Many writers [10,12,13,29,30,39] report single cases or series of cases of amenorrhea which were demonstrated to have been related to emotional dysfunction. One series[10] was specifically shown to exhibit a hormonal imbalance corresponding to Reifenstein's hypothalamic amenorrhea. Cotte[8] interrupts the autonomic discharge assumed responsible in amenorrhea and other pelvic disorders by the surgical procedure of presacral neurectomy, and claims good results over many years.

In studies[3,54,64,66] of large numbers of women in concentration camps, although the figures vary (as did conditions in the various camps), more than 50% of the women in all the series reported, except[66], developed amenorrhea immediately upon internment. Malnutrition was not considered an adequate cause, because the onset of the amenorrhea occurred before the effects of malnutrition could become important, because there was a spontaneous return of menses in a large percentage of the women while still interned under the same conditions, and because not all the women subject to the same nutritional deprivation developed amenorrhea.

The relationship between infertility and emotional factors has received less detailed attention. Selye[62] produced evidence that ovarian atrophy and diminished fertility result from emotional stress. Dunbar's[12] review of the literature includes cases of infertility influenced by hypnosis. Marsh and Vollmer[43] list five local somatic changes contributing to infertility which they attribute to emotional conflict: 1. vascular changes with genital and gonadal congestion; 2. endometrial hypoplasia due to hyperestrinism from anovulatory cycles; 3. irregular uterine motility; 4. excess cervical secretions leading to low grade vaginal infections; and 5. tubal spasm.

Tubal spasm has been most studied and best documented with respect to the role of psychogenic factors. Stallworthy[63] has demonstrated that at least 50% of apparent tubal blockage is due to tubal spasm, and believes that this spasm is probably related to autonomic nervous system activity as a reflection of emotional tensions, fears, etc. Fischer[15] and Kroger and Freed[33] support this view.

The function of oxytocin in sperm transport is believed by Heiman[24] to be subject to control by emotional impulses integrated through the limbic system and hypothalamus. Mirsky[48] has noted that noxious stimuli which release vasopressin in the hypothalamus do not release equivalent or proportionate amounts of oxytocin. This correlates with Sawyer's[59] observation that when histamine in the third ventricle produces a stress response in the rabbit, the essentially constructive event of ovulation does not occur; stress and ovulation appear mutually exclusive in his experiments. Adrenalin counteracts the function of oxytocin, although the site and mode of this antagonism is not clear. Heiman[24] suggests that pleasant emotions, specific sensory stimuli, and some conditioned responses stimulate the release of oxytocin, while emotional stress such as fear either centrally inhibits the release of oxytocin, or exerts this effect through the action of the adrenalin released in stress. Thus emotional stress can interfere with fertility through the inhibition of the elaboration of oxytocin, and/or the counteraction of its function, resulting in disturbances in sperm transport. He postulates a major neuro-psycho-hormonal reflex arc, with its center in the supraoptic and paraventricular nuclei of the hypothalamus. Its afferent limbs are sensory fibers from erotogenic zones, emotional and autonomic impulses, all integrated in the limbic system and funneled into the hypothalamus. Its efferent limb is hormonal. In this way, emotional responses exert their effects upon reproductive functions.

III

The recognition of the major role played by emotional conflict in the genesis of reproductive disorders has led to the attempt to discover whether specific emotional pathology could be correlated with specific somatic dysfunctions. If accurate, such correlations could advance the theoretical understanding of the interrelations between psyche and soma, and further the practical considerations of diagnosis and treatment.

Many workers in the broad field of psychiatric gynecology have attempted to delineate personality profiles, or descriptions of typical patients, to correspond with particular reproductive disorders. Mandy et. al.[40,41] describes two main types most likely to develop functional reproductive disorders: 1. *Physically and emotionally immature:* These women enter marriage to preserve the child-parent relationship, and can assume responsibilities only if a sufficiently dependent relationship is maintained; this relationship is threatened by a child. They are typically feminine in appearance, but are somewhat juvenile, shy, quiet, indecisive, easily embarrassed and fatigued, have multiple somatic disorders, and may collapse under moderate pressure into schizoid episodes. They seldom overtly reject a child; if they live in a protected environment with enough help, they may appear as sweet, gentle, devoted mothers. 2. *Aggressive, masculine-competitive:* These are strong, ambitious, dominating women with intense drives toward independence. They are often successful career women to whom marriage is a convenient social institution, and for whom a child would be in the way. They openly reject the feminine role, and regulate any child's life with absolute discipline and schedule.

Dunbar's [12] profile of the frigid woman is quite similar to that of the obsessive-compulsive character: not overtly sexual, socially restrained, dominating at home. She points out that not all women become frigid for the same reasons, and enumerates three different types, related to the unconscious motives. Kroger and Freed [34] describe the nymphomaniac as generally frigid, easily excited erotically but failing to achieve release of sexual tension, incessantly searching for the male who will give satisfaction, resorting to unusual practices, excessive masturbation, and great length of foreplay, and using sex to discharge non-sexual tensions. They express clearly, however, that many different unconscious motivations may lead to the end result of nymphomania.

Benedek and Rubenstein [4] demonstrated that typically there were specific unconscious emotional responses to the hormonal changes of the menstrual cycle. Their results are presented in considerable documented detail; in general, estrogen activity is accompanied by heterosexual interests and tendencies, and progesterone activity is accompanied by passive receptive and narcissistic attitudes. These changes in the direction of unconscious concerns reflect closely the fluctuations in the metabolic gradient of the specific gonadal hormones, and occur in emotionally healthy as well as in emotionally disturbed women.

A number of studies and papers have restricted themselves to the menstrual disorders, and have sought to delineate in particular the emotional conflicts which interfere with the menstrual cycle. O'Neill [52] considers amenorrhea to result from rejection of the feminine role, whether due to guilt and fear regarding sexuality, or to envy of the male. Nemiah [51] in a study of amenorrhea in anorexia nervosa, found three areas of conflict: problems of oral sexuality, inability to relate to the world in an adult manner, and immaturity, infantilism, emotional coldness, and poor interpersonal contacts. Moulton,[50] also studying the combination of amenorrhea and anorexia nervosa, considers these patients basically opposed to growing up, menstruating, facing men and marriage. She found increased symptoms with increased ovarian activity and suggests that the increased sexual stirring accompanying the high hormone levels may be responsible for the exacerbation of symptoms. Menninger [45,46,47] points out that women generally recognize that anxiety, depression, and other painful emotions can cause or inhibit menstruation. He lists the causes of menstrual irregularities as hostility toward the husband, avoidance of coitus, and the punitive symbolic self-infliction of the unconscious wish to castrate the husband. As emotions are "recorded" in the glands and smooth muscle, amenorrhea and dysmenorrhea, as well as frigidity, vaginismus, sterility, and pernicious vomiting, all record rejection of the feminine role. Kelley et. al.[30] studied intensively a series of cases of secondary amenorrhea, and found the following psychopathological correlations: psychosexual immaturity, oral conflicts, and schizoid thinking. They stress the fact that the unconscious can conjure up symbolic dangers to which the individual will respond as if they were real, and describe their subjects as all behaving, physiologically and psychologically, as though they had never reached puberty. It will be noted that the unconscious rejection of the role of the mature sexual woman is a characteristic in all of these studies of amenorrhea.

Other workers have studied the correlation between infertility and emotional conflicts. Deutch [11] comments upon the frequent association of sexual guilt with sterility, and states that the most frequent cause of sterility is unconscious fear of everything sexual. She enumerates five types of psychogenically sterile women: 1. women who are physically and psychologically infantile, but who have normally functioning organs; 2. women who channel their motherliness toward their husbands; 3. women who channel their motherliness toward other interests and ideologies; 4. women who are masculine-aggressive in character; 5. women who are severely disturbed emotionally, and who fear the additional burden of children. O'Neill [52] regards sterility as related to the unconscious rejection of pregnancy. Kroger [32] considers sterility a result of serious psychic conflict regarding the feminine role, pregnancy, and childbearing.

Brody [6] compared 20 functionally sterile women with 15 organically sterile and 20 fertile women, using the Rorschach, Thematic Apperception Test, and an autobiographical questionnaire. The functionally sterile group of women was characterized as functioning constantly at a regressed, neurotic, infantile level, and living in magic dependence upon mother. Among the 15 organically sterile women, 5 were psychologically normal, and 10 resembled emotionally the functional group; this suggested that organic infertility may be a somatic acting out of a neurotic conflict. Six of the functionally sterile patients were analyzed, and five of these six had children following the analysis.

Rubenstein [58] studied five sterile women, and determined the central conflict in all five to be a hostile identification with the mother. Four became fertile after analysis.

Kuhn [35] reports an 18 year old girl suffering from amenorrhea following the loss of her sweetheart. Her menstrual disorder was reversed during psychotherapy. Orr [53] is one of several to report a case of pregnancy in a sterile couple following the decision to adopt a child. In his case, both partners were analyzed, and in each there were factors mitigating against acceptance of a pregnancy: The husband needed to be dependent upon his wife as a mother, and encouraged her working and not having children; the wife's parents had wanted a boy, and treated her as a boy, and she found this same unwelcome situation repeated in her marriage. This couple made the decision to adopt only after they could modify the above problems, and pregnancy resulted before the adoption was carried through.

Of special interest, in view of the case to be reported in this paper, are the only two cases of patients in psychotherapy with hypoplastic uterus which this author could discover. Dunbar [12] quotes Wengraf as reporting a case of a 24-year-old frigid woman who had an "infantile" uterus with a plum-sized fibroma; after psychotherapy, her uterus had grown and the fibroma had disappeared. Jacobson [28] reports a woman of 35 who was amenorrheic for 19 years following two years of regular periods just after menarche. She had repeated gynecologic studies and hormone therapies to no avail, and examination revealed atrophic uterus and non-functional endometrium. This patient became pregnant in the eighth month of analysis, but no examinations were quoted regarding objective changes in uterine size.

It will be seen that a pattern begins to emerge from this welter of material. It is clear that, in general, none of the women studied with functional reproductive disorders were psychologically mature, and that this immaturity centered largely about the sexual functions. Women with amenorrhea and infrequent menstruation routinely reveal unconscious fear and avoidance of the adult sexual role of gratifying sexual intercourse, conception, and motherhood. Where persistent infertility is a primary complaint, intensely hostile emotions toward the mother become conspicuous additions to the above constellation. While certainly no one "type" of patient invariably develops one specific disorder, it is suggested that when a particular physiological function is fraught with fear and guilt, inhibition and disturbance of that function may frequently result, and that some similarity of persons with similarly centered conflicts and similar symptoms is not surprising.

IV

This paper is concerned with a patient who originally presented herself as a psychiatric problem, who was suffering from a severe hysterical personality disorder with symptoms of frigidity, infrequent menstruation, infertility and intense lack of self-esteem. There has been little written on the hysterical character and much confusion surrounds the term.

All of Freud's work on hysteria concerns the "defense psychoneurosis" of hysteria, characterized by the classical conversion symptoms. The closest he came to a description of this disorder was in his paper on libidinal types,[18] in which he described the "erotic type" as having her main focus on love and on being loved; this type is governed by the dread of the loss of love, and is particularly dependent upon those who may withhold love.

There was no clear distinction between hysteria and the hysterical character in the early literature. Reich[55] gave the first careful description of the hysterical character, emphasizing the obvious sexualization and provocativeness of behavior, the suggestibility and imaginativeness, compulsive need to be loved and admired, dependence upon others for self-esteem, intense feelings of inadequacy, great capacity for dramatization and somatic compliance, repression or acting out in concealed ways of any aggression, easy disappointment reactions, and the unexpected changes of behavior. He pointed out particularly the apprehensiveness when the sexual provocativeness seems close to attaining its goal. He believed that this represented fixation at the genital level, with its incestuous attachment; pregenital strivings represented repression of genitality, with the mouth symbolizing the female genital; this explained the frequent oral regression.

Wittels[67] emphasized fixation on the infantile level, and the tenuous contact with reality which the hysterical character has.

Fenichel[14] summarized analytic thought, and still makes no clear distinction between the neurosis and the character. He relates the character traits to the conflict between intense fear of sex and intense sexual striving. His description includes the characteristics already mentioned, and he terms the end result "pseudo-hyper-sexuality."

FitzGerald[16] doubts that the hysterial character develops without love deprivation in childhood, which leads to the habit of love-craving and emotional dependence. He notes that these persons generally become involved in hasty, incompatible marriages in order to escape from home. Their love-craving leads to insatiable demands, and they are often frigid. He also notes successful sublimations to be histrionic ability, humanitarian vocations, and skill with children. He states that "hysterical illness" is precipitated by emotional crisis in these people.

Horney[25] gives perhaps the fullest description of the kind of interpersonal difficulties which the hysteric's needs precipitate. The hysteric expects of love what it cannot give. Because the insatiable demands for love must remain unfulfilled, a self-perpetuating cycle of frustration is set up, in which the lack of fulfillment produces even greater needs and fears of rejection. Angry, resentful emotions reveal themselves in the coercive and accusatory quality of the dependency. The personal responsibility to deserve and maintain love is completely disregarded; the attitude develops that "if he *really* loved me, then I would be well, he would do anything for me, and he *should* love me because that's what I need."

Marmor[42] challenges the classical opinion that the hysterical personality is fixated at the phallic or early genital phase. He points out the general recognition of the prominence of oral mechanisms in hysterics, and urges that fixations at the oral period really determine this personality development. He believes that the blatantly sexual or Oedipal material conceals the more important, deeper oral dependency concerns. He supports his thesis by reasoning that if hysteria were a fixation at the most nearly mature level, it should be the most easily cured. This is clearly not the case as this pattern is most difficult to modify. Readily utilized severe oral regressions, such as addiction, depression, and even schizophrenic episodes, characterize the hysteric's reaction to stress.

Chodoff and Lyons[9] abstracted all the descriptions of the hysterical personality, and derived the following essential traits: 1. vain and egocentric; 2. labile, excitable, but shallow affectivity; 3. dramatic, attention-seeking, histrionic behavior; 4. sex consciousness and provocativeness; 5. frigidity and fear of sex; and 6. demanding dependency. In a study of 17 cases of conversion reactions, only three of the patients had hysterical personalities. Thus they delineate the hysterical personality as a separate entity, distinct from the conversions, and requiring independent consideration as an illness.

V

The patient whose history and treatment provided the stimulus for this paper was first seen in March of 1955, at the age of 20.

S. was a Jewish girl born in Chicago in 1934. Her early parental relationships, and the various relationships between her mother and a variety of father figures were quite confused. Her mother had eloped and married her first husband, A., at a very early age; the marriage was annulled. She then married her second husband, E., who was the father, presumably, of S. and of a four-year-older sister. This marriage was stormy, with violent arguments and many separations, and when S. was four, they separated permanently. S. never knew this real father until her adolescence; at that time, he was a "drunken bum." Her mother married her third husband, J.R., immediately following the divorce, and had, presumably by him, two more daughters, four and eight years younger than S. This marriage was equally stormy, but they managed to remain together through the time of S.'s beginning treatment. Throughout both latter marriages, her mother apparently had a continuous affair with A., the first husband, whom S. met when she was 9. S. idolized him, called him her "fairy godfather," and was encouraged by both her mother and A. to consider him her father.

S. thought that her mother wanted children, and was probably warm to her at first; her mother has in later years said that S. was her favorite. But from her earliest memories, S. had hated her mother. She was described as a vulgar, cruel, emotionally explosive person who made many suicidal threats and gestures. S. was usually farmed out to relatives during the many separations, and she doubted that her mother really wanted her. When, at age six, S. got her own room, she used it for a retreat from her mother and from the parental fights and would "write volumes" about her hatred of her mother.

She described her step-father, J.R., as a coarse man, with whom there was no early closeness. She envied her young sister, and felt left out, because J.R. was the sister's real father, whereas he was only her step-father.

The family and all relations were orthodox Jews, but S. could never recall sharing their religious views.

The family's socio-economic status was as unstable as was everything else about it; there were long periods of real poverty, with occasional periods of relatively comfortable means. Most of her childhood was spent in the tenement areas of Chicago, even when the family was in better circumstances; she remembers one fairy-tale-like apartment in a building in one of the city's worst areas. She was always afraid of the other children in these neighborhoods, and was closest to her older sister, who was her protectress. She was too frightened to fight back, and tried to gain immunity by being sweet and kind. She developed the technique, while still in her latency, of pleasing the other children by telling them her dreams or by making up fairy stories, and this was apparently quite successful.

After S. met her mother's lover, A., at age nine, she was used as the intermediary and confidante in the affaire. She delighted in this intrigue and in her part in arranging the assignations. She condoned everything, considered it a very sad love story, and often advised them to marry. She apparently repressed, however, any thoughts of intercourse between them.

S.'s earliest remembered sexual experience was at about age eight, when a man exhibited himself to her, and at which she recalls only fear. When she was nine, she had a recurrent experience with an older, strange man who would sit next to her in the movies; he would stroke her legs and genitals, but apparently there was no digital penetration of the vagina. She was tremendously excited, and very guilty, at this sex play.

When she was ten, her step-father began making these same advances to her, and for about two years there were frequent occasions of genital petting by him while she remained passively lying in bed with him. She was again terribly guilty and very excited, and longed to stop the activity, but the pleasure was so great that she would always answer no when he asked her if she wanted him to stop. He often told her never to let anyone do this to her, and warned her that if her mother ever found out, she would kill them both. She had no memory of ever seeing J.R.'s penis, of ever having an orgasm, or of her vagina ever being penetrated. She finally mustered the nerve to break off this relationship, and since that time J.R. has been repulsive to her.

Following the discontinuance of her sex play with J.R., she began a series of mutual mastubatory experiences with other adolescent girls, which lasted about three years; this consisted of genital strokings, again without digital penetration. She only engaged in this activity with girls she did not like. Again, there was the combination of great pleasure and intense guilt.

Menarche did not occur until age 14; she was prepared for it, and welcomed it as a symbol of maturity. She menstruated only about once a year, and at 17, she went to a gynecologist, who from her description, probably performed a dilation and curretage. Her reference to this experience was, "The doctor did some terrible things to me." Following this, she menstruated two to four times a year up through the time of entering therapy. Although the details were not available, she reported that she had numerous examinations by various gynecologists, and had had various forms of treatment, with no change in her menstrual function.

The constant moves of S.'s family resulted in frequent school changes which were always distressing to her. She would repeatedly go through the process of feeling a complete outsider, would strive for acceptance, and achieve it, only to have to change schools. Her efforts for acceptance included the playing of any role expected of her, including pretending fanatical Judaism during the period when her family sent her to a Hebrew parochial school because of her lack of religious convictions. She was always successful in becoming an important and popular member of her group, but this was "always because I was pretty, and always through boys"; this route to acceptance devalued the acceptance in her eyes. She dated more than average, but restricted her sexual activity to kissing and mild petting.

She met her husband, J., when she was 16, and was immediately attracted to him; he was handsome, gentile, "a man," and an "intellectual" in the bohemian sense of the word. He began making sexual advances to her on their first date, and within two months they were having intercourse. Their first sexual relationship was one in which S. performed fellatio "to avoid intercourse." Shortly thereafter, they began having intercourse. She was not orgastic, and was very disappointed: "the expected greatness didn't come." On one occasion when she was coming home disappointed after having slept with J., she got into a sexual conversation with the taxidriver, and eventually allowed him to masturbate her. This was the occasion of her first remembered orgasm, and this, like all of her sexual activity, was accompanied by extreme guilt. He was old and ugly, and her explanation was, "I didn't want nasty old sex with somebody nice and handsome whom I loved."

She and J were married when she was seventeen, and she was precipitated by him into a bohemian and carefree life among avant garde intellectuals. She felt she thrived in this life, and she began to turn her own considerable talent to various artistic and musical pursuits. She worked from the beginning of the marriage, often at quite responsible positions, which she usually fulfilled quite satisfactorily, although she had a compulsion for stealing countless useless objects such as paper clips, memo-pads, typewriter ribbons, etc., from her employers. When J. decided to enter medical school, they moved to the city in which they were living when she entered therapy.

Her sexual life with J. had been quite chaotic, and usually unsatisfactory. From the beginning she was unsatisfied with normal intercourse; she preferred clitoral manipulation, and was aware of distinct reluctance to have him penetrate her. A diaphragm and spermicidal gel were used for contraception, but the use was at best irregular. She had never become pregnant in spite of the irregular practice of contraception. (J. was known to be fertile,[49] having fathered a child prior to his marriage to S.) She would become most excited when he would verbally phantasize, while manipulating her clitoris, his having an affaire with another woman, during which they were saying degrading things about S. On such occasions, she had what she called a "clitoral orgasm." This complex was very guilt-producing, and she frequently would lash out at J., blaming him and venting her guilty rage upon him. There were also frequent episodes of threesome activity, always involving another woman along with herself and J. She usually instigated such activity, but was usually distressed to discover that the girl was more interested in her than in her husband. She often experimented with passively permitting sexual play and cunnilingus by the girl, but without deriving pleasure. She had fears of being "queer," and wished to stop this activity.

At the time when she applied for therapy, she was employed as personnel manager in a department store. She was afraid that she was going to have an affaire with her immediate superior, an older man, and this fear precipitated her application. By the time therapy began, she had had intercourse with him several times. She was again not orgastic, but, although guilty, she derived some pleasure because "for once someone needed me and not the other way around."

When she presented herself for therapy, she was very attractive, red-haired, dressed with dramatic flair and seductiveness, and made a great show of sophistication. Evident beneath this veneer was intense anxiety, and a complete lack of self-esteem and identity-formation. Her openly expressed—and more important—motives for therapy were the feelings of inadequacy, lack of identity, and guilt over her chaotic sexual background.

A Rorschach revealed a "markedly infantile personality, beset at present by preoccupation with sexual matters and anxieties ranging from the free-floating variety to definite phobic fears . . . Her emotional responsiveness is largely to the world around her, and it is somewhat uncontrolled and impulsive. She is obviously threatened by the male figure . . . Her emotional disturbance is so pervasive at present that the resources she might bring to therapy are not easily seen." Since the symptoms, the history and the Rorschach indicated the possibility of an underlying schizophrenic process, it was decided to begin her therapy on a less intensive basis (three times weekly), pending clarification of her basic ego integration, before commencing reconstructive (analytic) therapy.

At the outset of therapy, there was an overwhelming production of material, a compulsion to reveal all the "bad" things about herself, as in a confessional. But most important was her immediate use of her standard defenses in any relationship with a male: first was seductiveness, then the appealing helplessness of a child, and finally angry, demanding coerciveness. As one after another technique in her repertoire failed to elicit the usual male response, she entered a period of considerable depression, in which her feelings of being a worthless nothing came prominently into awareness. Her sense of loneliness and of being unloved in childhood by her mother produced intense needs to have the analyst be a mother to her, accompanied by hopelessness due to her expectation of a repetition of her unhappy relation with her mother. Some early associations began to emerge which revealed that her feelings of being "a nothing" were related to her being a woman and lacking a penis. The intensity of these feelings, plus a growing positive transference, led to a retreat to her earlier defenses, and there was a period of considerable vacillation between using these resistive defenses, and trusting the analyst and herself sufficiently to experience and explore her painful self-perceptions.

Her treatment behavior throughout these early months was largely coercive, and she was enraged that there was no response to her seductiveness and her helpless pleas by taking care of her like a magic parent and thus making her well without effort on her part. She regarded the analytic role as evidence of indifference to her. As she began to realize the motives of her seductiveness, she began also to depreciate herself as a purely sexual object to men, and some recognition of her actual dislike of sex began to emerge. These insights into her behavior and needs opened the way to the beginning of a more realistic evaluation of her marriage, which had been entered into for just such motives, and which was totally unhappy and unsatisfactory. She became more and more aware of her tremendous hostility to men as selfish and sexual beings who satisfied their needs through her, instead of fulfilling her own.

At this time, due to her own concern and request, she was referred to a gynecologist who specialized in problems of infertility. He first saw her on 3/6/56, and found a "hypoplastic anteflexed uterus; uterine sound passed with some difficulty, uterus measuring 5 cm." He placed her on "cyclic sterol therapy with various estrogenic hormones." S. reported to him that her menstrual cycle became more regular; in therapy she continued to report irregular, but somewhat more frequent menses. She reported that his younger associate had, like almost all the men of her acquaintance, made passes at her. Such a circumstance could throw some light upon her reporting a different result to him than she reported to me.

In spite of her awareness of her motives and of their inappropriateness in therapy, she continued to express both a refusal to work further on her behavior, and a decrease in therapeutic motivation. This situation existed at the end of the first year of therapy, and represented a fear of further exploration of her unconscious. Although this was a severe hysterical character disorder, it was now clear that there was no underlying schizophrenia. It was deemed advisable to test her motivation by offering her analysis if she wished to work on her conflicts, or termination if she did not. This precipitated her recognition of her ambivalence concerning growth, and produced a flurry of demands to "have her cake and eat it too," in terms of remaining in therapy while not modifying her treatment behavior, clearly revealing her frustrated omnipotence and rage at the environment for not changing to fit her expectations. She was unable to avoid more realistic insights into her motives and goals, and she began more accurately to perceive her marriage in the context of her neurosis. This brought about both a firm decision to grow up, and also the intention of leaving her husband. A severe depression resulted from her fear of separation and being alone with her inadequacies, and she began a period of intense sexual promiscuity, acting out her search for a father-mate who would fulfill the unrealistic needs that J. could not meet. Although she was non-orgastic, this acting-out gave sufficient pleasure through the overwhelmingly successful use of her primary defenses, that once again she refused to deal with her feelings, and a three-month time limit was set for her to demonstrate her ability to enter meaningfully into analysis. During this phase of promiscuity, as well as during all others later in therapy, S. practiced infrequent contraception though having intercourse with numerous men of proven fertility; she never became pregnant.

Her promiscuity continued unabated, but she began real introspective work. For the first time, it became clear that her inability to achieve orgasm was a refusal and inability to lose control in coitus. She now could recall orgasms in her sex play with her step-father, J.R., and that to avoid unbearable guilt, she pretended that she was not actually participating in the activity. She began revealing masturbatory phantasies in which ugly men would make advances to her under degrading conditions, and initiate sex play and coitus while being abusive to her; she would pretend to take no part in this, as though her own desires were not involved, thus denying guilt and achieving orgasm. She recognized that this was a recreation of the incestuous activity, and therefore the fact that the great pleasure of orgasm with J.R. produced even greater guilt. Thus, in order to avoid the guilt, she repressed the pleasure; sex was only acceptable as long as it was not pleasurable. A secondary gain of her non-orgastic sexuality was her ability thus to act out her rage toward men by making them look like fools, defeating and enslaving them by making them lose control sexually while she remained aloof and superior, non-participating and non-orgastic. Her marriage was therefore a haven from real sexual pleasure and guilt, and separation represented exposing herself to these dangers. Because of her chronic guilt, her promiscuity also served the purpose of furnishing justification for her guilt. She was able to see that when she felt guilt, she would transform it into guilty rage, which would produce further acting-out and further guilt, a cycle which had her promiscuous acting-out continuing at a feverish pitch, including some passive homosexuality. Material also emerged revealing that her behavior constituted revenge against her mother by outdoing her sexually.

The analytic work eventually produced an increase in self-esteem and a decrease in acting-out, culminating in a final and decisive separation from her husband. This action abruptly precipitated an outburst of even greater promiscuity, homosexuality, and masturbation, with degrading phantasies and homosexual phantasies, and brought on a real panic in which she begged to be stopped from her actions. It could then be interpreted to her that the real motive of her promiscuity with men was to protect her against the perverse thoughts and masturbatory phantasies, which provided the greatest pleasure and temptation, and thus the greatest guilt. By having a man make love to her, she was both persuaded that she was sexually normal, and protected from being alone and vulnerable to the most frightening phantasies. This was the purpose J. fulfilled, and as her relationship with him deteriorated, she needed more and more lovers to take his place. Since her intense sexual urges and pleasures were fixated upon objects and situations which symbolized J.R., the guilt became associated with sexual pleasure, so she could not allow pleasure even in appropriate circumstances. Interpretation of these major areas at the height of her panic had a dramatic effect in removing both her anxiety and her promiscuity.

There followed an extended period of working more deeply into her hostility to, and fears of, men. Her compulsive stealing and her feeling of never having received enough from men led directly into dreams and phantasies of openly castrative wishes: her frequent performance of fellatio was castrative, in that it reduced an erect penis and prevented penetration; intercourse was also castrative, in that she made the penis limp. In these ways, she used her sexuality to further hurt and retaliate against men.

During this time S.'s mother divorced J.R., and became a more openly sexual woman. This produced an increase of sexual feelings toward mother, and resulted in temporarily increased promiscuity. Constant homosexual feelings and activity accompanied this phase of work, which involved her extreme misconception of sex. Since her hostility toward men was castrative, her fears were also of castration: the greatest danger in coitus was castration through the mutilative attack and penetration of the penis. In her phantasies, this had already occurred, so that the fear and rage were reawakened with each sexual act. In this light, her homosexuality became a seeking of the reassuring absence of the damaging penis. In addition to the previously guilty associations with sex pleasure, the pleasureful aspects of sexuality were subjugated to the competitive aspects, both with mother and with men.

Working through these conflicts was followed by the beginning of real sexual feelings in the transference, in replacing the earlier defensive provocativeness. She recognized her anger and guilt at being the one to lose control with J.R., and was now reversing roles with men. She interpreted analysis as the analyst's wish for her once again to lose control and be orgastic, while the analyst remained non-participating, like J.R., and the development of an acceptance of sexual pleasure equalled a reenactment of the incestuous scene; she therefore had to resist analytic influence in order to avoid guilt. In this transference phase, however, she began to have more courage in feeling sexual desires, and could begin to imagine for the first time, mutual pleasure and mutual loss of control. She had intense phantasies of her incestuous desires, and for the first time experienced orgasm upon digital penetration. Phantasies of sex plus love in the same relationship were for the first time possible. This Oedipal transference was acted out as directly as possible by her having an affaire with a man whom she identified directly with the analyst. This afforded the most nearly normal approach to a combination of sexual pleasure and affection which she had not yet experienced, but the guilt was so great that she regressed again into a period of anxious acting-out, with a confusion of her ultimate goals, and a resurgence of seductiveness in the transference. Once again the transference situation was: to successfully seduce the analyst equalled getting his penis, remaining the man, remaining in control; the alternative was (in failing to seduce) to accept her role as a woman.

At this time, near the 350th session, S. met her future second husband, A.F. He was Jewish, fourteen years older than herself, quiet, loving, and considerate. She began to feel love toward him, and to experience regular loving orgasms through digital play, though not with the penis. S.'s conscious ego ideal had by now greatly modified; she now worked toward the goal of settling down into the role of a good housewife and mother. Toward this end, she was unconsciously hoping that her mother, on a forthcoming visit, would disapprove of her open sexual relationship with A.F., and thus reinforce her striving toward more acceptable behavior. The whole relationship with A.F. was seriously set back, therefore, when her mother, now living with and engaged to her first husband, A., visited them, stayed in the same apartment with them, and condoned the entire affaire. Once more, as during her pubescent relationship with J.R., mother did not apply an urgently wanted and needed control; her relation with A.F. therefore, became a re-living of the incestuous relationship, and there was increased guilt and decreased pleasure from her sexual activity. Sexuality with A.F. was hostile retaliation against mother, and therefore a further source of guilt. This led to her recognition that her adolescent homosexuality had been a retreat to a less guilt-laden and more acceptable form of sex.

These reawakened conflicts, which had been largely worked through, no longer had the same paralyzing force, however, and S. was able to reestablish her loving relationship with A.F., eventually achieving, for the first time, the ability to feel love and affection for the man during the sexual act. This realization of her sexual potential brought into awareness what appeared to be a truly nuclear anxiety: The fear that orgasm would be so overwhelming and intense as to disorganize her entirely and disrupt her ability to apply any controls to her sexuality, thus making her completely wanton and controlled by desire. She was firmly convinced that once orgasm was experienced, control was totally impossible, and her own background and experience affirmed her conviction; she had never known one man or woman, including her step-father, who had displayed sexual control in her presence.

The working-through of this phase proved to be the crucial point in analysis. She felt forced by her omnipotence and her retaliatory castrative rage to seduce and destroy the analyst as the one person who had withstood her advances; at the same time, she was terrified that she might succeed and so lose the only example she had that sexual control was possible to achieve. As her need to test out and resolve this conflict became clearer, her anxiety increased to near panic. Her agitation mounted and continued through about two weeks, during which she moved physically closer and closer, eventually sitting next to and leaning against the analyst as though in his arms. She did not act out further and terminated the physical closeness spontaneously, being thus confronted with both his and her own capacity to control. This opened the way for the major interpretation that her acting-out in the transference indicated that she herself had had the incestuous desires, demonstrated by the fact that she had made the advances when she could not force the analyst to do so; having to assume the responsibility herself for her desires had brought forth in full force the guilt of her own Oedipal wishes, and had resulted in her intense agitation. Her guilt was not primarily because of her sexual actions, but because of her desires; therefore, sex without desire could be tolerated, but the desire, and therefore the pleasure, had to be completely repressed.

This was followed by conscious phantasies of coitus with J.R., and a period of regression in her dreams and general sexual functioning. She resolved to marry A.F. as soon as her divorce was final, and began talking of termination. This seemed to be not only a hostile retaliation against the analyst and an avoidance of the Oedipal guilt, but also a testing to determine if she would be allowed to break away from her Oedipal attachment and move into a non-Oedipal one. As this was accepted, and it was indicated that termination was her decision, there was an intense period of working through remaining conflicts. She was able to recall conscious desire for coitus with J.R., and that on one occasion she did see his erect penis during sex play. She remembered not only her desire, but also her fear at the size of the penis as it appeared to a little girl. The infantile roots of her fear of intercourse were revealed in her memory of wondering what would happen to her if he actually penetrated her vagina with the penis: Would it keep growing until she died? Would it stay in her? Would it somehow do something to her that could never be altered? Would the feeling of orgasm be so intense that it would kill her?

Her regressive function subsided, and she regained greater orgastic capacity with A.F. She reported with great joy (February, 1958–no comment about this in the gynecologist's summary) that she had been examined, her uterus had grown, she was perfectly normal, and could now have children. She and A.F. were married in a double wedding, with A. and her mother. S. felt quite well satisfied with her general functioning. She had no further motivation for analysis at that time, although she still had one complaint: she still could not achieve orgasm on penile penetration alone, but required prior manipulation. However, she felt that this was not enough to motivate continued analysis in the face of her general self-satisfaction, and terminated with the anticipation of possibly returning to analysis after further life experience.

She terminated in March of 1958, and in April was found to be pregnant. A follow-up Rorschach administered in June, 1958, by the same person who had given her one previously, revealed ". . . none of the flightiness which characterized her previous record. The patient appears less anxious, for although there are still signs of anxiety on this record, they do not have the pervasive and panicky quality as before. She seems to be able to internalize some of her feelings more effectively, and there is little of the sexual preoccupation noted before. It is as if she feels more 'comfortable' with her sexual urges, and can manage them in not so destructive a manner. She still shows impulsivity in her reactions, and the general picture still contains elements of infantile reactions. But the overall impression is one of great strides in treatment." She had a normal pregnancy and delivered a normal male infant.

VI

Descriptively and dynamically, the characteristics of the hysterical personality correspond in all important modalities with those of the patient described. She perceived herself as a sexy-acting nobody, a pretty little girl who had been mistreated and unloved as a child and who therefore never found out who or what she really was. She liked to present herself as a sophisticated intellectual, and she cherished the phantasy that some day the world (her parents) would discover that the girl they had been neglecting as Cinderella was really a princess after all. Her most prominent adaptive pattern was the use of her extraordinary beauty to obtain the attention, love and care she needed, primarily from men. She made seductive use of her appearance, but was distressed and angered when men responded. Prior to analysis, she characteristically withdrew without sexual performance. Her combination of beauty, appealing child-like dependency, and satisfactory work performance, made it possible for her to achieve the status of favorite daughter to any employer. Her basic intelligence and dramatic ability, plus a creative imagination, made it possible for her to assume virtually any role required for acceptance in any group, including the reputation for hyper-sexuality without ever following through with performance. She thus reassured herself both of her adequacy as a sexual woman, and of her acceptability and loveableness as a person. She frequently found herself in conflict with women, and although this distressed her, she did little to modify it, generally ignoring them and feeling contemptuous of them.

She had no secure ego formation, and could derive no self-confidence from an inner evaluation of herself as an established and worthwhile identity, but molded herself invariably to fit external expectations. She had constant need for the love of a father, and used sexuality inappropriately and repetitively to achieve this status. This technique automatically resulted in conflict with mother, and fear of her retaliation.

She felt that she could only achieve the love she wanted by being a sexual object for father, and allowing him to gratify his sexual needs at her expense. This produced extreme rage toward father, plus fear of mother's retaliation. She perceived father as an attacking and selfish creature with a mutilating weapon (penis), from whom she wanted love, but who would damage (castrate) her if she submitted. Beneath these fears were her own Oedipal wishes, augmented by her hatred of her unloving mother; the wishes and the hatred-produced guilt. The guilt stemming from her Oedipal wishes was too great to sustain, so it was transformed into guilty rage, and added to her existing rage against father. The guilty fear over her desire to revenge herself upon mother by stealing father was also transformed into guilty rage against mother. She felt that if she only possessed father's weapon (the penis), she would be safe from the mutilating attack by father, which she phantasized had already occurred and castrated her. Each coital act stirred up fear and rage over this phantasized attack and castration. Her non-orgastic sexuality and preference for fellatio allowed her to avoid the guilt of her own desire for incestuous pleasure and revenge upon mother, by allowing her to maintain the phantasy of non-participation, and secondarily served the purpose of enslaving, humiliating, and castrating (by taking away his erection) the attacking male. Her homosexual phantasies and activity were a retreat from the guilt-laden Oedipal attraction, a seeking of sexual pleasure in the reassuring and less fearful absence of the penis-weapon, and a means of getting closer to her overtly sexual mother.

Her early childhood in the unhappy marriage of her rejecting mother and her unknown, thus obviously ineffective, father set the pattern for her lack of security and self-esteem. Her mother's third marriage, also unhappy, continued the pattern, and the advent of two younger sisters furthered her sense of not belonging. The world of fantasy early became a welcome escape from her unhappiness, and a means of imaginary retaliation against a mother who apparently took out her own frustrations upon her children. As puberty approached, and her sexual urges became more insistent, their aim toward the incestuous object was unquestionably increased by her need to retaliate against her mother. The eventual sexual activity with her step-father was undoubtedly a result of her seductiveness as well as of his own pathology. The fear, guilt, and rage thus stirred up determined the fixation of her own character formation; she repressed her sexual desires and capacity for orgastic pleasure in relationships with men, and retreated into homosexuality. Her subsequently reestablished relationships with men remained without orgastic pleasure, and repetitively reenacted her seductive attempts to gain father's love and to defeat mother, while also expressing her castrative rage toward father.

Her natural endowments afforded abundant success in her efforts to gain affection and acceptance, but the superficial results provided no real security or identity, and her underlying hostility and guilt prevented any genuine affectional relationships.

VII

Since this patient corresponds closely with the diagnostic criterion of the hysterical character, some correlation between emotional conflict and reproductive dysfunction may be discernible. One of the standard features mentioned in the description of hysterical character is pseudosexuality with frigidity. This, of course, was a main complaint in this case, and is also a major symptom in the more extreme development of this disorder, nymphomania. Particularly during the periods of promiscuity, S. was certainly nymphomanic; she had the chaotic sexuality, excessive masturbation, need for long foreplay, and the inappropriate use of sex to discharge non-sexual tension.

More specifically: in amenorrhea and infrequent menstruation, the emotional conflicts most frequently revealed were the rejection of the female role either because of sexual guilt and fear or because of penis envy, with associated infantility and the wish not to grow up sexually, avoidance of coitus, castrative hostility toward the husband, and oralization of sexuality. These traits are thoroughly descriptive of this case. When infertility is a factor, the hostility toward mother and the hostile identification with her become an additional consistent finding; this also rounds out the description of the case presented. This case bears out in every particular the emotional pathology which has been generally found to be associated with her type of reproductive system pathology.

The exact state of her endocrine function is unknown; that it was disordered is clear both from her menstrual disturbance, and from the fact that some change was effected by artificially introduced sterol cycles. It is possible to speculate, but not to document, that her type of amenorrhea was possibly the hypothalamic type as described by Reifenstein; the complicating psychogenic factors noted in this type were abundantly in evidence, and there was no evidence from other symptoms or organ systems of primary pathology in the anterior pituitary, the ovaries, or the endometrium. She was unquestionably under stress of the most severe and chronic nature relative to her sexual function, and Selye [62] has demonstrated that after puberty, such emotional stress expresses itself through endocrine balance shifts to produce amenorrhea and infertility.

The fact of this patient's hypoplastic uterus, and the absence of any indication that her uterus had at one time been normal in size and function, but had then undergone involution, suggests that whatever the neurohumoral dysfunction which produced it, it had existed before puberty. The same lack of evidence for any primary ovarian pathology again indicates that the uterine underdevelopment resulted from secondary ovarian hypofunction; in such cases failure of uterine development is linked to anterior hypophyseal hypofunction before puberty. Selye [62] has shown such gonadal developmental failure to be a specific concommitant of emotional stress with its accompanying hormonal shifts; the normalcy of other organ systems regulated by anterior pituitary hormones, rules out primary pathology of that organ. The history of this patient reveals that her sexual guilt, and therefore her emotional stress, was at a peak in the prepuberty period, at just that time when the gonadotrophic hormones show their highest increment of increased elaboration, and when maximum development of the secondary sexual organs occurs.

It seems reasonable, therefore, to postulate that the intense sexual guilt, fear, and rage which this patient experienced constituted adequate emotional stress to disturb the normal balance and elaboration of gonadotrophic hormones and thus to inhibit the development of mature reproductive organs and function.

One must be extremely cautious in designating the causes and reasons for the eventual mature development of this patient's reproductive function. Proper sterol therapy alone has sometimes overcome menstrual and fertility disturbances. That it did so alone in this patient is open to question. Her menstrual irregularity and infrequency improved, but there was an extraordinarily abundant testing of her fertility for almost two years following the cyclic sterol therapy, without pregnancy. It is probably not coincidental that her final reproductive development and capacity for more mature sexual function coincided with her working through most of her sexual conflicts, and with her emotional readiness to assume the mature role. The premise supported by this paper is that emotional and physical aspects of an individual's life are inseparably interrelated, and it would seem insupportable to claim the validity of either emotional or physical influences to the exclusion of the other. In this case, as an illustration of many others, it seems reasonable to assign a significant role in the inhibited development and the eventual maturation to long lasting emotional influences in life and in therapy. These findings warrant further investigation in the area of the inhibition of physical maturation and function concommitant with emotional conflicts centering about the specific organ system.

REFERENCES

1 Alexander, F., *Psychosomatic Medicine,* New York, W. W. Norton, 1950.

2 Allen, E., and Doisy, E. A., "Ovarion Hormone; Preliminary Report on Its Localization and Partial Purification, and Action in Test Animals," *J.A.M.A.,* 71:819, 1923.

3 Bass, F., "L'Amenorrhee au Camp du Concentration de Terezin," *Gynaecologia,* 123:211, 1947.

4 Benedek, T., and Rubenstein, B. B., "The Correlations Between Ovarian Activity and Psychodynamic Processes: I. The Ovulative Phase," *Psychosom. Med.,* 1:245, 1939; II. The Menstrual Phase, *Psychosom. Med.,* 1:461, 1939.

5 Bos, C., and Cleghorn, R. A., "Psychogenic Sterility," *Fertil. and Steril.,* 9:84, 1958.

6 Brody, H., *Psychologic Factors Associated with Infertility in Women,* Doctoral Dissertation, New York University, 1955.

7 Cannon, W. B., *Bodily Changes in Pain, Hunger, Fear and Rage,* New York and London, D. Appleton, 1929.

8 Cotte, G., "Techniques of Presacral Neurectomy," *Am. J. Surg.,* 78:50, 1949.

9 Chodoff, P., and Lyons, H., "Hysteria, the Hysterical Personality and Hysterical Conversion," *Am. J. Psychiat.,* 114:734, 1958.

10 Decourt, J., Joyle, M. F., Laverge, G. H., Michard, J. P., "Amenorrhea of the Mental Anorexias; Clinical, Biologic, and Biochemical Aspects," *Ann. d'Endocrinol.,* 11:6, 1950.

11 Deutch, H., *The Psychology of Women,* Vol. II, New York, Grune and Stratton, 1945.

12 Dunbar, H. F., *Emotions and Bodily Changes,* New York, Columbia Univ. Press, 1954.

13 Easser, R., "A Case of Amenorrhea Showing Psycho-hormonal Interrelationships," *Psychosom. Med.,* 16:426, 1954.

14 Fenichel, O., *The Psychoanalytic Theory of Neuroses,* New York, W. W. Norton, 1945.

15 Fischer, I. C., "Psychogenic Aspects of Sterility," *Fertil. and Steril.,* 4:466, 1953.

16 FitzGerald, O. W. S., "Love Deprivation and the Hysterical Personality," *J. Ment. Sci.,* 94:701, 1948.

17 Ford, E. S. C., Forman, I., Wilson, J. R., Char, W., Mixson, W. T., and Scholz, C., "A Psychodynamic Approach to the Study of Infertility," *Fertil. and Steril.,* 4:456, 1953.

18 Freud, S., "Libidinal Types," in *Coll. Papers,* Vol. 5, London, Hogarth Press, 1952, p. 247.

19 Friedgood, H. B., "Neuroendocrine and Psychodynamic Factors in Sterility," *West J. Surg.,* 56:391, 1948.

[20] Fuche, J. and Kahlson, G., "Histamine as a Stimulant to the Anterior Pituitary Gland," *Acta Physiol. Scandinav.*, 39:327, 1957.

[21] Harris, G. W., "Hypothalamic Control of the Anterior Pituitary Gland," in: *Ciba Foundation Colloquia on Endocrinology*, New York, Blakiston, 1952, p. 106.

[22] Heath, R. G., et. al., *Studies in Schizophrenia.* Cambridge, Harvard Univ. Press, 1954.

[23] Heath, R. G., and Leach, B. E., "Multidisciplinary Research in Schizophrenia," in: *Changing Concepts of Psychoanalytic Medicine*, ed. S. Rado and G. E. Daniels, New York, Grune and Stratton, 1956, p. 201.

[24] Heiman, M., "Reproduction: Emotions and the Hypothalamic—Pituitary Function," *Fertil. and Steril.*, 10:162, 1959.

[25] Horney, K., *Overemphasis on Love*, ACAAP Lecture Series, 1946.

[26] Hume, D. M., "The Role of the Hypothalamus in the Pituitary-Adrenal Cortical Response to Stress," *J. Clin. Invest.*, 28:790, 1949.

[27] Hume, D. M., "The Relationship of the Hypothalamus to the Pituitary Secretion of ACTH," in *Ciba Foundation Colloquia on Endocrinology*, New York, Blakiston, 1942, p. 87.

[28] Jacobson, E., "A Case of Sterility," *Psychoanalyt. Quart.*, 15:330, 1946.

[29] Kamman, G. R., "The Psychosomatic Aspects of Sterility," *J.A.M.A.*, 130:1215, 1950.

[30] Kelley, K., Daniels, G. E., Poe, J., Easser, R., and Monroe, R. R., "Psychological Correlations with Secondary Amenorrhea," *Psychosom. Med.*, 16:129, 1954.

[31] Klinefelter, H. F., Albright, F., and Griswold, G. C., "Experience with a Quantitative Test for Normal or Decreased Amounts of Follicle Stimulating Hormone in the Urine in Endocrinological Diagnosis," *J. Clin. Endocrinol.*, 3:529, 1943.

[32] Kroger, W. S., "Evaluation of Personality Factors in the Treatment of Infertility," *Fertil. and Steril.*, 3:542, 1952.

[33] Kroger, W. S., and Freed, S. C., "Psychosomatic Aspects of Sterility," *Am. J. Obst. and Gynec.*, 59:867, 1950.

[34] Kroger, W. S., and Freed, S. C., *Psychosomatic Gynecology*, Philadelphia, W. B. Saunders Co., 1951.

[35] Kuhn, R., "Zur Daseinanalyse der Anorexia Mentalis," *Nervenarzt*, 24:191, 1953.

[36] Leach, B. E., Heath, R. G., and Strohmayer, F. B., "Effects of Subcortical Stimulation on 17-ketosteroid Excretion in Monkeys," *Fed. Proc.*, 14:242, 1955.

[37] Lesse, H., *Fed. Proc.*, 16:343, 1957.

[38] Lesse, H., et. al., "Rhinencephalic Activity During Thought," *J. Nerv. Ment. Dis.*, 122:433, 1955.

[39] Loeser, A. A., "Effect of Emotional Shock on Hormone Release and Endometrial Development," *Lancet*, 1:518, 1943.

[40] Mandy, T. E., Scher, E., Farkas, R., and Mandy, A. J., "The Psychic Aspects of Sterility and Abortion," *South. M. J.*, 44:1054, 1951.

[41] Mandy, T. E., Weinberg, P., Rudolph, A., and Mandy, A. J., "Psychosexual Conflicts: Their Implications in Functional Pelvic Disorders," *South. M. J.*, 48:533, 1955.

[42] Marmor, J., "Orality in the Hysterical Personality," *J. Am. Psychoanalyti. A.*, 1:656, 1953.

[43] Marsh, E. M., and Vollmer, A. M., "Possible Psychogenic Aspects of Infertility," *Fertil. and Steril.*, 2:70, 1951.

[44] Mazer, C., and Israel, S. L., *Menstrual Disorders and Sterility*, New York, Hoeber, 1947.

[45] Menninger, K. A., "Somatic Correlations with the Unconscious Repudiation of Femininity in Women," *J. Nerv. Ment. Dis.,* 89:514, 1939.
[46] Menninger, K. A., "Psychogenic Influences on the Appearance of the Menstrual Period," *Internat. J. Psycho-Analysis,* 22:60, 1941.
[47] Menninger, K. A., "Influencias Psicogenicas en la Aparicion del Periodo Menstrual," *R. Psicoanal. B. Aires,* 6:141, 1948.
[48] Mirsky, I. A., "Physiologic, Psychologic, and Social Determinants in the Etiology of Duodenal Ulcer," *Am. J. Digest Dis.,* 3:285, 1958.
[49] Monroe, R. R., Personal Communication.
[50] Moulton, R., "A Psychosomatic Study of Anorexia Nervosa Including the Use of Vaginal Smears," *Psychosom. Med.,* 4:62, 1942.
[51] Nemiah, J. C., "Anorexia Nervosa," *Medicine,* 29:225, 1950.
[52] O'Neill, Desmond, "A Psychiatric View on Gynecology and Obstetrics," *Postgrad. M. J.,* 26:64, 1950.
[53] Orr, D. W., "Pregnancy Following the Decision to Adopt," *Psychosom. Med.,* 3:441, 1941.
[54] Peretz, –, "Gormin Psihosomatiyim b'alveset," *Harefuah,* 46:189, 1954.
[55] Reich, W., *Character Analysis,* New York, Orgone Institute Press, 1949.
[56] Reifenstein, E. C., "Psychogenic or 'Hypothalamic' Amenorrhea," *Med. Clin. North Amer.,* 30:1103, 1946.
[57] Reynolds, S. R. M., *Physiology of the Uterus,* London, Hamish Hamilton, 1939.
[58] Rubenstein, B. B., "An Emotional Factor in Infertility," *Fertil. and Steril.,* 2:80, 1951.
[59] Sawyer, C. H., "Rhinencephalic Involvement in Pituitary Activation," *Am. J. Physiol.,* 180:32, 1955.
[60] Scharrer, E. and Scharrer, B., "Hormones Produced in Neurosecretory Cells," in: *Recent Progress in Hormone Research,* ed. G. Pincus, New York, Acad. Press, 1954, Vol. 10, p. 183.
[61] Selye, H., *Textbook of Endocrinology,* Montreal, Acta Endocrinologica, 1947.
[62] Selye, H., *Stress,* Montreal, Acta Endocrinologica, 1950.
[63] Stallworthy, J., "Facts and Fantasy in the Study of Female Infertility," *J. Obst. Gynec. Brit. Emp.,* 55:171, 1948.
[64] Sydenham, A., "Amenorrhea at Stanley Camp, Hong Kong, During Internment," *Brit. M. J.,* 2:159, 1946.
[65] Weinstein, B. B., Personal Communication.
[66] Whitacre, F. E., and Barrera, B., "War Amenorrhea," *J.A.M.A.,* 124:399, 1944.
[67] Wittels, F., "The Hysterial Character," *Med. Rev. of Reviews,* 36:186, 1930.

Psychoanalytic Psychotherapy and Casework: Treatment of Choice

by Frank Winer, Ph.D.
Postgraduate Center
for Psychotherapy

Frank Winer, Ph.D.

The author is principally engaged in private practice, and is on the staff of the Psychiatric Clinic at the Norwalk (Conn.) General Hospital. He is currently on leave of absence from the Postgraduate Center for Mental Health, where he is a senior staff member of the Research Department.

PSYCHOTHERAPY is, by definition, a psychologic treatment method for emotional disorders. Casework is directed at the resolution of social problems. Whether or not it is treatment, will vary with a given instance.

Casework and psychotherapy may be utilized concurrently, as in child guidance where members of each discipline work as a team, each maintaining separate functional responsibilities.

However, there is an aspect of casework which does constitute treatment and which in certain instances, is appropriately to be regarded as an alternative to psychoanalytic therapy. It concerns primarily, efforts to alter deviant and pathologic behavior. It is carried out by psychologic processes, rather than by administration of social resources. Historically, it represents a departure from the point of view that social problems can be understood only in terms of economic causation, and arose out of a recognition, sharpened by psychoanalytic insights, that social problems of the individual can also be understood in psychologic terms. Its object, however, is not fundamental psychodynamic alteration but the maintenance or increase of the individual's ability to deal effectively with his environment. It seeks to do this by strengthening the ego's capacity for integration through techniques of a supportive nature, and clarification of feelings as well as through educative and informational techniques. Its area of study is the ego.

Casework treatment is frequently referred to as counseling. It is carried on extensively in family service agencies, where the problems presented lie in the area of interpersonal adjustments within the family, between husbands and wives, and parents and children.

Though an individual with a given neurosis has the tendency to react in a predictable way from situation to situation, the same individual may also react in significantly different ways in different situations. The reason for this becomes clear when we direct our attention not only to the character of the neurosis, but to the meaning of the situation, as well. A particular environmental situation may serve to promote or disturb the individual's adaptive capacity. Ackerman illustrates this in the following way: "For example, a psychoneurotic male with strong castration fears may be totally impotent with his wife, and strong as a bull with another woman. In other words, though he is affected by or, we might say, enjoys the same neurosis in both relationships, as a person he is differently integrated in the two situations, and the psychosocial consequences of neurotic conflict are correspondingly different." [1]

This phenomenon is seen frequently in family relationships. Sometimes, as one member of a family gets better in therapy, other members may also show improvement—or they get worse—but, in either case, this illustrates that maladaptation is not only a function of neurosis but of interaction with others in the environment. We often see how two neurotic partners may, in their interaction, support each other and make for more adequate functioning of each. The quality of a relationship, therefore, cannot be understood in simple terms of health or ill health of each member, for traits that would be considered liabilities in two individuals may be complementary when the same individuals live with each other.

The implication of this phenomenon is that psychologic help need not be directed at the resolution of neurotic conflicts, but at the establishment of a balance between people in a relationship, however neurotic each of them may be.

It is this unitary nature of inner and outer forces as they merge in ego functioning that makes for an inevitable overlap in the activity of caseworker and psychotherapist, but each has his characteristic orientation to this phenomenon which must be preserved. When the psychotherapist concentrates unduly on helping the patient effect a balance of relationships, his attention may be diverted from intrapsychic factors; and, likewise, when the caseworker focuses on the neurotic psychodynamics, this may result in ignoring the problem of reality adaptation for which help is being sought.

Workers in both fields, then, are interested in the problem of adaptation; but in line with their unique traditions, professional purpose and competence, each approaches the matter differently. Casework endeavors to promote constructive reciprocal interaction by working with more than one family member, and by attempting to achieve a workable and mutually gratifying balance between them. In psychotherapy, the individual is helped to interact with his family through resolution of his own neurotic conflicts. This means, further, that in psychotherapy help is limited to enabling the individual to use his own resources for the solution of his problems, while casework help may even involve the use of occasional concrete resources or environmental manipulation, if it will promote equilibrium.

Casework treatment is often geared to the resolution of crises and emergencies in the family which may threaten its equilibrium or its unity. Psychotherapy views the situational crisis as symptomatic, as a by-product. Each field operates on a different psychic level, the content of psychotherapy being the analysis of the defense mechanisms and unconscious conflicts, while the caseworker's area of analysis is confined to the mostly conscious aspects of the ego's adaptation to reality.

With respect to the psychodynamic process involved, psychotherapy depends largely on the interpretation of the transference for stimulating significant insights, while the casework process depends on a warm, positive relationship which is felt as supportive and conducive to the acceptance of encouragement, guidance, and learning.

Psychotherapy can be effective only when the patient is dissatisfied with himself and is seeking self-improvement. Successful casework requires that the individual be dissatisfied not with himself, but with his social situation, though he must also be willing to alter his own behavior in relation to his situation.

With these differences in mind, let us turn to the question of treatment of choice. What criteria can be utilized in determining treatment of choice? Since psychotherapy is the more intensive process and operates on deeper levels, it has been maintained in the past that treatment be determined on the basis of the severity of pathology, with the "less ill" as candidates for casework treatment. But experience teaches that, as a criterion, the degree of pathology has limited validity. In some instances, the severity of pathology may make an individual a poor candidate for therapy, and a more suitable one for casework treatment. In actuality, the people who present themselves in family agencies for help with interpersonal problems suffer no less from psychopathologic disturbances than those who seek the services of the psychotherapist. This opinion is supported by the findings of Coleman,[2] who studied and compared a psychiatric clinic and family service agency in the same city. In his words, "On the whole, it may be said that people with very much the same kinds of problems come to the attention of both agencies. They are people with long histories of chronic maladaptation, with rather poorly developed psychologic coping capacities, and with relatively little expectation that they are likely to receive the help they need or are looking for."

If we turn to what the patient asks of us as a criterion for treatment of choice, we are on more solid ground, since what he asks affects his motivation for change. But even his request is still not a definitive factor because, as therapists, we must decide whether we should regard such a request as a resistance to be worked through, or go along with the patient's definition of his problem in terms of his reality or interpersonal situation. Because psychoanalytic psychotherapy is directed at uncovering the roots of the maladjustment, its results ordinarily promise to be more far-reaching, reliable and durable. For this reason, as a general rule, it is to be regarded as the treatment of choice. The fact that the patient presents his complaint as a marital conflict, rather than as a neurotic disability may, in this sense, be regarded as a resistance to be worked out. However, there are general circumstantial factors in which the patient's focus on his reality situation leads us to regard casework as the treatment of choice. These factors are:

1. When the resolution of a social emergency in the life of an individual (or his family) takes precedence over resolution of his intra-psychic conflicts.

2. When the individual's personality limitations make his unconscious conflicts inaccessible to him for all practical purposes, but permit his working out his reality problems with the help of the caseworker.

3. When a family is (a) so deteriorated that the children are neglected or encouraged to delinquency; or (b) so disorganized that the family is in danger of disintegrating, despite the wishes of the parents to hold it together; or (c) so lacking in gratification, and so full of conflict and frustration, that the individual's reality problems appear overwhelming to him and prevent work on intra-psychic conflicts.

Clearly these are general criteria. In a given case, a decision as to treatment of choice will depend on a total evaluation of diagnostic and prognostic factors. I would like now to elaborate on each of these circumstances.

1. *When the resolution of an emergency or a crisis in the life of an individual (or his family) takes precedence over resolution of his intra-psychic conflicts.*

At times, the most pronounced manifestation of developing mental illness will involve the threatened failure of the individual to discharge his social roles. Apart from its meaning as a manifestation of illness, the failure to perform certain social roles is a social crisis in the life of the individual and his family, the resolution of which may take precedence over psychotherapy itself.

When key members of a family, such as father or mother, are in danger of collapsing in the performance of their roles, the future of the entire family may hang entirely in the balance. In the face of possible collapse of a family, the most pressing problems are realistic, practical ones. The question for the helper in such an instance is "How can we bolster this individual so that he can continue to function?" The solution of such a problem often requires vigorous activity on the part of the helper, with firm guidance and encouragement of the patient, manipulation of his environment, education of significant people in his life so that they may be supportive to him, or neutralization of their destructiveness to him—the kinds of activity which family agencies are particularly able to perform, by virtue of their structure, function, and experience.

Even when such efforts prove to be in vain and the individual does collapse, the effects on the family are, in general, less deleterious if, in the meantime, the family has been induced to adjust to the patient as the ill member of the family, or is assisted in carrying on without his aid.

Furthermore, from the point of view of the therapeutic outcome, there is an advantage in working with a patient who continues to function, rather than with one who has already withdrawn and found comfort in the secondary gains of his illness, or whose hopefulness and self-esteem have been damaged by incapacitation. This is often especially true with children, whose withdrawal from peer relationships, for example, is characteristically accompanied by feelings of worthlessness, inferiority, and hopelessness about ever being able to compete successfully with others. This point is well recognized by children's workers, who advocate the child's continuing in school, even in the face of his anxiety about leaving his home, or developing the child's learning skills which will assist him in relation to other children.

Situations in which the social crisis takes precedence are analogous to those situations in which a medical crisis takes precedence. If an individual suffers from a psychosomatic illness which endangers his life, it makes no difference that the etiology may be rooted in psychic factors. What is required is medical intervention to keep the patient alive. And so it is with social crises which, if not resolved, may have disastrous consequences and may later render psychotherapeutic treatment impossible.

2. *When the individual's personality limitations make his unconscious conflicts inaccessible to him for all practical purposes, but permit his working out of his reality problems with the help of the caseworker.*

With regard to the individual's accessibility to treatment by psychoanalytic psychotherapy, though we would all agree that limitations do exist, it is scarcely possible to mention a specific limitation without its sounding too arbitrary. The development of new or modified techniques, many of them based on reality-oriented measures, has taught us to think less absolutely and with more hopefulness about personality limitations. Furthermore, variations between individuals are such that general rules cannot be established. For example, though old age restricts flexibility, it does so in varying degrees, from individual to individual. No single criterion is sufficient for deciding on the suitability of a patient for psychoanalytic therapy. A total evaluation of strength and pathology is required. Even individuals whose motivations for therapy seem minimal can sometimes become significantly involved when character defenses are penetrated. In a particular case, whether the prognosis justifies the time and effort involved in remobilizing the latent conflicts, will depend on the diagnosis, including the patient's readiness and ability to understand and cooperate, as well as on his flexibility.

Certain patients with character disorders display a complex of characteristics, which often make them better candidates for casework treatment than for psychoanalytic therapy. They are of two types, (a) certain oral narcissistic characters, and (b) certain obsessive characters.

(a) The narcissistic characters: I am speaking here of individuals who feel so deprived that they retain a semblance of integration only if their egos are utilized in securing gratification for themselves, with little or no capacity to "give" or relate themselves to anyone else. Because they must "give" to themselves first, their anxiety is experienced in relation to being cut off from external supplies, and motivation for treatment is the desire to change the frustrating environment, rather than to change the ego. Their tolerance to frustration is low, with ego functioning becoming quickly impaired when postponement of gratification is necessary. In desperation, they tend to act out explosively, violently and destructively to themselves and everyone else.

Because their defense of narcissism is syntonic, they can be approached in treatment only if they are helped to achieve the narcissistic gratification they seek—if it is not too difficult or does not take too long. They can be aided only to the extent that they recognize what behavior on their part defeats the narcissistic purpose, and what behavior serves it.

Scherz [3] has presented in some detail the technical method involved in working with marital partners with narcissistic disorders. In a marital case which she describes, the behavior of both husband and wife was characterized by pervasive immaturity and repetitive impulsive acting out, with infantile neurosis incorporated into the character structure. Husband and wife fought incessantly, and each complained constantly about the other, neither showing discernible signs of self-awareness, guilt or anxiety. They fought constantly with words, as well as, at times, with teeth, fists and unbolted household equipment. They fought about money, frequency of sexual intercourse, and their respective responsibilities regarding earning a living and preparation of meals. The wife's motivation for seeking help was her fear of being deserted by her husband. His was expressed as "Marriage is better than nothing," illustrating his narcissistic attitude toward marriage. Both husband and wife were looking for a strong, protective mother, and the caseworker fulfilled certain aspects of this role in their lives. He was active, did things in their behalf as, for example, agreeing to contact the husband to invite him in for discussion. At one time, he went so far as to visit the wife at home when she was ill and unable to come to the office. Thus, pushing through resistance, he handled destructive behavior by firmly holding both partners to their responsibilities to each other—his to earn money, hers to cook—and by appealing to their narcissism, as when he told the wife that if she cooked, her husband would probably give her more money. All this was done with continued careful assessment of their low tolerance for reality demands, and full recognition of the psychic economy of the acting-out. Scherz, in her summary, says, "In a sense, the clients incorporated to the extent they could the caseworker's ego and super-ego. They learned from him specific desirable ways of handling themselves, personally and socially." [4]

It is clear that no psychodynamic alteration was sought, nor could reorganization of ego structure and defenses be reasonably accomplished by such an approach. But by "borrowing" from the caseworker his ego and super-ego, the couple sufficiently strengthened their own egos, so that their reality adaptation was increased and a significant improvement in their functioning took place.

(b) Certain obsessive-compulsive characters also lend themselves better to treatment geared to improving their function in various social roles, than to treatment aimed at psychodynamic changes. Some mothers who seek help primarily not for themselves but for their children fit into this category. They are able to see their problem essentially as one of management of the child, since the child's behavior is felt as a threat to their compulsive character structures. On this basis, they are able to accept specific advice on child-rearing (which they apply rigidly as rules) with some constructive results for the child and themselves. Glover calls this kind of treatment the substitution of an "artificial compulsion" which is less costly than the original.[5]

Some time ago, when a patient was expressing guilt about a hostile feeling he had, I pointed out that though we can assume responsibility for our behavior toward others, we cannot decide as to how we should feel. For weeks afterwards he referred to this comment as the most helpful one in his therapy. He used it to control hostile behavior and to reassure himself with regard to his feelings. He repeated it to himself in one life situation after another, often under inappropriate circumstances. Certainly, no psychodynamic alteration of his personality is involved; but there is no question that the integration of this "rule" into his compulsive structure was strengthening his ego.

3. (a and b) *When a family is so deteriorated that the children are neglected or encouraged to delinquency, or so disorganized that it is in danger of disintegrating despite the wishes of the parents to hold it together.*

A family-centered approach to treatment may be advisable in certain severe cases of family disorganization, especially when there are young children who are grossly neglected and abused physically and mentally. I am referring to situations which seriously violate our social standards regarding parental responsibility for the care and rearing of children. On the basis of his broader social obligation, the psychotherapist may decide that he can best discharge this responsibility by referral to a social agency. The resolution of such a situation, because it involves the participation of both husband and wife and their cooperation with each other, can best be handled in the family agency. Treatment in such cases must be directed toward breaking a vicious circle of retaliation and counter-retaliation between husband and wife, as a result of which the children are either neglected or used as pawns in the struggle. Sometimes, for the children's protection, and to minimize the destructive parental effects, other community resources, such as day care centers or community recreational facilities, may be utilized.

(c) *When a family is so lacking in gratification and is so full of conflict and frustration that the individual's reality problems appear overwhelming to him, and prevent work on intra-psychic conflicts.*

The woman patient who shows up for a treatment session with a black eye or other evidences of ill treatment by her husband is probably not only acting out her masochism, but is also presenting us with a reality problem that cannot be analyzed. Such a patient may be seeking sympathy from her therapist, on whom she wishes to project the power of protecting her from her sadistic husband. She may view herself as a "bruised child" who is responding (appropriately) to a hurt. Whether such a patient can be helped to gain insight into her behavior cannot, of course, be answered *a priori*, but it seems to me that the more realistic the sadism of the husband, the less favorable are the possibilities of the patient's understanding herself. In a given case, it may be necessary to refer husband and wife for marital counseling as a prologue to psychoanalytic psychotherapy.

Conclusion. In view of the vast shortage of personnel that exists, it is especially important that our efforts be expended as efficiently as possible, so that each individual practicing therapy perform with the highest possible skill in response to the needs of his patients. The referral of appropriate cases to family service agencies is not only of benefit to the patients referred, but also makes room for patients who can best use the service of psychotherapists. At this time, the criteria available for the choice of treatment—casework or psychotherapy—are crude and must be largely descriptive. It is to be hoped that in the future it may be possible to develop and refine such criteria; but this will come only if collaboration grows between the various disciplines engaged in promoting mental health.

REFERENCES

[1] Ackerman, Nathan: "The Diagnosis of Neurotic Marital Interaction," *Social Casework*, v. 35, April, 1954.

[2] Coleman, Jules, R. Janowicz, S. Fleck, N. Norton: "A Comparative Study of a Psychiatric Clinic and a Family Agency," *Social Casework*, vs. 37 and 38, January and February, 1957.

[3] Scherz, Frances: "Acting Out Character Disorders in a Marital Problem," *Social Work*, v. 2, January, 1957.

[4] ——. ibid. p. 50.

[5] Glover, Edward: "The Therapeutic Effect of Inexact Interpretation," *International Journal of Psychoanalysis*, v. 12, 1931, as reported in Fenichel's *Psychoanalytic Theory of Neurosis*, p. 557.

Therapeutic Problems and Techniques in the Analysis Of a Case of Character Neurosis; with Special Reference to the Concept of "Line in Therapy"

by Vincent S. Conigliaro, M.D.
Postgraduate Center for Psychotherapy

Vincent S. Conigliaro, M.D.

Dr. Conigliaro is assistant professor of psychiatry at Fordham University's School of Social Service, Associate Professor of Psychiatry at the Iona College Graduate School of Pastoral Counseling, and Director of Curriculum for the St. Francis Institute for Pastoral Counseling. He is also Director of Therapeutic Services at the Metropolitan Consultation Center in New York City, and has been associated with the Postgraduate Center for Mental Health as an instructor and community mental health consultant.

THE case of Ray being presented here illustrates the therapeutic and technical concept of "line in therapy." The concept of "line in therapy" emphasizes the importance of selective focusing and holds that unless "a line" is followed, therapy will be chaotic and disorganized or, at least, unproductive and inconsequential.

To "have a line" means: to focus only on those productions of a patient which relate to the phase of therapy, the patient's ego strength and defenses, and the readiness to utilize a given intervention and psychodynamic level of interpretation on the analyst's part. Therapeutic intervention is visualized as multipronged; but only one "prong" is permitted to *openly* stimulate the patient at a given time or period of therapy.

In view of the many considerations that must be observed in selecting a line, it is not possible to follow the same line with all patients, nor to formulate a universal blueprint that will apply to all cases. The concept that line-focusing should retrace, in reverse, the stages of psychodynamic development is too rigid and will excessively straight-jacket the analyst. In Ray's case, the oedipal line was gradually substituted with an oral line before the oedipal material had been completely analyzed; anal focusing has not yet become significant and will probably be utilized only after returning to the oedipal line. The patient's transferential postures and verbalization content remain a basic guide in the selection of a line, with two important qualifications; the analyst will have to be selective, and will have to determine whether resistential maneuvers are in operation behind a patient's seemingly genuine offering of a line. This was clearly borne out in Ray's analysis, where the patient's oedipal overtures were, at times, compulsively ego-syntonically determined and, at other times, subtly offered "red-herrings." There is also the possibility that the analyst's counter-transference will contribute to the selection emphasis or prolongation of a given line of therapy. Possibly, the only universal rules of lines are: (1) A line should be followed that is consistent with the phase of therapy; (2) A line should be flexible in all cases.

Ray's case was selected because he had been in therapy over two hundred hours, thus offering the opportunity to visualize the course of his treatment. He is a bright, verbal, dynamic individual, whose developmental defenses have been complex and have resulted in his involvement in complicated, realistic or intrapsychic predicaments which are, psychodynamically fascinating.

Ray is a soft-spoken, poised, sophisticated thirty-two-year-old Negro. He has been in treatment at the Postgraduate Center for Psychotherapy, on a twice-a-week basis for approximately four years. For the past two months of therapy he has come once a week.

Ray is Chief Psychiatric Social Worker in the children's unit of a state hospital. Over the past year, he has practiced psychotherapy as a member of the staff of a metropolitan community clinic. He has a Master's degree in Social Work and is currently pursuing studies leading to a doctorate. He is in his third marriage—to Pat, an American Negro divorcee, formerly a Psychiatric Registered Nurse with the same hospital that now employs Ray. His first marriage (to May, an American Negro woman, three years his senior) was dissolved in 1958, shortly after Ray had become the father of a male child. His second marriage (to Ida, an Afro-Cuban divorcee) was also terminated by divorce, early in 1960.

I saw Ray for his first session on October 13, 1959. He was handsome, neat, well groomed and spoke smoothly with perfect "Caucasian" inflection. His verbalization was slow and thought-out, as if he were weighing his words for their potential impact. He used a rich vocabulary, frequently interjecting appropriate psychiatric terms. He politely waited for me to "start the session," spoke only after being spoken to, never interrupted, and was always relevant in his replies. When his guard was lowered he was more openly compliant, deferrent, or even submissive. As all this was done with utmost dignity, one could miss both the passive compliance and the subtle pomposity underlying his politeness and courtesy; or mistake this pattern of behavior as simply a cultural reaction. He strove to convey a feeling of self-control, "reason-over-emotions," at-easness with himself.

His main lines of defense had been intellectualization, compulsivity and "role playing," and in his first meeting with me he illustrated these characteristics by presenting his history in an orderly, unspontaneous, constricted and artificial manner. Ray was playing the role of caseworker (was being the "caseworker of himself") and playing the role of patient as well. It was significant that he was not entirely successful in reducing his first sessions into letter-perfect ego-syntonic rituals; thus, while "giving the history" on mother, data pertaining to his wives or his babysitter seeped through; or, while talking of father, he might talk of his wives' paramours.

Ray stated he was seeking therapy because of marital discord; frequent sexual impotence *(impotentia coeundi* or *ejaculatio praecox);* occasional homosexual thoughts and homosexual anxiety of moderate intensity. All these symptoms he dated from about the time his first wife became pregnant. Ray also complained of "a tendency to get involved with too many women . . . extramaritally . . ."; generalized restlessness and tension; dissatisfaction with his status and his "performance as a husband, a professional, a student"; and feelings of boredom.

Ray was born and raised in Staten Island, New York, in a prevalently Negro neighborhood which was part of a larger, ethnographically mixed section of the borough. His parents were both born in New York. They had moved to Staten Island shortly after their marriage. Ray was the oldest of four children, having a brother three years younger, and two sisters, nine and thirteen years younger.

Ray's mother was a passionate woman, of strong convictions and volatile emotions. She was demanding, domineering, seductive, flirtatious. She was interested in community affairs and especially in civil rights. An active member of the N.A.A.C.P., she willingly devoted much time and energy to these matters. She had little interest in housekeeping and spent part of the day "in bed, smoking, eating crackers, listening to the radio—while father and I did housework." She often paraded around the house only partly dressed or, very casually, would drop in bed with Ray. (Ray remembered an instance, at the age of four or five, of being in bed with his mother, feeling highly aroused and rubbing himself against mother "who at times ignored me and went on reading—at times would abruptly tell me to stop squirming.") When Ray was younger, mother depended on him for menial household chores. Later, she would depend on him for "more important matters—things she should have discussed with father." At the same time she continued to engage in a bland, casual seductiveness.

Ray spoke of his father with intensity and a significant combination of grudging admiration and subtle contemptuousness. Ray's father was the fifth of six children, and because of financial difficulties could not finish high school. "He regretted it very much—he liked to study—he preached to us on end on the importance of education." He worked as a technician at American Cyanamide and as a part-time chauffeur with a limousine rental agency. He was sentimental, easily stirred by emotions, friendly, and jocular. He was firm and authoritarian with the children, whom he punished corporally "very harshly—but not cruelly—and never impulsively." He held Ray responsible, as the first-born, for his younger brother's mischiefs. When Ray was older, father would remind him that, in his absence, Ray was "first in command."

Ray's parents argued frequently, usually about trivial matters. "Mother always had her way—she was the power on the throne and behind the throne." After arguments, Ray's mother would often use Ray as a pawn against her husband. She would either take Ray and put him in bed with her, or get into Ray's bed herself.

Ray's relationship with his brother was openly competitive, at least through the first decade of Ray's life. Ray remembers with great clarity being seduced, around the age of four, by a baby-sitter, a girl in her late teens, whom Ray described as "demanding, impulsive, domineering." She engaged with Ray in an imitation of coitus. This "affair" continued until Ray was approximately seven, at which time the girl lost interest in Ray's penis and only wanted to "play," similarly, with his four-year-old brother. Ray remembered feeling "furious at the girl for her fickleness, and at my brother."

Ray was a precocious child, both intellectually and sexually. Sex was very much on his mind a great deal of the time. When he was not being stimulated by his mother's seductive behavior or by the baby-sitter's open seduction, it was one of his friends' mothers who occupied his mind. By the age of eight or nine he entertained frankly phallic daydreams concerning his friends' mothers or older girls in the neighborhood. Already, at this age, he was prone to become involved with older phallic, promiscuous girls. Still very vivid in his mind is the memory of a huge, muscular, athletic girl in her mid-teens, by whom he was fascinated when he was eleven or twelve. One day he tried to touch her breasts and she knocked him down.

In his teens, Ray was less openly timid and passive, more competitive but "smooth" in his "operations" (he saw everyday interpersonal relationships as "dealings" or "operations"). He was a good student through high school and college. With his instructors he was always formal, reserved, distant. He was reasonably interested in athletics but was handicapped by a lack of any really strong desire to be "first."

He was particularly interested in the opposite sex. He was more aggressive if he was certain of the girl's interest in him, but retained his qualities of surreptitiousness even then. When confronted with a woman already involved with another man, his interest would double and his approach become even more subtle. In his unassuming courtship, he actually "worked hard" at making the woman interested in him by collecting, in advance, jokes, conversational pieces, interesting information to entertain her and "to sweep her off her feet." He dated frequently, and had complete sexual relations from the age of fifteen. He went through periods in which his romantic life almost took on the characteristics of Don Juanism, but he was always cautious to avoid involvements and entanglements. Much as he enjoyed the sexual relief in itself, he enjoyed "performing" adequately, impressing his dates with his potency and smooth competency, showing off around town his most attractive conquests.

Ray first met May in 1949, when he was nineteen and a junior in college. She was twenty-two and a trained psychiatric social worker. Both he and May felt conscious of the age difference, and, Ray at least, of the difference in professional status. Ray courted her aggressively, but it was on May's initiative that, about eight months later, they became sexually intimate.

For a few months "it was a very pleasant relationship—she was attractive, intelligent—there were no ties." When they became fonder of one another, Ray felt "as if I was going to be trapped in something I knew nothing about." Ray began to feel that May had developed interest in "older, more accomplished men" and felt intensely jealous. Yet, when May reassured him that there was no one else in her life, he felt just as tense. When May told him that she wanted to get married, Ray broke the relationship twice, finally enlisting (September 1951) in the U.S. Air Force and fleeing to Texas for Cadet Training School. About six months later, May wrote to him in Texas, saying she was upset, had developed a duodenal ulcer, and a forty-two-year-old widower wanted to marry her. Ray wrote back immediately, announcing that he would marry her as soon as he could obtain a leave. Two months later he finally arrived in New York, planning to postpone the wedding until completion of training school. When May told him that unless he married her then, she would marry the older man, Ray gave in and married her. Thus, the first cycle of Ray's matrimonial tugs-of-war was completed.

Ray was nominally married to May from 1952 to 1958. Shortly after the wedding he returned to Texas and continued to behave as if he were still single. His letters to May were rare and sporadic. Between his compulsively active social life, and the fact that he did not study very diligently, he could not graduate, either as an officer or as a pilot.

Cadet School was much more than an escape from May. Ray wanted to become an officer. His personal responsibilities were again limited, and he was again allowed to be part of a great "happy" family. After the disturbing features of the involved heterosexual relation with May, he was now in the comparative safety of a uni-sexual environment, where women existed only peripherally and could be allowed in, or shut out, at will. It is not surprising that in the midst of his conflicts with May he should have sought out, adaptationally, this, and not another, type of environment. The fact that he managed to flunk out was a measure of his masochism, of his ambivalence about being first, and of his conflict between autonomy vs. dependency.

Discharged in 1953 from Cadet School, Ray returned to New York without notifying his wife and was reunited with her after a three-week "Roman holiday" in the city. During this interlude no one, not even his closest friends, knew that he was in New York. Once back with May, he tried, as compulsively as he could, to make a go of his marriage; "I tried to be a good husband." (Note the preoccupation with roles: In the Air Force, the role was "the gay and irresponsible cadet"; in the three week holiday in New York the role was "the reckless soldier on leave"; now he was going to be "the husband.") The next three years were comparatively calm. Ray enjoyed May sexually and intellectually. Everyday companionship with her was "taxing at times—for she was opinionated, dogmatic, domineering—but on the whole, not unenjoyable." She did not make many demands and, primarily, was a "dependable girl." On May's urging, and with her financial help, Ray decided to enter a school of social work (originally Ray had planned to become a lawyer). He never regretted this decision, and in 1957 he obtained his Master's degree. He began work in an institution for aggressive youth and found this work thoroughly enjoyable. But then, in 1957, May became "accidentally" pregnant.

Ray dates the beginning of the deterioration of his marriage from around this time. As we shall see later, the fact that May became pregnant and the mother of Ray Jr. did play a very significant part in the reactivation of Ray's problems. However, another important factor had been the following: In response to Ray's subtle bragging about his previous sexual exploits, May once reacted by flinging into Ray's face the fact that she too had had several sexual affairs before Ray's time. It was shortly afterwards that May became pregnant. It was also around this time that Ray had some minor sexual difficulties.

After May became pregnant, May and Ray became less interested in each other sexually. Ray spent more time away from home. At the beginning "May was so absorbed in her pregnancy that she did not ask too many questions." Later she would "bother and harass me incessantly with her jealousy." About five months later, at an alumni picnic, Ray met a young Afro-Cuban girl in whom he was soon to become very interested.

Ray described Ida as an "extremely attractive" divorcee, despite the fact that she had sustained a major amputation of her left arm. He mentioned her amputation very casually and only much later in therapy did he verbalize his feelings about it. He was equally casual in relating the fact that she had been married before. On their very first meeting, Ida told Ray very extensively of a U.S.A.F. captain, at the time in Germany, in whom she was very interested. Ray liked Ida and managed to meet her again at parties, social gatherings, and meetings of the N.A.A.C.P. About two months later Ray told Ida that he was married and that May was seven months pregnant. When Ida finally invited him to her apartment and Ray realized that they were going to be sexually intimate, Ray was concerned as to "what kind of sexual performance" he would give. Fleetingly he also thought: "Will I be able to satisfy her as much as Al?" With Ida taking the more aggressive role, they became lovers, and began to see one another frequently.

Ray decided to divorce May shortly after his son was born. He felt he had not really wanted to be married to May in the first place. He found Ida sexually more enticing. When Ida suggested marriage, Ray agreed. He told May that he no longer loved her, obtained a divorce settlement in which he left Ray Jr. to May and agreed to pay her alimony, and late in 1958 married Ida.

Ray found that Ida, too, could be "bossy and nagging—but as long as we had a satisfactory sexual relationship, life with her was not unpleasant." Ida was seductive and flirtatious, but initially did not give Ray reasons to be jealous. Ray was aware that Ida had had a rather "intense" sexual life before meeting him but "I did not let it bother me." Ida occasionally complained of Ray's intellectual, impassionate approach to everything.

A turning point in the relationship occurred when Ray was sexually impotent for the first time. Ray heard Ida whispering with a girl friend about a former lover of hers, extolling his virility and personality. "I heard her commenting on the size of his penis—on the wildness of his love-making—she said she used to be both aroused and frightened when he approached her—she said he was so big, once he hurt her deep inside." Ray felt tense and disturbed through the rest of the evening. When night came, and Ida, very passionately, wanted to make love, Ray was extremely anxious and completely impotent.

After the first three or four episodes of sexual impotence, a very stormy relationship ensued. Ida was often impatient, hostile, and contemptuous. Ray remained controlled and reserved, attacking her with cerebral sarcasm or by "psychoanalyzing" her behavior. Ida often delighted in telling Ray about her previous lovers or in comparing their sexual prowess with his. Ray lingered out of the house more and more and engaged frequently in casual, heterosexual relationships. When Ida began to suspect his extramarital philandering, she became even more resentful, hostile and sarcastic. With his wife, Ray was more and more frequently impotent. He had no sexual problems extramaritally. He began to be preoccupied with homosexual thoughts and occasional homosexual anxiety. He felt under great pressure stemming from payments to May, suspiciousness about Ida's behavior, and doubts about his masculinity. It was at this point that he decided to enter treatment.

Ray had been first diagnosed as, "anxiety neurosis, passive-aggressive personality, Oedipal problem." Ray's anxiety did not have the clinical features that would justify a diagnosis "anxiety neurosis."

I saw his anxiety, rather, as part of the generalized restlessness chronically experienced by character neurotics, and known to break, more or less frequently, through the characterological armor surrounding the ego. Being impressed by Ray's emotional isolation, general fastidiousness, concern with roles, performances and ego-syntonic rituals, my diagnosis was one of severe personality trait disorder, with compulsive and passive-aggressive traits. Dynamically, there was more than an Oedipal problem.

Early in therapy, I felt that Ray had a strong problem of identification. Ray's father was omnipotent with the children but dominated by his wife. He could lecture his children on the importance of education and self-sufficiency, but could not interfere with his wife's domination of Ray. Mother was inconsistent and elusive. She could ignore the pleas of an aroused Ray and entertain strangers in the parlor. She wanted at times to be a child herself. She could be a very hard master, who wanted to be served, and could be very demanding. To please her one had to be passive, or be used like a housemaid, or be used against father—or, as with the babysitter, used sexually only as long as one's penis is small enough. Identification with an incorporation of an often weak, feminine father and an often phallic, masculine mother had much to do in structuring Ray's polar characterological postures.

There certainly was an Oedipal problem but, even more, an oral problem. As I found later in therapy, the phallic conflicts and interests of the Oedipal stage were intimately interlocked with oral wishes and fears. Throughout his life, Ray had sought out women who were duplicates of mother. He had sought relationships that would duplicate his relationship with mother. *On the Oedipal phallic level,* to seduce a woman was to compete with, and triumph over, the paternal figure. The necessity to compete was omnipresent if Ray were to keep on defeating father and please mother. To be potent, meant to be as sexually omnipotent as the omnipotent father and to be impotent meant to avoid rivalry and castration. *On the oral level,* the necessity to work hard was equally omnipresent if Ray was to extract supplies from an ungiving mother, before anyone else extracted the little that could be gotten. To be impotent carried frightening oral threats just as it fulfilled frightening desires for passivity. I saw Ray as strongly fixated and deprived at the oral level and, later, strongly stimulated and frustrated at the phallic level; trying to express through his phallic sexuality, not only genital, but also pregenital (sado-masochistic, oral and narcissistic) aims.

As I found later, his general attitude with men was energized by the above dynamics. At one level, men were dangerous antagonists, at another useful protectors. On another level they were mother symbols. At one level they induced competitiveness and hostility, to ward off the mature masculinity one fears, and to avoid castration, (to learn from them how to best defeat them in the pursuit of mother); or one might be dependent on them in order to be feminine, thus avoiding the danger of being controlled, dominated, incorporated by women (mother) as man (father) was; and, finally, one could be dependent on them as one is dependent on a mother. His homosexuality was both related to the identification problem and to the dynamics for passive dependency on men.

Ray approached his analysis intellectually and compulsively. In the early phases of therapy I attempted to render his posture less intellectual by trying to elicit the personal experiential meaning, the feeling, the affect of the words and psychiatric terms he was using so liberally. Otherwise I was minimally active, offered no interpretations, gave no support beyond the support inherent in listening attentively and with sympathetic, though non-committed, interest. At this stage, I was seen as a benevolent, patient, undemanding parental figure, whom Ray was cautiously testing, as he confided, "confessed," and primarily complained about the pressure he was experiencing in his marital and extramarital life.

The first line focused on in therapy was the theme of his extramarital acting-out. Ray concentrated on this subject—and on the allied subject of the difficulties caused him by Ida—rather consistently. I decided to focus on it because, in my estimation of Ray's psychodynamics, this seemed to be a significant and promising line, and because his "philandering" was to him a source more of realistic concern and discomfort than of pleasure.

Initially, Ray saw his "philandering" through a smoke-screen of rationalizations some of which, although utilized by Ray defensively, reflected significant unconscious feelings and fantasies, i.e., "I philander because Ida does not give enough" (oral language), "because with Ida I am impotent," "because, perhaps, I am oversexed." He spoke of the elation with each successful sexual experience and of the depression with each episode of impotence. He spoke of the necessity to avoid any new involvement: "I could not afford to—I already have to feed two wives" (oral language again). The extramarital acting out concerned him, not only because of the necessity to guard himself against being trapped into closeness, but also because of the complicated triangulations it often "webbed" him in. When his casual paramours already had a lover, he was concerned with the other man in the picture, feeling both competitive and concerned about "being caught red-handed." When his girl friends had no lovers, he would worry about Ida catching him "red-handed" (at the same time being concerned as to whether Ida was philandering too).

Ray began using the couch around this time. From the very beginning he adopted a very suggestive posture: Completely flat on his back, his pelvis slightly raised, hands on his abdomen, patting his stomach from time to time with the flat of his hand. The nonverbal communication was passive, seductive, oral. He was saying: "Screw me, mother—but feed me. My stomach is empty." Through this period, there were dreams of impotence; of absolute mastery over several women; of being seduced, and then rejected, by Ida or by his current girl friends. There were dreams relating to deeper problems and concerns (oral fears, castration fears). Material relating to deeper dynamics was emerging also in association or in the relating of everyday events. Even the pressure to tell me about his multiple extramarital involvements already had transferential dimensions (i.e., "showing off"; testing, transferentially, my responses and my permissiveness; telling me: "Look, father, how horrible is mother"). Ray did gain some initial, tentative understanding of his doubts about his masculinity and his need to dilute his emotional involvement with any one woman by involving himself, superficially, with many. Coincident with this phase of therapy, Ray went through a prolonged period of complete sexual impotence with Ida, related, I believe, to the emergence of Oedipal material (and therefore, transferentially to his having earlier set me up as the father-rival), and to the emergence of fear and projected hostility toward women.

As Ray increasingly verbalized (and "felt") his feelings about women, he began to enter the area of his relationships with his parents (his mother first, his father later) *on the Oedipal level.* This was to represent a large portion of Ray's analysis. It was only in this year that the analytical field was expanded to include his relationship with his parents *on the oral level.* This stage covered approximately two years of time, encompassed about 150 sessions, and spanned two summer separations. During the first (August 1960) Ray divorced Ida. During the second (August 1961) he married Pat. He told me of both important developments *post facto.*

At first Ray showed feelings of resentment toward Ida and May, still tempered by the feeling that "he had no real right to experience anger at them as long as he had been sexually incompetent." As he related more details of his relationships with his wives, the sado-masochistic, passive-aggressive, dependent-controlling features of both relationships became more apparent. He complained about May's and Ida's looseness and past promiscuity, and their dogmatic, domineering attitude. He felt particularly vulnerable to Ida's contempt and sarcasm when he was impotent, and to her discussing with him her former lovers' sexual vigor. He began to realize that it was not accidental that he should have become so often involved with the same type of woman. He then returned to mother, recognizing the similarities between her and May, Ida and Pat. As he kept on talking of mother, he left aside anger and resentment and focused mainly on her seductiveness. He began to remember the romantic or more frankly sexual feelings he had experienced for her or for his friends' mothers at various times in his childhood. Dreams were produced in which he found himself in bed with Ida (or May or Pat): "At the moment we were to become intimate, she suddenly looked like my mother—and then nothing sexual would take place"; or dreams in which sexual exchanges took place between him and mother. In these dreams he almost invariably assumed passive, receptive, postures and anxiety was invariably experienced either during the dream or upon awakening. It was at this time (10th month of therapy) that Ray asked if he could come twice a week.

In these first ten months, I was still only moderately active, and primarily concerned with remaining in the background (to facilitate transferential developments), and maintaining the line of therapy. At this point, too, material was being produced that related to deeper levels of personality, and was thus extraneous to the main line of production, i.e., fantasies and/or dreams suggesting the latent fear and desire to be nourished, taken care of, absorbed, swallowed, incorporated by mother. Even his request to come twice a week indicated more than merely stronger motivation or greater anxiety. It also reflected specific transferential positions related both to the Oedipal phase we were approaching (i.e., involving me more in his triangulations) and to deeper transferential levels (i.e., making me the gift of himself; homosexual dependency in exchange for my protection against women). The latter material was not interpreted or focused on at that time.

In the period of therapy just described, Ray reached the outskirts of the Oedipal phase of his analysis. That he should have actually gone that far was a function, I believe, of the specific significance that Oedipal relationship had to Ray. In these ten months of therapy Ray had already begun to touch on pre-Oedipal problems (anger and resentment at mother; having to "serve" mother). To rush into the Oedipal stage was a relief, as talking Oedipal language was, to Ray, less frightening than talking oral language. In terms of "line of therapy" I was consciously interested in dealing with Oedipal problems, and I believe that I did encourage, counter-transferentially, the early Oedipal focusing. As I was letting him provoke me with rich verbalization on philandering I may have, at times, sounded competitive, set myself up as "the other man" or, even, sounded more judgemental than I consciously felt. I may have unconsciously needed (as well as consciously wanted) to bypass and ignore the pre-Oedipal messages being sent to me all the while. Later, the question arose in my mind as to whether the Oedipal phase of Ray's analysis had been drawn out and if so, whether counter-transferential insistence on the Oedipal aspects of father-son relatedness had unduly contributed to its length. I believe that, since the early counter-transference was caught in time, the *later* Oedipal emphasis was no longer motivated counter-transferentially. I believe Ray kept his father in the transferential picture mainly because he felt continuously exposed to the even more frightening emotions concerning oral wishes and fears about his mother. Father (the rival but also the protector) and therapist were kept as buffers between himself and mother (or between himself and Pat).

As Ray started coming twice a week, the tempo of his analysis quickened. More emotionally-charged memories and/or fantasies of erotic relatedness with mother came to the fore. Mother was always seen as the initiator of any erotic exchange, and Ray always placed himself in the familiar, passive, receptive posture. This is seen in the following dream (76th session):

> Ida came in my bed . . . I did not want her there, as I felt tired . . . but she came in anyway and began to play with my penis . . . suddenly she was my mother . . . and I was a little child . . . and she was over me, rubbing my penis . . . and smiling . . .

As I was interested, at this point, only in facilitating insight on how much he associated Ida with his mother, I only focused on that aspect of the dream, and commented, at the end of the session: "In your dreams you certainly keep on seeing your mother in this woman." I ignored, for the time being, the line of his passivity or other latent contents.

In the immediately preceding phase of therapy, Ray had become aware of his anger at May and Ida. Now he became more aware of resenting mother for being first seductive and then ungiving. The resentment at the ungiving mother related to a mother both phallically and orally ungiving. However, in his associations Ray focused only on his anger at mother for not giving sexually and recalled many instances from his childhood, exactly mirroring those aspects of his dreams. In obedience to the principle of selective focusing, I did the same, and my only comment, in reaction to his dreams and associations, was: "You must have been very angry at her for doing that to you."

At first Ray saw his sexual impotence as related to his anger at women for being seductive and then ungiving. In relating to persons like May and Ida, and in being resentful toward them, he was truly recreating the situation he had experienced with his own mother. He could see that his problem was one of generalized, rather than just genital, potence-impotence and that his resentment not only caused him to deny himself to women sexually (the genital impotence), but also motivated other of his attitudes with them—his reserve, intellectualization, competitiveness, etc. It was at this point that he began to experience transient periods of relief from his impotence or, when impotent, from the feelings of helplessness. I helped him along by pointing out to him that as long as he visualized Ida as a mother figure and had to "serve" her with an impeccable sexual performance, and as long as he used sex to serve and please, rather than to enjoy himself, he would necessarily find it very difficult to be potent. In this phase of his analysis there was initially a somewhat diluted father transference, and only its positive components were consciously experienced. He was moderately, and not too openly, dependent on me (or, more intellectually and abstractly, "on therapy"); looking up to me; experiencing me as "a more experienced man, who is at my side" and who "approved" of his sexuality. As he began to correlate more and more his sexual impotence (and his excessive dependence on Ida) to the incest taboo and castration fears, he entered more fully the oedipal phase of his analysis and a full transference developed rapidly. In these sessions he was often anxious. A typical comment, at this stage of therapy was: "I thought I knew all about this incest stuff—but it's another story when you feel it within yourself." What he still did not know was that what made him anxious was the incest taboo *and* the concomitant oral fears and threats, as indicated by the following dream (84th session):

> I was walking uphill with my mother . . . open country, Staten Island, I believe . . . I was very young and mother was pulling me by the hand. We see this metallic shack, on the door it said, 'Canned Food' . . . my mother disappears. I was to enter the shack, but I see no door . . . then I see, on the front of the shack, this gaping hole with jagged edges . . . I go in, careful not to get cut. Inside I find a crowd of people . . . there is a woman nursing this baby . . . I feel excited and urinate in my pants . . . there is a feeling of great danger, as if someone were coming from behind to hit me over the head . . . but nothing of the sort happens . . . I look around, I press a button and a trapdoor opens under my feet . . . I fall and fall, swallowed up in the hole, like Alice in Wonderland . . .

Keeping in mind the stage of therapy we were in and the principles of line of therapy, I focused only on the Oedipal phallic dimensions of the dream content—i.e., entering the hole, urinating in his pants, being in a Wonderland, being hit over the head by father—therapist, etc. I completely sidestepped the oral features; the metallic, ungiving mother-therapist; the dry, canned food; the nursing baby; the being swallowed up, etc. Striving to facilitate both insight and transference, at one point in that session I said: "You wanted to enter the hole." At the end of the session, after he had associated with some thoughts on Rose, an Italian girl he dated from time to time, I said: "I wonder if you think I am going to hit you over the head from behind . . . because of Rose." My comments were sparing, as this made interpretations simpler and more understandable; did not overwhelm him with a variety of multipronged comments; and gave him food for thought, thus placing on him the responsibility to follow through with more of his own thoughts and associations.

As Ray entered more fully the Oedipal phase of his analysis, I became the loved and hated rival, the dependable authority and dangerous antagonist, the contemptible weakling and the strong protector. During this stage of therapy, his analysis moved productively.

In reality, Ray's father had inconsistently interfered with Ray's Oedipal feelings—at times too little, at times too much; and mother herself had interfered with the development, of "healthy" Oedipal feelings. Dreams, fantasies, early memories contributed abundantly to this stage of therapy. There were dreams and fantasies with a homoerotic manifest and/or latent content (being naked in my presence; coming to therapist with his fly open); dreams of being guided by me "by the hand" up the glittering road leading to mental health; of seeing me as "a giant towering over him"; more directly Oedipal dreams and fantasies (in which Ida's former husband is a famous European psychiatrist, or an unethical physician who chisels on Blue Cross and Blue Shield; or in which I call on Pat and end up in bed with her) attempts at involving me triangularly with Pat ("You should see her once or twice . . . it would help her . . . you wouldn't mind it anyway . . . she is quite attractive"). This was a stage in which I was more active in my interpretations, which I directed both at the content of his communication and at the quality of this transference. Initially, I kept my interpretative activity strictly within the boundaries of the phallic-Oedipal line. Later, whenever the analytic material permitted, I directed my interpretations also to include other aspects of therapy, i.e., the oral features of his problem. I believed this would facilitate the development of the maternal transference. At the beginning of the phase of therapy now being described, he dreamed (87th session) in the following terms:

> I was living in Vincent's Price's house . . . I was his secretary and I had stolen something very valuable, perhaps one of his paintings . . . he was going to kill me, so I ran away . . .

As this dream was communicated just after he had been talking of Rose, my interpretation was in the form of a question: "What do you think you have stolen from this 'Vincent,' Ray?" Later, the transferential reference was brought back to father and mother, as he associated with "one of his paintings" to mother. When Ray was a child, father used to say "mother is as pretty as a picture." The primary mother transference became more evident.

The transferential connection therapist-father was often inclusive of other authority figures or male rivals. In the 126th session, he presented this dream:

> I had spent the night at Pat's. Calvin (Pat's former husband) showed up. He still had some claims on Pat and began to argue with me. He became bigger and bigger . . . I was afraid he would stab me in the back.

My comment was: "You always get involved with women on whom some men have claims . . . or whose men are going to give you a shellacking . . ." ("To give a shellacking" was the expression Ray had consistently used in referring to father's disciplinary methods.) On the 133rd session he produced the following dream:

> This big white fellow and I were hunting after this Negro desperado. We were in mining country, Virginia perhaps. I wasn't sure of my companion, was he friend or foe? I checked my pistol . . . the pistol was okay but the bullets were too small for the caliber of the gun. We entered the abandoned mine . . . the earth was soft and could cave in anytime and swallow us up. The man was ahead of me . . . suddenly turned . . . we began to shoot. My bullets fell short of him . . . his bullets were coming out of his gun all right, but never hit me . . .

This dream again contained both the Oedipal phallic theme (being chased by father-therapist for having been a desperado with the virgin-mother; impotent pistol; contest of guns) and the oral theme (mining country; ore; supplies; caving-in earth; being swallowed up). I commented: "I wonder who is really hunting you?" Shortly afterwards (141st session) he spoke again, and with renewed animation, of his feelings about "big shots." "They hold a position of power and they don't want to share it—so I am deferent to them—it angers me—they don't give anything in return—they just screw me up—same thing as with my father and mother, my father especially—he came home and laid down the law". Toward the end of the same session, he had this fantasy:

> I'm bigger than you . . . I feel anxious as I tell you this . . . first I was standing next to you but now I don't see you anymore . . . but I hear your voice asking me "are you through?"

As the ground had already been prepared by previous communications and interpretations, my comment was a direct interpretation: "You were talking of being screwed up by big shots who don't care for your feelings—in your fantasy it's you screwing me, rendering me feminine, having no concern for my feelings." In that particular session, I was specifically addressing myself to one transferential aspect of the fantasy—the feeling that father, therapist, "big shots," first seen as "big," exploitative and castrators, are rendered small, exploited, and castrated. The fantasy, however, had a much more inclusive meaning and more aspects of it were analyzed in the next several months when the lines of therapy had shifted accordingly. Another important aspect of the fantasy was that the "big shots" to whose power he defers are not solely *father* symbols. He himself had said, before verbalizing the fantasy: "They . . . just . . . screw up . . . same thing as with my father and *mother*"; and his complaint was not only that the "big shots" don't want to share the power (competitiveness with father) but also that "they don't give anything in return" (just like the orally ungiving mother). The "big shots," thus, are not only the pompous, authoritarian father but also the ungiving, egophylic mother; and Ray's anger at them is a function not only of frustrated competitiveness, but also of frustrated dependency. In spite of his deference and passivity, the "Big Mothers" still don't give a hoot about his comfort and don't feed him. This was one of the openings I utilized later on to suggest to Ray that he saw me, transferentially, not solely as the competitive father but also as the ungiving mother.

To the theme of "the big shots don't want to share their power," Ray associated memories of father telling him that he "could be 'first in command' when he, father, was not home." He remembered how he felt both angry and relieved when father returned home and relieved him of the honor and the onus of "being first." He realized that at that time, to have power and responsibility was entirely dependent on his father's absence and his mother's willingness to let him be "in command." This gave me the opportunity to analyze further his dependency, and I pointed out: "even today you act as if wives or strangers were your father and mother on whose permission you must depend if you are to exercise power and assume responsibilities." He realized how he permitted even his sexual power "to be dependent on Ida's moods or whims." He saw how conflictual he had been since childhood on the matter of "being first" and how often he had elected to be second—to avoid responsibility, not to antagonize father, to avoid castration, to be able to be dependent on mother. He realized how much he magnified the importance of being "first in command" or his own importance in general: "At times I felt like a god—a little god at least." He realized how often he undercut his own efforts so that he would not even be second: "If I could not be first all the time, I'd rather be last." (To which I added: "If you could not be as omnipotent as father, you'd rather be impotent").

The grandiose self-expectations of Ray's personality were becoming more evident, as in the following dream (143rd session):

> I was carrying this teacher of mine (a big woman), in my arms, up this hill in Staten Island . . . I had to prove to her that I could . . . I found it very difficult . . . I was not as strong as I thought . . .

Associating to the dream he said: "My mother always thought I was very strong; stronger, physically than my father—yet in the dream I could not carry this woman up a hill." I asked: "How strong must you be, Ray, to please your mother?" He answered: "Strong enough to be stronger than my father," then associated to May and Ida: "Performing sexually to impress them . . . is hell . . . they are not easy to impress . . . they have been already well 'impressed on' by other men." I pointed out that he acted as if he had to buy their acceptance by "serving them a good sexual performance . . . just as you had to serve mother dinner in bed." Later on, utilizing his need to impress Pat, I could take up this theme again and replay it to him in less projective terms, i.e., it was not so much mother who thought he was stronger than father, but he, Ray, who needed to conceive of himself as stronger than father and wanted to impress this fact on mother. It was he who needed to be depended upon by mother. Taking up from his competitiveness with Pat (working, successfully, in the same hospital where Pat had worked and failed; using his professional success to "make an impact" on Pat), I could also show him the multiple needs served by his wanting to impress women—impressing, serving, in order to be served (orally); impressing sado-masochistically (fantasies of hitting them over the head with the omnipotent penis and killing himself with hard work in the process of doing so).

As indicated earlier, Ray had married Pat in the summer of 1961: "I did not want to say anything . . . you may have objected . . . I did not tell my parents either." Pat was also a "woman with a past" (promiscuous adolescence; married and divorced young; graduated from a school of nursing, "and settled down . . . has been a 'good girl' for years") and, like May and Ida, a woman of strong personality. Ray married her basically for the same reasons he had married, and divorced, May and Ida; but found her not quite as phallic and depriving. Ray had found it possible, with her, to work through some of his oedipal problems and, I believe, he may also be able to work through some of his oral problems—in spite of Pat's present pregnancy.

Shortly after the marriage, Ray had the following dream (156th session):

> Father and mother are divorcing . . . I was glad but also alarmed. Father told me, sarcastically: "This will be good for you." I felt guilty. I saw mother, signaling me to get into this house . . . I felt as if I were being sucked up into a hole . . .

I related this dream to the recent marriage. Ray verbalized anger at father "for not protecting me from mother—I had my hands full with her—needed his help—I guess I didn't ask him because I doubted he could help." In that, and in the next several sessions, I pointed out that he had not really made up his mind if he wanted to be protected by father against mother (or by me against Pat). After all, he was alarmed but also glad at his parents' divorce, alarmed but also glad to be taken care of all by mother; and I asked why it was that he expressed more anger at his father (guilty of not having protected him against mother) than at his mother herself (from whom, he stated, he needed protection).

As I stated earlier, with Pat, Ray could work through some of his problems with the Oedipal parents and with the ungiving mother. Pat and her past were a fresh stimulus for the "return of the unconscious." In session 165, he brought up a dream with the same characters of a previous one but with a different solution:

> Calvin is in Pat's house . . . now my house as well. Pat tells me that Calvin Jr. had asked him to stay. I politely asked him to leave . . . he left never to return again.

In his associations Ray focused on his preoccupation with his "women's ex's" which, he felt, was based on past preoccupations with mother's boy friends: "I react with the past in my mind—not Pat's past but my mother's." I added: "And your own past—you keep on interjecting another man, next to your mother—just as you tried to interject yourself between father and mother." He moved back to the theme of "the other man as a protector," remembered "how much after all I wanted my father to stick around the house when I was very young" and became more conscious of his ambivalence on the amount (and the quality) of protection from mother he wanted.

The later phases of this stage of his analysis included:

(1) The analysis of more dreams and fantasies depicting triangular situations: "the other man" often being me, in a less and less latent content.

(2) The analysis of dreams, fantasies, associations, memories indicating greater insight, on Ray's part, into his own role in the oedipal triangle; greater awareness of his own activity, hostility, and competitiveness; fantasies of interfering with father's sexuality and of castrating father (as contrasted to the former, more projective attitude, when he saw father's hostility against him, father competing with him, father checking Ray's sexuality and interfering with it.)

(3) The analysis of his homosexuality, which, at this stage, was mainly related to the dynamics of his passive-dependency on men.

(4) The partial working through of his competitiveness, dependency and hostility, as these characterological attitudes were being de-energized by the partial working through of the oedipal problem. (It was at this point that I best realized that both the oedipal stage in his therapy, and the problems connected with it in his life, could not be adequately worked through without, first, a long analytical excursion in the area of his orality and mother-transference.) During this period, Ray became more assertive, more independent, more successful in school and at work and happier about it.

(5) Better understanding of his feelings about May, Ida and Pat, primarily, but not solely, on the oedipal mother level (and timidly and tentatively, on the oral-mother level): "Women like them attract me . . . as if they fulfill some crazy need inside of me" (patting of abdomen); recognition of his own need to be castrated,

tormented, dominated by them and of subtely doing the same to them. (It was at this time that Ray became more aware of his feelings about the castrated—amputated—Ida and could see that it was no accident that he had felt attracted to her); some dim recognition of the fact that being mother's prey, being dependent on the castrating woman, serving, was also his way of achieving ultimate comfort with mother.

(6) A growing realization that father was not "the only villain," as he so vehemently felt in the transferential peaks of this stage of therapy and many times throughout his life. A direct quotation is here in order, as it shows more openly the mother transference underlying the father transference: "Father is not, after all, the villain with the slick black mustache" which I heard as: . . . the villain with the slick black mustache (therapist—I have a mustache) is not father . . . is mother.

With fewer and fewer axes to grind against father, less protected against the mother transference, Ray entered another phase of his therapy. Pat became "accidentally" pregnant (July 1962). Ray resumed (though much less frenetically) his extra-marital acting-out, and insisted that the following September he could only come once a week. He gave Pat's pregnancy, and the attending higher expenses, as his reason for cutting down therapy. Actually, he was running from me, i.e., from mother, as he had run away before from May and Ida. This was clearly corroborated by all the material brought up in the last 3-4 weeks of therapy before the summer interruption. In session 197, he brought up the following dream:

> I must have been about four. Mother got in bed with me. She had flannel pajamas on and was eating a strongly smelling type of cheese, dropping crumbs all over the floor. I moved closer to her, but she went on eating. Father entered the room. She jumped out of bed and left me holding a very small piece of cheese and a copy of '*Good Housekeeping*.' I felt some guilt and fear in relation to father, but, mainly, I felt anger at mother . . .

In his associations, he first focused on Pat, who in the winter wears flannel pajamas and who reads *Good Housekeeping*. He then tried to use the Oedipal red-herring again by talking of father's entrance into the room and his fear. Keeping in mind the line now being pursued, I reminded him of the anger he felt against mother. He responded by associating to mother eating in bed and dropping crumbs all over the floor and talked, with animation, of her sloppy housekeeping, of the fact that he and father had to do her housework, that he could not bring any friends home for dinner, that quite often she altogether forgot to cook. I commented: "You must have been very angry at her for not giving you enough"; and he responded by saying: "Yes, I felt angry all right . . . this, I think, plus the . . . incest stuff, explains why I felt, so often, like running away from her whenever, as a child, she wanted to kiss and embrace me . . . later, when I left home, I never visited her more than twice a month . . . she would complain about the rarity of my visits." I said: "You often said I don't give enough in therapy . . . don't talk enough . . . don't commit myself enough . . . am 'as dry as a stone' . . . and you felt that in doing that I was being like your father . . . yet, isn't this what you are accusing your mother of—and aren't you cutting down your visits to me, now?" He replied, indirectly, by talking of how he had often felt, with May and Ida: "In moments of passion . . . I suddenly wanted to get the hell out of there . . . or become impotent." (In this context he verbalized fantasies of "maternal" woman feeding on his penis, fantasies of vagina dentata, fantasies of utter helplessness in a woman's embrace; then, somewhat more intellectually, thoughts about intercourse as "La Petite Mors.") I pointed out that he had wanted to run away in all situations of excessive involvement; and wasn't this the way he felt about therapy at the time? He "replied" a few sessions later when he spoke of his resentment at his "boss" (an authoritarian woman psychiatrist) for having invited him to a Fourth of July party and "expecting me to go . . . whether it is convenient for me or not . . . I will not go"; (in other words, seeing me as a "boss" who wanted Ray to come and serve him for my own, rather than Ray's convenience).

Ray's fear of involving himself further with a therapist whom he saw, transferentially, as a symbol of the seductive and then ungiving mother, and his apprehensions about the safety of investing too much with someone who was going to prove as undependable as the undependable mother, had possibly been strengthened by my announcing that I would take, that summer, a longer (six weeks) vacation. But his fears and apprehensions were to receive a strangely fateful validation when, only one month after my return from Europe (and after only four sessions of therapy) I fell ill and "abandoned" him for three months. In his 206th session (the second after my return to work after my illness, and the last, up to the time of this writing), he brought up the following dream:

> I was giving a ride back home to this teacher friend of mine, driving Pat's Volkswagen. When we were almost home, he got sick . . . some sort of a heart attack. He wasn't frightened, he knew it wasn't serious . . . but I was very frightened. We got to his house on Long Island . . . it was a twenty-or thirty-year-old house. I drove up his driveway, feeling uncertain as to whether I was supposed to or not. His wife came to the door . . . looked like Rose . . . pretty, but more housewifely than Rose. My friend got out of the car, still staggering a little. As I looked back, I realized that I had driven the car too far against the porch of the house . . . the front, where the trunk is, was all dented . . . the front bumper had fallen off . . .

After a long pause, Ray said: "I feel this dream recapitulates my whole analysis . . . and yet . . . it says something new." As he associated to the dream he again used Oedipal language. Going with Rose means trespassing on the Italian therapist's hunting ground . . . "this teacher has a black mustache" . . . "the house makes me think of my mother" . . . "Rose looks maternal" . . . "I got dented in front because I drove up my father's driveway again" . . . "when you aren't around, I start philandering again . . . and with an Italian girl," etc. Not much feeling accompanied these associations. He then moved to a deeper line as he began to talk, with more feeling, of the father as the protector, rather than the father as the antagonist: "When you are not around, I get more easily tempted into philandering . . . more easily attracted into other men's driveways." To this I reacted, since I felt it was a line that could allow us a more direct thrust into oral territory and into more open mother-transferential postures, I commented: "In your early childhood, you felt there was not enough to prevent you from depending too much on your mother . . . did you feel she was dependable?" He said: "I feel the dream gives some sort of an answer . . . of course, the dream has to do with your absence . . . with my father's absence from the house . . . the teacher in the dream stands for you, that is, for my father . . . I think?" In this last questioning doubt and in the growing realization that he might be talking, and dreaming, of me as mother (the mother who first entices him into driving deep into her until his front is dented, his defenses battered, his bumper lost—and then leaves him by "getting sick on him"; the mother he must carry home and nurse to health, the mother who needs more mothering than she can give) rather than of me as father, lies, I believe, the next theme in Ray's analysis.

Ray's analysis has been primarily the analysis of his transferential postures. In the initial phase of his analysis, I was confronted with guarded, intellectual, passive, deferent postures. This phase basically coincided with the "first phase" of therapy. As a relationship was being built, I was a vague, generically benevolent, parental figure with whom Ray was tentatively relating. More specifically, Ray was relating to me with the same courteous agreeableness, polite compliance and submissiveness, hostile-dependent postures he had used in relating to both his parents.

In a more advanced phase, as he entered the Oedipal area, I was confronted with true, specific transference, as I became the father figure: at first the rival-father (the rival he feared; the rival who interfered with his sexuality); then as the rival he, Ray, wanted to dethrone and with whose sexuality he, Ray, wanted to interfere); and then the ally-father (who might, or might not, protect him from mother and his desires for mother). As I persisted in systematically frustrating and analyzing, his transference became more acute and transparent, until in his feelings about, against and for me, Ray could recognize the equivalent feelings involving his father and relive, in the here and now of the transferential experience, feelings and experiences dating to earlier times.

In a further phase, that we have just entered, the mother-transference begins to appear more openly, a transference that should enable us to work through his problems of oral dependency and oral control. Mother transferential postures, of course, might very well have been present from the very beginning of therapy. In his first session on the couch, for instance, the non-verbal communication was unmistakably oral and directed at the mother-in-the-therapist. Practically and clinically, however, for reasons already explained, a mother-directed transference neurosis has not yet fully developed.

Ray has already achieved good insight into his involvement with his parents on the oedipal plane. Both the erotic and the hostile components of this involvement have been to a large extent elicited and worked through. But as long as Oedipal, phallic conflicts are, as I speculated earlier, intimately related to oral conflicts, no complete working through of the former should be expected without first working through the latter. In the current phase of his analysis, we shall, I believe, deal with and, hopefully, work through, such problems as: egocentricity and grandiosity of his expectations of women; dependency on women for oral supplies; oral expectations of mother; oral frustrations caused by the depriving mother; anger at the orally frustrating mother; passivity and servility as ways of exacting and extracting supplies needed for oral comfort; fear of the risk inherent in being passively dependent on an undependable, volatile, impulsive mother; symbiotic fantasies with mother, with fears of loss of identity; fear of his own desires for symbiotic relatedness with mother.

To the extent that predictions are possible in psychoanalysis, I think that subsequent to the oral, mother-transference, line, we shall return to an Oedipal transferential line. At that time, it will be necessary to evaluate very carefully whether Ray's return to the Oedipal line will be related to resistance to further explorations of oral material or to truer readiness to analyze and work through the Oedipal problems.

Anal dynamics have received, so far, little attention in Ray's analysis. Yet anality pervades Ray's entire personality, both characterologically and psychodynamically. I have already described how fastidious, meticulous, "neat," and retentive he is. His anality is found in his orality as well as in his genitality. Even his compulsive concern with erection and genital potency has anal dimensions, as he compulsively and omnipotently visualizes himself as someone who must compulsively have an erection at all times, with all women, regardless of whether he likes them or not or whether they love him or hate him. His difficulty in letting himself go and play, freely and spontaneously, at work or in sex, has stringent anal-retentive features. Also with anger, he is basically constipated and only capable of a slow, almost hemorrhoidal, expulsion of feelings. As I have seen his feelings of frustration, rage and anguish mount within him and as I have seen him laboring, working himself, in painful peristaltic waves, up to a final soft frizzle of mild resentment or mumbled protest, he appears to feel he is so filled with raging, omnipotent excrements that, unless he carefully controls his sphincters, he will drown the entire world, and himself, in a raging sea of feces. I am not sure I fully understand why so little of his anality has come through, so far, in his analysis. Probably, anal retentiveness is the ultimate defense, to be given up, if at all, only after all the other defenses (and fears) are worked through. If this is so, anal focusing will take place in the terminal stages of his analysis.

History and Treatment of George K: A Gifted Actor in the Grip of an Active Homosexual Syndrome

by Janet Jakub, M.D.
Postgraduate Center for Psychotherapy

Janet Jakub, M.D.

Dr. Jakub is affiliated with the Postgraduate Center for Mental Health. Her private practice is concentrated in the areas of homosexuality and impotency.

THE patient's complaints upon first applying to the clinic were: great tension, anger, a terrible temper, chest pains, numbness in hands and legs, frequent insomnia, fatigue, depression, and an incapacity to work. At two interviews he stressed that he "didn't want to be a homosexual," and that he had "great fear and guilt over it." His manner indicated extreme anxiety as to whether or not he would be accepted for treatment.

Despite this, the patient did not appear for his first therapy appointment. Playing a hunch, the analyst decided to telephone him at the end of the hour. He cut the analyst short abruptly, explaining that he had overslept, and hurriedly promised that he would be there for the next appointment.

Over a period of three years there were approximately 250 therapeutic sessions.

BACKGROUND

The patient was born in 1932, in Khartoum, African Sudan, of Greek descent and into the Greek Orthodox faith. He is tall, fair, very slim, lithe and sensitive-looking. He speaks with a foreign-tinged English accent, is generally dressed meticulously and presents a sophisticated, upper class appearance. He smokes a great deal, using a thin, gold cigarette holder and a matching lighter. He usually carries an expensive, brown leather overnight bag which he places on the floor each time he comes for therapy.

When the patient, the only child of unhappily married parents, was born, his mother was 24, and his father, 38 years of age. The father, a rich, respected businessman, was away a good deal because of business and, subsequently, the Abyssinian War. With considerable resentment, the patient explained: "Father was absent both physically and emotionally." The patient was left to the care of his mother, his maternal grandmother and Sudanese "black" servants. He has little recollection of this early phase of his existence. The patient originally described his mother as "a very beautiful woman who was in society but not 'sexual'." Because of the war in Abyssinia, the family returned to their native country; the father remained in Africa until 1940. Subsequently, the father failed in business (loss of caste is a sore spot with the patient), and was treated by the family with contempt, especially after the mother became the chief breadwinner.

The patient was a gifted, highly intelligent and intellectual child with strong leanings toward art, literature and acting. An avid reader, he read Dumas, Dostoevsky, Nietzche, Tolstoi, and the classics generally before and during early adolescence. This achievement alone was not sufficient. He walked around town with books under his arm to draw attention to his superiority.

He remembers his mother stressed appearance and superficial achievements. She encouraged him to perform in front of her friends and contemporaries, making him the center of attention. His only participation in children's activities was a short period with the Boy Scouts.

The patient remembers being seduced at the age of 7 by a priest, who was his math teacher. According to the patient, the priest both "seduced" him and "forced" him to perform fellatio. This event occurred only once.

At the age of 10 or 11, a servant girl both "seduced" and "rejected" him on many occasions. He considers this his first heterosexual experience, the emotional content of which is decidedly painful for him to this day.

Except for these two occurrences, the patient does not consider that his sexual experiences differed significantly from that of other children between the ages of 7 and 16. The exploratory play between the sexes was, according to him, "par for the course." At 16, however, he met a "brilliant, handsome" French actor of 24, with whom he developed an intense friendship. The patient thought of him as an older brother. When this friendship was terminated by the departure of the actor, the patient began to phantasize sexual relationships with his friend, to the accompaniment of excessive manual manipulation of his own genitals. The phantasies haunted him to such an extent that he began to fear that something dire would happen to him if he did not seek help. He had already "absorbed" Freud and was terribly afraid of becoming a homosexual.

After a few sporadic homosexual relationships with pickups, he gravitated to his native circles in London, for social reasons. He met a rich, "ugly" Greek girl who was most "sympatico" to him. They became fast friends and he confided his previous homosexual experiences to her. In a short time, they married, with the girl's parents "footing the bill." The patient's description of his wife abounds with adjectives such as "spoiled," "self-centered," "ugly." He claimed that she had temper tantrums; was unreasonable, jealous (especially of any friendships he formed with men), and that she tried to "swallow and incorporate him" into her being. At the same time he claims that their sexual relationship was most satisfactory and about a year later a son was born. Nevertheless, the marriage was dissolved after two and a half years. During this relationship there was no overt homosexual activity. After the break-up, the patient left England and emigrated to America in 1954, on a student's visa. His wife returned to Greece with their child and has since been married three times.

Before he came to the clinic in 1960, the patient lived here for six years. He got a job in the garment district as a shipping clerk when he first arrived, at the same time enrolling as a part time student in the Actors Studio. He soon came to the attention of the directors, passed the exams and was accepted as a full time student. Soon parts of greater or lesser importance came his way, and he had an uneven work record encompassing roles both as actor and director in T.V., summer stock and Broadway. He lived in a cold-water flat and money was always a problem.

During this period, he deliberately separated his artistic and sexual drives, despite the establishment of deep rapport in friendships. For sexual expression, he resorted to pick-ups of husky, truck-driver types in Turkish baths, and to cruising the city streets in search of the ideal muscular, tall and hated image. He remained the aggressor, the humiliator, the penetrator, who forced his partners to perform fellatio on him.

A crisis in the patient's life was precipitated by his association with Jones, a rising director and writer, with whom he was collaborating. Jones attempted to involve the patient in a homosexual relationship. However, the patient fought Jones' demands with rage and denial. He could not work, sleep or function and finally sought therapy on the advice of Alice, a close friend, when the manifestations of his anxiety could no longer be hidden.

FIRST PHASE OF THERAPY

The patient admitted in later sessions that the therapist's phone call was the determining factor in his beginning therapy. His anxiety, his fear of failure, rejection, submission and humiliation were quite palpable. In an incredibly short space of time, he spewed forth a steady stream of words, thoughts, phantasies, images and childhood recollections. The patient continued to talk until his fears of analysis were allayed, and he developed enough trust in analysis to let the therapist fulfill her role in a wider sense than just being a sympathetic ear. The resistance at this time seemed due to anxiety inherent in the treatment situation itself, to ambivalence toward a female therapist (a foreigner, who was Jewish) and behavior indicative of an obsessive-compulsive character.

In subsequent sessions the patient continued to talk and talk, letting fall bits of significant material pointing to the kind of transference which was taking place:

> When I left you last time (this, after the second meeting) I started to cry. I cried for about ten blocks. I usually cry when I'm frustrated, but this time I was surprised, because I realized I liked you. When I got home, I looked at the photographs of my mother and I was disappointed. She was not as beautiful by half as always I imagined her. I also had a funny dream. Not really funny, you understand, as a matter of fact it was quite unpleasant and all in technicolor. No, that is not quite right either. They were earth colors, ochres and browns and terra cotta. I was on the Third Avenue El, going to a dentist in Brooklyn. On the way I stopped off to go to a second-hand store. I walked and walked and suddenly there was a very insistent noise. It was a bell, clear and loud. 'Next case, George K., Professional Actor.' I knew my case was up. I ran up a big marble staircase standing in the void without any banisters. I was in a big room closely resembling a Greenwich Village espresso joint. All sorts of men, youngish and thirtyish were sitting and lounging around. I asked one man with a face like a death mask where the court was. He told me and I ran down to the street. I realized that my case was being tried and that I was not there to defend it.

On several occasions the patient reverted to this dream. A point had been reached where mutual discussion was possible and the patient was asked if he were willing to explore this dream. He assented and then added: "At 15, I was accused of stealing a watch and I did not do it. Other times, I did all sorts of things I shouldn't have, but nobody accused me of anything."

The components of the dream were interpreted as follows over a period of time:

1. He had been on trial all his life but had never been able to defend himself.

2. He admitted that he was looking for punishment.

3. The marble staircase was a status symbol to him, similar to "marble halls," etc. Its being "in the void" meant that in essence it was unattainable to him. Its lack of banisters meant that even if he could reach it, he would be unprotected and probably fall.

4. Going to a dentist implied fear of being hurt or castrated.

5. His not being able to speak in court symbolized his "resistance to treatment." He was afraid to talk about his doubts concerning the analyst and analysis. He was not at all sure the analyst would be able to help him, or whether his feelings and sufferings would be understood. His friends all had Park Avenue analysts, while he was in the clinic. And that is what the clinic was, a secondhand or second-rate bargain basement. He became

quite emotional over not having sufficient means to afford a more "high-class" kind of analysis.

Thus the nature of the transference at this time denoted a hidden resistance. The immediate goal of treatment, therefore, would be to make these negative feelings conscious, to make the patient aware of his hidden sado-masochistic pattern, a probable outgrowth of the sado-masochistic relationship inculcated by his mother.

The patient had stated that his homosexual activity had markedly increased since his analysis started; after each session, he went out cruising, having a compulsive need to do so even if it did not succeed in releasing his tensions but in fact increased his guilt feelings.

PROBLEMS OF THERAPY

The patient's increasingly verbalized identification of the analyst with his mother, which started directly after the first session, continued. The negative reactions as expressed in his "marble staircase dream" increased in intensity for a while, and resistance to analysis continued. He looked up the doctor's qualifications in the medical directory and the APA directory to make sure that the doctor possessed all the necessary degrees. He continued to be disappointed that he had to see the analyst at the clinic and not on Park Avenue. He claimed resentfully that he was frightened of the analyst because he knew he was being condemned as a liar, a shoplifter and a homosexual. When asked why he thought he would be judged as a shoplifter, he answered: "You know damn well I stole a pair of cuff links from Tiffany's." To the question, "Did you?" his answer was, "Yes, I did, but that was long before I came to you." Then he continued to berate the analyst by berating himself. His insomnia, the paralyzing numbness in his hands and arms, his increasing homosexual experience with greater aggressiveness were the fault of the analyst since the analyst did not really understand him in spite of the omnipotence with which he invested the doctor by assuming that the facts of his life were known in the analytical situation though he had never stated them. This phase lasted about a month.

In the fourth month, the patient attempted to "placate" and "please" the analyst by concentrating on his primal relationship with his mother, which he felt was fulfilling the role of a cooperative patient. The patient recalled how his mother called him her "little man." He hastened to explain that in Greece, as in many other cultures, the expression "little man" means penis. Then he related how she used to dress him with "refinement" and "elegance," and how they used to stand in front of the mirror admiring themselves and each other. "I used to wear mother's clothes and act out parts in front of the mirror for hours. I still comb my hair for hours. The rotten part was, though, that Mother would alternately cuddle and punish me without any reason. I really don't, that is, I never knew where I stood with her." His repetitive concentration upon the past instead of the present was recognized as resistance.

In the weeks that followed, interpretations were offered about his resistance and his negative transference. The patient's compulsive tempo of speech slowed down. He occasionally paused voluntarily to wait for a comment and showed no irritation even when the analyst deliberately interrupted him once in a while, to ask a question, or to stop him from digressing when it was felt he was covering up a painful memory which he was afraid to touch. His dawning confidence in the analyst seemed to be genuine.

His behavior outside the therapy situation began to alter as well. He excelled in school and got himself a teaching job.

Ironically enough, his friendship with Alice (who had originally sent him into therapy) began to flounder just as the crack in his homosexual leitmotif began to make itself evident. Although for three years he had maintained a platonic friendship with her, he began to have sexual phantasies, with her as the central figure. Several times, as they embraced each other, whether in greeting, departure, or just out of friendly enthusiasm, he experienced an erection. He daydreamed about their being lovers. Alice, who was going through a difficult period herself—she was currently starring in one of the season's most exacting plays in addition also to being in therapy—sensed the change in him but did not welcome it. They began to quarrel, and the patient, true to the hostile element involved in his homosexuality, stated that in his most recent phantasy, he saw Alice as the possessor of a huge phallus. They did not break up their friendship, but loosened the ties to some degree.

The patient's friendship with June, a much younger girl and fledgling star, continued unabated, however. As he and Alice grew cooler, June and he became closer. At her request, he began to coach her for an important role in a Hollywood movie offered to her. Although expressing the warmest feeling for June, the patient did not have any sexual phantasies about her. Nevertheless, at this period, he mentioned that he had given up cruising.

He considered this as "mastery" over himself—a great victory. His self-confidence increased, both spuriously and in a real sense. Although a healthier personality was emerging, he was warned about mistaking a sense of euphoria for a cure and told that he still had to face many unresolved problems. He claimed he knew that, but anyway wasn't going to worry about what didn't bother him.

At the end of the fifth month, he went to Hollywood on a temporary job with June to continue her coaching. Just before he left, he admitted that he had started cruising again, but not very often, and that his guilt feelings about it were even greater than before. He said that when he returned, he would like to continue his analysis if the doctor still wanted him.

THE NEXT SIX MONTHS OF THERAPY

Six months later, in October, 1961, the patient returned to New York and almost immediately resumed analysis, this time privately. His account of his experiences in California was not promising. Although busy coaching June until the movie was finished, he found himself in all sorts of emotional difficulties. He had experienced extreme pangs of jealousy of more famous actors and actresses. He grudgingly admitted that this was even true of his feelings toward June whom he thought of as his personal protegee. He felt extremely insecure, had temper tantrums in public and had even gotten into difficulties with the police through shoplifting minor and inexpensive items, and cruising. June's work had been very much praised, which redounded to his credit. Nevertheless he was in such inner turmoil that he had consulted a psychiatrist on the West Coast who gave him supportive therapy.

Additional complications were plaguing him. His parents had recently arrived in New York, and it tortured him to think that they would observe his mediocre existence, his lack of fame, the unacknowledgement of his genius. Their visit lasted two weeks. During this period he saw the analyst every day except week-ends. The beginning of insight was visible in his verbalized attitudes, despite the California setback:

> It's funny, how differently I see my parents now, a difference as great as that between the real world and the realm of the imagination. My mother is not and was probably never as beautiful as I remember her, and my father is not the total nonentity I used to despise. You know, he really is quite good-looking, tall and muscular, as a matter of fact, a physical type I admire. Funny, as a kid he represented everything I disliked in men. And yet, I know that my father would be willing to risk everything for what he considered to be right, whereas my mother, well, for my mother, honesty means something to act by only when it suits her convenience.

The analyst considered it important for the patient to examine his attitude to his parents more thoroughly. More submerged memories of his father began to crop up both in his conscious thoughts and in his dreams.

> I never thought my father had any real feelings. Now I realize he couldn't have had much of a chance to express them because of my mother and grandmother. I guess I did love him once, because I distinctly remember feeling jealous of a dog he used to fondle. Funny, it just occurred to me that I often see myself in dreams as a dog. I realize that my father is able to love; he loved the dog.

During the ensuing weeks the patient's turbulence abated considerably. He requested and rejected interpretations by turns. The result was often a stormy session, and not wholly because of the patient.

COUNTERTRANSFERENCE

As the quantity and the quality of the sessions became intensified, the analyst found herself looking forward to the patient's visits with anticipation, only to experience a sense of letdown at their termination. This happened with such frequency that the analyst was finally forced to evaluate her own feelings, actions and motivations. The analyst had lost a measure of objectivity concerning the patient and his problems. She was annoyed when, despite his brilliance, he failed to grasp or accept interpretive material which she secretly considered quite perceptively acute, and even more annoyed when the resultant insight which she thought should have automatically followed did not occur. A case in point was the patient's seeing himself as a dog in his dreams, and his own connection of this with his father's love of a dog. The analyst expected the patient to recognize on his own, or certainly to accept her pointing out to him that he really wanted his father's love as indicated by the related symbols.

The analyst was annoyed because he saw no connection between his description of his father as "good looking," "tall and muscular" and a physical type he admired, and his constant hate-love chasing after men who were good-looking, tall and muscular.

The analyst was annoyed that the patient, who could be so brilliant and entertaining a conversationalist when he pleased, was so often childishly silly, babyish, petulant and mawkishly depressed in the analytic sessions.

The analyst was annoyed that he, who lived in the glamorous world of the theater and rubbed elbows with the famous, gifted, and renowned, before whom golden doors stood open, should, by refusing to accept the full measure of help she was ready, willing and able to grant him, prevent her from pushing him through the same golden doors to the promised land. If she had been graced with gifts of the physical beauty and talents he possessed, how differently she would have used her opportunities.

Her annoyance must have showed. It then occurred to the analyst that the patient was not so much resisting the interpretations she so freely handed out to him as responding to the underlying feeling tone behind them. If so, he was justified in not letting her push him around physically even if it was "for his own good."

The patient was a patient and not a friend. Although it was all right for the patient to see the analyst as "the good mother," the analyst was neither his mother, potential sweetheart, or the patient himself. The analyst was merely his physician. With objectivity restored, it was not difficult to prognosticate that future sessions would have to be conducted differently.

PSYCHODYNAMICS

The patient used homosexuality in various ways: as a weapon of frustrated rage, a shield against overwhelming, self-searing anxiety, or as an acting-out of the hate-love feeling he held for his father (open hate to please the mother and secret yearning love which he could not control) and fear of his incestuous wishes relating to the woman-mother-maid whose rejection of him was implicit in her embrace. The patient's pathologic dependency, said by Bieber et. al. to be "a characteristic of the majority of homosexuals," was evidenced by his early relationship to his close-binding intimate mother (CBI) and later on to others. *Homosexuality, Basic Books, Inc., N.Y.P. 309.* According to the same source, (ibid; page 315) "Where a father has been devaluated by a wife's contempt while the son has been elevated to a position of preference, and where the father's potentially supportive role is undermined, a highly unrealistic and anxiety-laden grandiosity is promoted in the son." These words, verbatim, describe the patient's initial psychic makeup. The patient used the act of fellatio both in practice and symbolically to act out his oral passive-aggressive fixation, a character trait pervading every aspect of his behavior pattern. The duality of his compulsion also was manifested by his narcissicism and by his anxiety in regard to the adequacy of his own penis which led him to bite and internalize the sexual organs of his male partners, or else "humiliate" them by reversing the process. Despite his overt, active, promiscuous homosexual behavior, *it did not seem that the patient was a truly physically committed homosexual.* It seemed rather that his homosexuality, like his stealing, was an expression of a child's unspecified and polymorph perverse reactive behavior to an environment so confusing that he could not differentiate its individual components. On an emotional level, the patient simply did not know the difference in roles pertaining to men and women, boys and girls, mothers, fathers, and children. Nor did he know the difference between friendship, love, dependency and the varied emotions they evoked in relationships. Sex, to him, was a thing apart, wholly divorced from judgment and almost wholly from emotion, except when anger prevailed. His "guilt feelings" about his homosexuality, were the result of fear of his own underlying anger, violence and hostility. This fear led directly to his powerful masochistic drive for punishment. Since these marked characteristics influenced his life, the unconscious factors, the pre-Oedipal, oral and anal fixations and Oedipal anxieties had to be interpreted to mean that his homosexual activities were a defense against his hostility to men (his father), and a fear of castration by women.

The patient appeared to be moving from a homosexual fixation loosened by analysis toward heterosexuality. This was indicated in the transference as well as through the manifest and the latent contents of his dreams. According to Bieber, "the reparative mechanisms, usually unconscious and irrational, operate to restore heterosexuality."

MID-PHASE

In the tenth month of therapy, the patient arrived for his first session of the week in a mood that can best be described as "high."

"You can throw away the couch," he announced airily. "I won't need it any more." He added proudly that he and June had "made music" together the night before. This was the patient's first heterosexual experience in six years. He had stated more than once how much he liked her, and there were indications that the quality of his feeling differed in some way from his previous "platonic" relationships. He reported that he had been phantasizing about her for some time, but had made no advances to her because he had not been sure of his reception.

Two sessions later he reported a dream. "It was really very short and I know just what you're going to say, so don't bother, I can interpret it myself. I was dancing with a wonderful girl. We were dancing together but she couldn't follow me." He related June's father, who would stop June from *following* him, if he could, to the dream. "I am in competition with her father for June, and for her father for myself, just as you said last time. It's also true that he's the type who used to attract me, but you're wrong if you think I want him that way now. I'd like to have him for a father, that's all."

After ten months of therapy, the patient once again left for the West Coast with June, she to star in a movie, and he to coach her for the part. They remained away for six months. Again, the patient consulted a psychiatrist but this time more from force of habit than from any great urgency. When he returned to New York, he resumed therapy on an average of three sessions a week.

The patient discussed his homosexuality with more objectivity in this new phase of the therapeutic relationship. "I really don't want to be a homosexual, and I hope I'm not using June to escape being one. But people say that an analyst is a crutch. Maybe everyone needs a crutch now and then. I'm not ashamed of it. I like having you behind me. It gives me a sense of security."

June and the patient had been living together for seven months. He was not only her coach but he assumed the role of building her up physically and emotionally. He saw to it that she kept appointments with her own analyst, stopped her overeating and self-induced vomiting (one of her major neurotic symptoms), helped her to look more feminine and attractive, and to decorate her apartment. He was not only her lover, but "confidante" and mother. Her career was at its height, and in this the patient played a major role. Their interdependency grew and grew. Through increased interpretation, the patient became aware that aspects of this relationship were a repetition of his childhood relationship with his mother. He had been mother's "extension" and now became June's "extension." Without analytically discussing any of the oedipal and pre-oedipal unresolved conflicts underlying his behavior, the patient was aware that his only aim was to please June, to make her important. His own ambitions became of secondary importance.

June's own personality make-up became identified for the patient with that of his mother. June was self-centered, narcissistic, moody, unstable, very confused in identification, and gave the patient the emotional roller-coaster ride he identified as love, by alternately loving him and rejecting him strictly according to her need.

In the treatment situation, some of the underlying factors in the patient's neurotic pattern were coming to the surface:

> Maybe I want to be an extension of June. I think of *you* as an extension of myself. I *do* think that June is like my mother, and I'm beginning to resent it. I think that people in analysis always discover that their parents are bitches. Maybe that's the real goal of analysis. I'm sorry, I really didn't mean that. I realize that criticism can be constructive. I always thought my mother was a human being, that women were strong. Actually though, I always knew way down deep that she was a conniving, lying, thieving bitch. She beat me unjustly, she protected me unjustly and she literally stole my father from me, by turning me against him. He used to drive me mad when he couged or went to the bathroom, it made me so aware of his presence.

In the same session he related a dream:

> I was in my apartment and everything was clean. I had a small French desk. I opened every drawer and everything was in order, but in the lower drawer there were small little curled black things. It was rat shit. I said, 'There's a rat in my desk.' It worried me, but I decided to put off doing anything about it till tomorrow. It didn't smell, this rat shit. That's the end of my dream. I'm thinking now that when I lived with my wife and baby in London, we were on a train and I happened to look out of the window. Outside on another rail, a sleek, horrible rat was slinking along. I keep thinking about Diane and my Mario Angelo and also know that I'm neglecting him. I'm not really a father to him. I don't want him to visit my mother. I couldn't trust my mother to bring up my child.

The rest of the session took the form of a dialogue:

Analyst: Why do you associate a rat with your wife, child and mother?

Patient: It isn't the rat. It's the rat shit. She used to roll me in shit. (Pause)

Analyst: Why do you see yourself rolling in shit?

Patient: Hell, she used to connive with me to steal, she even gave me high moral principles about it. I was never to steal from a friend. I remember dreaming the other day that I was in London, in the house of a friend, completely nude, but I was not ashamed. I did not want to hide. I concentrated on my penis. It was half erect and I was proud that people would see how well developed it was. Suddenly, it went to a normal position and I thought that now the people would say how small it was, but I still was not ashamed of being naked. When I woke up I wished that I was here with you to tell you that I realized I was making a parallel about nudity and being adjusted. My problems and my penis.

Analyst: You say you were not ashamed of being naked and showing yourself?

Patient: Yes, I did not panic. Also, I used to think the physical pains I had always started when I was coming to a session. That's no longer true. I like the fact that you don't make any demands on me, or at last demands I can't meet. Funny, although I'm pretty sure I love June, it suddenly occurred to me that I'd like to be able to sleep with many women. I think it is probably more fun to be promiscuous with women than with men.

Patient: (In another session.) I dreamt I was some place in California. I was there with Alice's new boy friend. I was in some kind of police station. I escaped and found myself hanging on to a rope; below was a highway and bushes and trees and a running stream. I hung on to the rope, but I was sort of sliding down very fast. I was not tired and I jumped down and came to a small village with small houses. I had no money, only a dime in my wallet. I knew I had left my money at the hotel. I wanted to use the dime for a phone call and I saw a policewoman who stopped me. There was no violence in the way she did it. (The policewoman, I think, is you. Someone who puts me on the line, makes me face the truth, my feelings and duties.) I didn't have my bag with me.

Analyst: The bag you always carry when you come here?

Patient: Yes, I am not sure what that means. Is it my masculinity? Is it an escape? The village and houses, they were so modest, pretty and small, they are all female symbols to me. Why was the dream connected with Alice? I don't care about her that way. Why wasn't it about June? It's her I want, but she really doesn't want to commit herself, I know. I realize that I want to be loved but I'm afraid no woman will love me unless I buy her off or steal from her.

CRISIS

The patient continued to discuss the problems of his life, and it was obvious they were again coming to a crisis.

As stated before, the patient was utterly blocked in all matters pertaining to his early life in the Sudan. He also had a marked preference for the color "black," in clothes and decor, and thought that Negroes were "sexier" than whites, a trait of which he approved. In phantasy he always saw his mother in a black dress—by no means *her* favorite color—and this bothered him. Again and again this was brought up; Why did black mean something to him to such a degree that it disturbed him, and what did it symbolize?

One day he came to the office obviously very much excited. He had seen the movie, *David and Lisa,* and began to describe a scene in which Lisa climbs up to the arms of a black marble statue representing a mother and child. Suddenly the patient started to sob. When he was asked why he was crying, he replied, "I don't *know!*" He was asked to associate to "black" and "mother." He paused and suddenly shouted: "Fatima! My old nurse! *She* was the one who used to hold me in her arms, not my mother. Black means love and Fatima loved me. Maybe you doctors are not so wrong after all. I always wanted to please my mother so that she would love me as unconditionally as Fatima loved me. That's why I let my mother beat me. I wanted her to beat me."

The patient himself began to connect his warm, almost foetal symbiotic relationship with Fatima, with the self-incorporating relationship he desired with his mother, his father and June. He soon presented a dream as follows:

> My agent told me I was to paint a canvas. It was a big canvas and he was telling me what to paint, but I had already splashed it with vivid Gauguin-like colors. My agent pointed to the painting and said: 'In the center you have a banana tree with about two hundred bananas on it and these bananas are very bright yellow. Also, all the crossroads lead to the banana tree. The roads are brown, the grass is green, and the sky is blue. I see you have painted June and your analyst together on one road, and yourself on another.' Then, we all met close to the banana tree.

The patient labeled the banana a phallic symbol, and claimed that he was very angry with this dream. He resented that June and the analyst were on the other side, and he resented his agent.

Although his dream had put both June and the analyst on the other side, possibly because he had a desire to walk alone, he resented the two women being there because he feared that without them he would skip back to the banana tree (homosexuality). When the three persons did meet, it was *near* the banana tree, which showed how close to the surface his fears were on all levels; fear that the analysis and heterosexual relationship might not work out and therefore he would have to have recourse to homosexuality again. The patient resented the latter part of this interpretation, claimed he was not at all afraid of losing June, and was sure that therapy was making a new man of him.

Two weeks later the patient called up for an unscheduled session. His voice was hoarse with urgency; he had to see the analyst at once and could not wait until the next day. When he came in, he took the chair instead of the couch, and was the picture of utter dejection. June had decided to break off with him. She was not ending their friendship but wanted to live separately and stand on her own feet. She assured him she was not in love with anybody else. He said he didn't feel like living any more. By helping him to verbalize his anger toward June, he felt sufficiently relieved to state that he would come back the next day.

The next day he came in looking like death itself, and wordlessly pushed a cable in the analyst's hand. His mother had just died. Faced with the actual physical loss of two people so necessary to him, superimposed on the psychic trauma of his disturbed mother-child, male-female relationship in general, he felt unable to cope with life. The analyst responded to his mood of the whole world crashing around him with the one weapon that could never fail at such a time: sympathy.

This was an extremely critical period for the patient and there were times when the analyst could not be sure that he wouldn't commit suicide. His sessions were increased and the analyst continued to be as supportive as possible. In time, his repressed anger toward June as well as his mother was brought out in the open, and discussed.

PRESENT STATE OF THERAPY

The patient and June continued to see each other platonically. He moved out of her apartment by stages, and slowly began to adapt to the new situation. They continued to work as before but when June left for the West Coast without him, contrary to their work-contract, the patient went into a rather deep depression again. Parallel with his depression, and perhaps buttressing it, his masochism came to the fore, and he spent far more time, money and effort than he could afford in buying June expensive gifts.

The state of his analysis in the months since the break-up is marked by recurrent depression. Nevertheless, with the ventilation of his angers, fears, and anxieties, the patient is managing to function on his own. With the exception of one regression to a homosexual episode consisting of mutual masturbation (committed at the time when he was angry at the analyst for going on vacation) he has not regressed to homosexuality, despite frequent panic and temptation.

At present, the patient has grown a beard, which seems to be a sign of his desire for both true masculinity and adulthood. He has had a few dates with women. His professional strivings have increased and the analyst feels that the patient is gaining insight into the self-defeating emotional patterns at the root of his neuroses.

ADDENDUM

The necessity of condensing the voluminous material gleaned from and about this patient suitable to a short paper of this type, perforce caused the omission of much pertinent data of therapeutic importance. This patient's active, intense life situation, unlike those of many neurotic patients who vegetate and brood from session to session, was incredibly complex, brimful of incidents, personalities, hectic action and inter-action.

For these reasons the analyst could touch only lightly on his deep masochistic drives, expressed among other ways by biting his fingernails to the quick, walking for hours at a time until he was "ready to drop," seeking self-humiliating incidents, and causing many psychosomatic symptoms. All physical findings concerning his ailments proved negative. At various times, according to the transference, the analyst was a symbol of the loved mother, the hated mother, the loved-hated mother, the good mother, and in line with the patient's homosexuality, the mother-father figure. The latent content of many dreams suggested incestuous wishes toward all these figures, and his own identification of the analyst with June as well as his sometimes coy manner of alluding to sexual terms, including punning, indicated some mixed-up sexual phantasies toward the analyst. He also feared that he wouldn't be understood by a woman, which seemed reinforced literally by the fact that the analyst was a foreigner. On the other hand, he also believed that women were stronger and more understanding than men, so he felt inferior to the analyst. He expected the analyst to "beat" him until he bled as his mother did and at times tried to provoke this to happen. When he started to grow a beard, he commented that it would make him look older, and added "so now I'll be more on an equal level with you."

The prognosis in this case could be seen as a good one and it may be that heterosexuality, while it may take a long time to achieve, along with all the other goals, is possible in the future.

Psychodynamics and Psychosomatic Symptoms

by Jack L. Rubins, M.D.
American Institute for Psychoanalysis

Jack L. Rubins, M.D.

Since publication of the paper herein presented, the author has served as Associate Clinical Professor of Psychiatry, New York Medical College, Attending Psychiatrist, Flower Fifth and Metropolitan Hospitals, and Consultant Psychiatrist for the New York City Board of Education. He is Associate Psychoanalyst with the Karen Horney Clinic, and has lectured at the New School for Social Research and the American Institute for Psychoanalysis. Dr. Rubins was president of the Association for Advancement of Psychoanalysis from 1961-63, and is President-elect of the Queens County Psychiatric Society.

THE term "psychosomatic" refers to the appearance of physical symptoms in relation to emotional states or mental activity. From a dynamic viewpoint the term seems grossly inadequate. In the first place, it indicates little about the particular patient before us in analysis. Secondly, it tells nothing about the psycho-somatic relationship, and thirdly it lumps together, indifferently, manifestations of quite different order and dynamic process.

In one case the somatic symptoms may be the physiological component of a healthy, affective state of simple order; in another the affect may be compulsive or irrational. Or anxiety may be involved. Generally, this is considered an affect, resulting from the interplay between "simpler" emotions, so that although a large volume of experimental work may give factual evidence of particular somatic changes being "produced" by particular affects, it does not help too much in understanding the patient, whose emotional states are more complex, or unconscious, or cannot be easily identified either by patient or observer.

Still other somatization reactions, such as the "conversive" symptoms, may not only involve affects but conceptual ideational complexes in conflict. And even more complex clinical syndromes, such as asthma or tuberculosis, have been related to personality types or "profiles" or groups of character traits. In these cases not only is the psychosomatic relationship often most strained, but the origin and nature of the psychological state is difficult to explain.

Most attempts to explain these symptoms have focused on the nature or type of affective-ideational factor, and on the relationship of such a particular condition to a type of somatic response. They assume an interaction between more or less definable psychic and somatic events. These theories have been well reviewed in a recent article [1] and it is unnecessary to detail them here. Suffice it to say that degrees of relatedness have been seen, varying from a close, precise specificity (affect→symptom, personality→syndrome) to a limited specificity (non-specific anxiety→symptom or syndrome) to complete nonspecificity (any affect producing any somatic reaction). In the latter group, any consistency of pattern of somatic reaction in one individual, or differences between individuals, is vaguely attributed to temperamental and/or constitutional predisposition, to total life experience, or to development of a "psychosomatic character."[2]

While this emphasis on the type of psychological state and type of somatic response may be necessary to lay a foundation for describing psychosomatic relationship in simple observable experimental terms, I feel it has many limitations and may even obscure further understanding of the total clinical picture. This is because it takes one aspect of function out of a context in which the total human being is functioning in a total situation that is both immediate and historical. Moreover, while it may correlate psychic and physical events, this correlation is primarily descriptive rather than dynamic, so that we are still left with the basic problem of how these spheres relate. This question is inherent in the cause-effect concept of causality upon which such theories are premised. A duality or dichotomy is thus implied, when in reality we may be dealing with some other form of correlation, perhaps only aspects or modes of function of a unitary process, as Kelman has suggested in regard to anxiety.[3]

As I see it, any explanation of the process of somatization must include three aspects, involving questions which the aforementioned theories have failed to clarify adequately.

First, why does a particular individual show particular symptoms at a particular time (and show different somatic reactions at different times)?

Second, does somatization per se (regardless of the particular symptomatic form) have any basis as a form of experience? Why is it that an individual should somatize his psychological processes instead of experiencing them in some other way? Is there some element of purposeful selection, conscious or unconscious, and if so, to what extent? Is it a trial-and-error process? Is it just a minimizing of "unpleasure" or anxiety? Or a moving toward safety or love or security or selfhood? Would such motivations necessarily determine more than general defensive moves, e.g., neurotic attitudes, or is some other determining quality also necessary to channel modes of self-expression to the body?

Third, what occurs as the psycho-physiological correlation during somatization? That is, although there may be motivational forces to "explain" somatization, what is the psychological process by which these motivational forces result in the symptoms?

Since the analytic process brings into play emotional forces (including anxiety) to a considerable extent, it is to be expected that psychosomatic symptoms will occur therein. In fact, one could legitimately ask whether a treatment is truly psychoanalytic without the occurrence of such symptoms. In my own experience, every analysis of adequate depth and length has been accompanied by some somatic symptom formation. However, it is not usual for somatic symptoms to occur so constantly during analysis, and to be of such a nature that they permit a close correlation with the dynamics of the neurotic process. It is the purpose of this paper to present such an illustrative case, to evaluate the observations made during this analysis, and to present some pertinent conclusions which may help to answer some of the questions set forth above.

The patient, a thirty-year-old woman, was in analysis for about four-and-a-half years. Her presenting symptoms were recurrent attacks of trembling of about two years' duration, which had become progressively more severe and frequent; at times, a nondescript, transitory skin eruption; nausea and diarrhea of several months' duration; an extreme feeling of tension and fear of insanity; and a chronic respiratory allergy which began at age two, with asthmatic attacks in the winter and rhinitis in summer. In addition, she was having difficulty with her job notably because of chronic lateness. In her social relationships, she was finding herself unable to get along with people (particularly with her mother, whom she used to idolize), and with her girl friends. She was finding them dishonest, catty, and critical. She had one friend, an ideal, whom she found to be charming, clean-cut morally, and physically alert and quick-witted. She complained that she herself was extremely shy, timid, unable to talk back, never able to do enough for anyone or live up to their demands, and that she was resentful when she was not liked for what she was.

During her first session, she appeared to be under considerable pressure. She hurried through a list of symptoms and present circumstances, as in a prepared recital, wishing to cover as much as possible without showing she was hurrying. She seemed anxious and fearful, but trying desperately to keep these feelings under control. Her physical appearance carried a sense of incongruity; although she was above average height, rather heavy and massive, her gait was light and bounding, her face was cute and childlike, her voice soft, and her limbs contrastingly thin. During the first three years of analysis she usually wore a mannish jacket with a skirt-blouse combination or slacks, then, occasionally, a dress until during the last year it became her preferred style.

Her family history was not presented in any consecutive fashion, but as a composite of spread-out details. For a long time she reiterated how poor, vague, or dreamlike her memory was. It was only during the third year, in spite of much previous encouragement, that she expressed an insistent desire to look back. With this she had considerable anxiety and feelings of being in a trance.

Her mother was the guiding figure in the household, a dominating personality who took the major responsibilities, paid the bills, etc. One outstanding memory was of mother smiling all the time. She never permitted the children to experience or see any unpleasantness or tragedy: no disagreements were voiced in front of them. By the same token she seldom showed any natural or spontaneous affection. Her mother encouraged her to be tough, unemotional, independent and self-sufficient.

While her mother was relatively uninhibited with the children about the body and natural functions, she never discussed the sexual facts of life. During adolescence, the daughter always felt ashamed to mention to her mother such questions as her menses, wearing a brassiere, etc. And although the mother was quite socially minded and modern in the use of make-up, she was rather indifferent about her own appearance. Nonetheless, she always wished her daughter to wear nice clothes—and complained about having to make a fuss even though she was pleased.

Although the daughter felt that her father had played an important part in her life, she was not sure how. She felt she never really knew him, that mother kept him away. He was a contrast to his wife. He was rather introverted and disinterested in the home life. When he had a comment about the children, he would tell his wife rather than speak to them directly. He worked long hours and was seldom home. Although his business affairs were generally fairly prosperous, he had severe reverses at times. On two such occasions he had a depression and the daughter felt that such an illness made him despicable and dirty. Thus, although usually quiet, he was often nervous and moody. Sometimes feeling this way, he would flare up in protest, and she was afraid of his temper. She recalled her mother crying once during such an occasion, and she reacted intensely by crying also, blaming and hating him. Only once did he ever hit her brother and she recalled thinking it was strange that he should be interested enough to do so.

He tended to be rather untidy and unconcerned about his appearance and personal habits. He would walk around the house unclothed and it was always an embarrassing fear to walk in on him this way.

There was one brother to whom she was—and is—quite devoted, minding and protecting him. He also had frequent respiratory and gastric symptoms requiring medical care. He was quite intelligent, but very shy—although very demonstrative with his affections—which often embarrassed her.

Her past personal history was predominantly tinged with an atmosphere of sickness, which she recalled as far back as she could remember. Her frequent asthmatic attacks sometimes required bed rest; often she had difficulty in calling her mother to help her. She was seldom taken to a doctor, but told she should be smart enough or strong enough or controlled enough to overcome them. At times she was given foods, to which she was known to be sensitive, just to test her condition. At times she could bring on such an attack just to get attention from her mother, and she loved to be indulged then. There were occasions when her brother was ill and getting such attention, and she looked on with an eerie lonely, left-out feeling. She especially disliked his making her laugh or otherwise react suddenly, since this might bring on an attack.

Until about the age of nine, she was painfully shy and sensitive. She was so shielded from unpleasant events that when she did come in contact with something sad, she often felt she did not know how to react. She was an obedient child, since she felt mother expected her to be good, nice, and smart. She herself felt that since she wasn't healthy or beautiful, she had to be smart, though not smarter than her brother. Although she experienced her mother as controlling, it was not in an overt way. She always felt she had to ask permission to do anything, though mother never refused. By contrast, outside the home, she was strong, a leader among her friends, doing things for others she felt to be weaker.

Her appearance always was a problem about which she felt sensitive. Mother wished her to look nice, but would make her feel guilty about it. She herself considered clothes to be unimportant, as being merely to cover herself. She was a plump child and felt herself to be homely and distasteful until high school.

Her early school life was associated with feelings of insecurity and unhappiness. She was usually in the top ranks, but always felt her good marks were only luck, that she didn't deserve them. She had few friends. Once she was elected a class officer, but she did not like being in a position of authority. When she was twelve, she had an IQ test and was told she had the intelligence of an older girl. To her this confirmed that she was above the average of all other pupils. But after this she felt competition to be keen and the pace rapid, and even though she was smarter, she felt fearful of having to work much harder.

During this period she had frequent asthmatic attacks. She also became aware of a new feeling toward her mother. Since the domination was not overt and so could not be rebelled against, she discovered that she could avoid being touched by it by just not being there emotionally.

Her high school life was quite a contrast, because here she felt she found freedom. It became more real than her home life. She now found herself pretty and socially popular. She felt important and really smart. Feeling hard and strong, she not only wished to be like boys, but to surpass them; she liked to play rough games and beat them.

Her feelings about sex were confused. While it had never been brought up by her parents, neither had she asked about it. When she had been found exploring herself and her little friends, her mother had said nothing. She had felt that sexual parts were just not supposed to be there. During adolescence she had felt ashamed of her maturing body, her periods, and her breasts, and unable to ask her mother since she felt the latter didn't accept them. No limit was placed on her dates and she was encouraged to bring boy friends home, but when her parents said nothing, she felt they were not interested in her. In general, she felt boys weren't important. Taller than average, she had to go out with big fellows; she always admired bigness, anyway. On dates she had to get dressed up, but in ladylike garb she felt no freedom or naturalness.

She never permitted more than mild necking. At times she felt afraid to kiss, lest the boy back away and reject her. Anything more than this was promiscuous. Since she was so cool, she could not understand why she was so popular with boys. Her girl friends considered her sexy, but she felt that anyone interested in real sex was abnormal. At times she would consciously tease a boy friend by exciting him sexually, then ask him to leave. She was never sure of what love really was, and felt you could love more than one man, provided they were the strong, persistent types. However, she always experienced a wall between her and the man.

She met her husband shortly before the war. What attracted her particularly was his being openly affectionate and warm in front of her parents. After several months he left for military service. On his return, about two years later, they were married. The marriage itself had an impersonal dreamlike quality about it. She was primarily concerned about the number of people present and felt a vague guilt feeling. She claimed that her sexual relations were good in a conventional way, without being an unusual or special experience; it was a good feeling, and she usually had a satisfactory orgasm.

She worked at several jobs before and after marriage, each of them usually lasting a few months. She never really liked to work. She was afraid of the bosses; she felt they never praised her, but only criticized her mistakes, and she felt unable to do anything well. While at work, her nasal symptoms occurred particularly often and intensely. She was often ashamed and humiliated in front of the other girls, but she felt she had to smile and be in a good humor, nonetheless. At times, with these symptoms, she also felt a desire for sex.

She felt that marriage made a great change for her. While previously she had lived in a dream, her husband tried to bring her down to earth. She soon took over the major responsibility for their affairs, such as paying the bills. Arguments often occurred, however, over questions relating to managing the household. The trembling spells began to occur concurrently, without her being able to control them. Occasionally, she felt she could bring one on consciously, in order to get sympathy. Although arguments decreased during the next few years, the trembling persisted until she entered analysis.

During the first few hours of analysis, her associations gave some indication of her conception of me and of the analytic relationship: she was experiencing me as an awe-inspiring teacher (representing her standards of intelligence), plus a powerful (male) mother-figure who would magically make things come out right if her wishes (implicit and unexpressed) were obeyed. I was to let her get away with things—namely, to avoid awareness of anything sick in her through intellectual psychologizing, while relieving her somatic symptoms.

COMMENT

From the history, symptomatology, and first few analytic hours, certain dynamisms were deductible which may contribute to understanding the patient's somatization.

1) In her early relationships with her dominant mother, she had adopted a personality orientation of compliance-submissiveness-dependency, in return for which she felt entitled to approval and protection. However, strong expansive trends (particularly perfectionistic standards) in the areas of intellectual and physical performance were evidenced outside the home; these were especially notable in her sexual relationships, and during her adolescence, when reinforced by her growing sexual drives.

2) The idealized self-image she slowly created and which she then felt expected of her from others (externalized) included being good, nice, friendly; being charming and seductive; being smart, alert, and quick-witted; being stoic and non-emotional; being healthy, strong and self-sufficient. This constellation of personality traits was associated with—and symbolized by—her mother and idealized femaleness. By contrast, she associated what she felt to be negative aspects of herself—including dependency, weakness, emotionality—with her father, with maleness and feelings of self-contempt. She had hitherto been able to avoid awareness of the essential contradiction between some of these by a tremendous emotional control, and by distancing herself from all inner emotional experience and deep personal contact which would call up such emotions. Most of what she claimed she felt was a spurious, intellectualized sort of emotion, based on what she felt she should feel.

3) During her pre-adolescent years she had begun to experience a new way of relating, both to her mother and herself—namely, through emotional detachment, "not being there" for others, a distancing mechanism which forestalled genuine emotional closeness.

4) "Sickness" had a particular and intense emotional significance for her. It had become part of her major orientation to life. This was not the typical hypochondriacal, obsessive preoccupation with particular organs or body functions, although comparable dynamic functions and "uses" the so-called secondary gains—were present here, too. In fact, although she did have variations in intensity and form, she was rarely free from some somatic symptom for any length of time—except during several years of her adolescence. This latter period corresponded to a hiatus in her anamnesis, which she did not recall until late in her analysis and associated with strong feelings of self-hate. In other words, to see herself as sick was a psychological necessity to fit into the facade, the version of herself which would satisfy the greatest number, and most advantageous of her compulsive qualities. And as part of her idealized image, she had intense pride vested in being healthy and denying the reality of illness, physical or emotional.

5) As a result of the association of particular desired or rejected personality traits with femaleness or maleness, the blurring of her own identity was characterized by a blurring of her sexual identity. This included a distortion of her body-image; she rejected herself as the physical woman she was, as well as having "feminine" personality traits compared with other girls or boys.

THE COURSE OF ANALYSIS

During the first four months she was completely free of somatic symptoms. She brought up mainly her complaint and perfectionistic tendencies as she was consciously aware of them: her need to be liked, to be generous, self-sacrificing and forgiving, and, at the same time to be more intelligent and better-informed than others. She constantly felt she was not being any of these, even to a normal degree, and called herself—and felt that I was calling her—stupid and selfish. Although she spoke insistently of feeling affection, resentment, and so forth, it was completely intellectualized, as if occurring in someone else. She discussed her ways of handling upsurges of anger: by being sick, by forcing herself to like people, by absolute physical control, by feeling guilty, and by externalizing.

After beginning to look at these qualities, she reacted with a series of dreams dealing generally with the theme of uncovering and hiding. She recalled fears she had had of sex and of being pregnant. She was troubled by a desire to steal little things, which she acted out by taking paper towels and magazines, then telling me about it each time. This seemed to be a testing of how far she could go against her own restrictions and me.

From this time on, until she left analysis, she experienced various and changing somatic symptoms almost constantly. These often changed from day to day, week to week, or even during the same hour. This first period consisted of nasal congestion and asthma or nausea and dizziness, lasting about four weeks. With them she often had an urge for food and for sexual intercourse. During the sessions she fluctuated between extremes of feeling helpless and insecure, of hating herself for this and feeling that others hated her too, and feeling abused because others were indifferent. She began to see insincerity everywhere, emphasizing in herself the compulsiveness of her having to be so compliant. She then began to bring up incidents from her adolescence which were associated with change, spontaneity and aggressiveness; and at the same time, feelings about sex and "feminine" functions which she despised.

She became pregnant during the eighth month of analysis; her associations and dreams indicated considerable anxiety about this "growth" within her, which she was consciously unaware of. Her nasal congestion was interspersed with periods of running nose, but otherwise she was free from somatic symptoms. She seemed to have distanced herself emotionally and was unwilling to become involved in any sensitive question. The analysis was "smooth" in the sense of her not having any intense psychic swings. She might bring up some emotional theme, usually in externalized form, for one or two hours, then abruptly change the subject. She often spoke of spilling things or "cracks in the wall" with such shifts. Nevertheless, in spite of this elusiveness, we touched upon several of her claims: for affection without giving any, for attention devoid of emotional accompaniment, for freedom to "get away with" whatever she might want. Following this she began again to have the attacks of trembling. Although she related this primarily to sexual exposure, she gradually became more aware that this included other areas, such as sickness and tragedy, to which she could not expose herself. Now anxiously preoccupied with her forthcoming delivery, she was somewhat aware of her numbing herself to it, to the inner movement; relating this to her remoteness and not participating completely in personal relationships with others.

Her attacks stopped with this awareness, but she kept having a constantly changing somatic symptomatology from day to day. It seemed she was experiencing a consistent, though lower, level of anxiety, with rapid small swings into and away from it. This same movement was evidenced toward me in general questions or in asking directly for reassurance. Before discontinuing, although she kept emphasizing her unconcern about doing so—how unimportant and unreal it was—she brought up early memories of the few times she should have felt sadness but had not. She was angry, too, at people who did not understand her need for help. She could not ask for understanding; it would be a favor; she would feel guilty about it.

During her absence, she was free from her habitual allergic symptoms. She had occasional tremors which became more frequent before her return. For some time after she began again, the constellation of her dependency feelings was in the forefront. We worked on this, emphasizing the difference between neurotic help-demanding and the healthy asking for help as self-assertion. She was experiencing conflict between her dependent needs and her needs for self-sufficiency, both on the reality level (between the demands of her baby son and her mother) and on the symbolic level. She felt confusion, caught between the acting-up and not-following-routine of the baby, and her mother expecting him to be healthy and well-behaved. Her need to feel she could handle anything prevented her from admitting her need for help. As she kept elaborating upon these needs, she began to make little moves toward a greater involvement with me and with her analysis—for instance, by commenting in a positive sense on the office or my appearance. To each movement she reacted with a headache or other somatic complaint, and often she would complain of difficulty in relating to her mother.

She shifted from the couch to the chair. Then, after remarking that she noticed for the first time that I was human, she felt like fighting and yelling and pulling me down to her level. This was followed by a stormy period of reaction: congested nose, cough, backaches. She missed several hours because of hoarseness. She kept feeling hostility toward everyone, and while complaining that I did not give her enough reason to get angry with me, she projected much of this hostility onto people who were petty about money, easy-going, and who showed little expansiveness.

On several occasions she spontaneously related her clogged-up feeling to her husband's asking for sexual intercourse; then, more particularly, to her letting-go, as in real closeness and in orgasm. She began to question her feelings about being a woman and to recall past incidents when she had preferred being strong, like a boy. Her usual respiratory reactions to such upsurges did not follow, but instead she was now having diarrhea. The theme of dishonesty was now coming up more frequently. She was asking what she was really like, what her appearance was like. Asking her mother for help—to which she had previously related her asthmatic attacks—now began to appear as a demand for attention. She kept seeing frustrated aggressiveness in everyone.

While considering this aspect of herself, she had a running nose, urinary frequency, and hives. She consciously felt superior and smarter than her friends, able to disagree with them or with her family. A long series of dreams was largely about violent animals and mother going away, or about outright aggressiveness and giving up her controlling "shoulds." Her having to control came into focus: her asthma as controlling her mother, intelligence as controlling others, her feeling of strength in being able to control her asthma, her sexual desire, and her orgasm.

She began to bring up what it might feel like really to be a woman and felt less self-contempt therewith. For some time she questioned her mother's perfection, her idealized version of woman. Being a woman meant having a female body. She brought up her feelings about sex, in some detail. She seldom wished to have sexual relations and felt coerced by her husband's desire, though it was her duty not to refuse. She often felt disgust and unexpressed resentment. She recalled having felt her mother's condemnation of sexual parts. This body also meant having insides which was anxiety-creating, not only in the possibility of experiencing pain, but also in requiring her to give up some of her compulsive intellectualizing. Finally, it could mean having children, being a housewife, taking responsibility and caring for, instead of being the child who was cared for. As she brought up each of these attributes, she felt anxiety at times. At other times she felt self-hate with awareness of her lacks. She responded in her usual defensive ways: somatization, externalization, becoming mildly depressed, or acting out.

Her dreams at this time had a recurrent theme of fatness and thinness in people with her preferring the latter and not wishing to be in contact with the former. Being fat she associated with being warm, loose and womanly, also with "taking license" to do what she wanted. She began to see in a somewhat deeper sense that she had played a role by doing what others wanted—"what she should do." She had admired men and wished to be one because of their freedom, as she saw it, to do as they wished. With this movement, her nose was running constantly now. She began to experience a desire to be closer to her mother, brother, friends, but likewise to experience a blocking, a wall between herself and others. Enlarging upon this latter feeling, she began to sense "dullness," "passivity," and "thinness" in others, and "far-awayness" and "emptiness" in herself. There was a fear of feeling her own inner emptiness and for some time her sessions were characterized by long silences.

She was more and more concerned with restrictions and demands: those she made on others and those she resentfully felt put upon her. She alternated between hours concerned with others (externalizing) and hours focusing upon herself. She seemed to be gradually becoming aware of the extent of her externalizing and taking some back into herself. In this connection, the significance of her rhinorrhea and sneezing appeared to be abortive crying; she was now feeling on the side of her restricting herself. While she often felt conscious anxiety, or "falling apart," she also became aware of a certain pleasure in it, like scratching an itchy throat.

As the intensity of her restrictive "shoulds" came more into awareness, questions relating her honesty, pretense, and duplicity occurred to her. Her father arose as a symbol, both in the sense of his being weak and secretive, and his being hard and stern. She then associated him with authority and the analyst. With this latter concern, her somatic symptoms again became acute. She experienced attacks of wheezing, nausea, trembling during the sessions, backache at home. Unable to deny "sickness" (father) totally to herself any longer, she now began to often feel her members falling asleep, being cold or numb.

A series of dreams pictured her generally as being pretty, well-dressed, a good homemaker, a good sexual partner, seductive, and so forth. She became aware of her pride in being able to handle everything, in her seductiveness, in her narcissism. In the analysis her behavior and dress took on a new, seductive quality. She appeared with new hair-do's and new dresses: she changed her chair several times, even trying my own. Working on this charming-manipulative aspect of herself, she recalled how, as a child, looking pretty helpless brought attention. As an adolescent she had used sexiness to dominate. Since then, she had employed other qualities—flirtatiousness, physical appeal, intelligence. The claims she asserted with these attitudes were for receiving without giving out anything, without effort.

With these awarenesses, she began to wonder whether she might not like to be a "typical" woman. She became more interested in housework and felt she was making friends with herself. But with each move toward self-acceptance, she reacted with nasal congestion and increasing sensations of pressure in her head or chest. Although she came close to tears several times, she was not yet able to cry.

She returned from a summer vacation during the fourth year with consciously experienced anxiety, although without having had any somatic symptoms during the break. She described this anxiety as different from that previously felt. The usual frightening quality was absent. Her analytic hours felt different also. She participated more fully and more actively. She seemed to have less of a need to control through intellect; her associations showed less consistency, and it was difficult—at times impossible—to follow underlying themes.

Conflict came through all her recurrent associations: becoming involved versus withdrawal; opening up, and warmth, versus blocking passages and being cold; tight and tense versus loose and smooth. These involved many areas of her experience: reactions toward the analyst and the analysis; toward her parents and son; toward her husband socially and sexually; toward herself. She often felt nausea or diarrhea, had a congested or running nose, and experienced much gut-rumbling and girdle-loosening during the analytic hours. She began to find it more enjoyable to visit her mother and found her parents less demanding. Her father was now seen with mixed emotional value. He represented the average, accepting limitations and illness, possessing humility—qualities usually despised from the viewpoint of her perfect image of herself and feared as threatening to her total neurotic position. At the same time, although unable to express it, she began to see him more positively as good, natural, enduring, and with more feeling than her mother.

She decided to take courses in art and psychology at a local school (which seemed to represent both a constructive move and a move back to her old neurotic solution of "knowing"). In these she was able to act out many of her attitudes toward authority, such as abused feelings, claims for special attention, for understanding without effort, for the magic solution. Once she reacted with an argumentative outburst toward the teacher, which was duplicated to a lesser degree in the analytic hour. After it she felt out of control, then depressed. It was followed by unusually painful and overabundant menses. Working on her expansive trends, aggressiveness, independence, and rebellion, she began to distinguish between healthy self-assertion and compulsive acting-out.

Subsequently, she felt "more like a woman, with its softness and fragility." She came close to crying several times on recalling childhood events when she had had to be strong and unexpressive. As she let into her experience the deep, hitherto unacceptable feelings of loneliness and of wanting help which underlay this stocism, she was more able to distinguish emotionally between a healthy request for help and compulsive dependency. As her pride in her masculine strength lessened, so too did the contempt for her weakness, her womanly qualities. Sickness was less terrifying. She challenged her "shoulds," identifying herself with the authority instead of feeling herself the little girl subject to irrational discipline. She was afraid that if she gave up her perfectionistic goals, she would be bereft of all existence. Death themes recurred, but she found them less frightening and counterbalanced by life and growth themes. She brought up past events on the positive, achievement side: an early interest in art, her real ability in school, her vivacity.

At one point, after a very scanty menstrual period, when she was feeling nauseous and thought she felt some breast tenderness, the possibility of pregnancy occurred. This produced a reaction involving the entire gamut of her neurotic defenses: numbing and removing herself; control through domination or seductiveness, or absolute emotional squelching; appeals to love; appeals to magic. Her rapid shifting indicated that none of these solutions was working adequately. However, she tolerated her anxiety and stayed closely involved with it.

Soon thereafter her somatic symptoms began decreasing in intensity and frequency. Recurrent dreams of her father's death indicated that he symbolized her detachment and non-involvement, particularly as these referred to her major solution, perfectionistic intellectualism. She seemed to be radically revising her picture of herself. The "opposites" she had become aware of now no longer appeared as necessarily contradictory. She apparently was unifying her fragmentation, encompassing her conflicts. Her references to "back and forth" feelings were now often interspersed with expressions of "mine," "wholeness," and so forth. During the last few months of her analysis, she was free of somatic symptoms, in spite of her being aware of a certain low level of tension—and in spite of which she was able to enjoy her various activities, to laugh, and to cry freely.

COMMENTS

In this analysis, the pattern of somatization had some particular characteristics. 1) For the first few months after beginning analysis, the patient was free from the symptoms previously experienced. 2) The somatic symptoms occurred in cycles of varying length and intensity. Usually, there was a sudden onset, then a gradual decrease of replacement by others. 3) The system affected varied: at times it was respiratory (nasal or bronchial), gastrointestinal (diarrhea-constipation), generalized motor (trembling), ocular (tearing or itching), genito-urinary (pollakiuria, pseudopregnancy). 4) At times the symptoms seemed to be related to anxiety in direct proportion, at other times not: they decreased even though the anxiety was high, increased when the anxiety was lessening. 5) Symptoms decreased toward the latter part of the analysis and finally disappeared.

PERSONALITY ORIENTATION

The presence of certain dynamic personality traits in a particular functional organization seems to be necessary, or at least seems to predispose, to the appearance of somatic symptoms. I do not feel that these constitute a "personality profile" or character typology, such as various authors have described, since these are not static or descriptive attitudes or behavior traits. They are, rather, driving or energizing forces which we might variously call needs, demands, dynamic attitudes which have a peremptory effect and direction, but which may or may not be concretized into behavior.

The first of these is a pride-invested glorification of absolute health, both emotional and physical. It constitutes a predominant aspect of the idealized self-image or concept, implying a feeling of omnipotence in being able to overcome any physical illness-imperfection. It results in corresponding claims on life—namely, that the person be invulnerable and immune to physical ailments. While such feelings may be partly conscious and behavioral, their intensity, compulsiveness and ramifications are unconscious.

They are entwined with other personality traits, for instance, in this patient, with perfectionistic strivings and expansiveness.

As a derivative of this idealization of strength, "sickness" becomes highly charged emotionally, again both on a conscious and unconscious level. It becomes synonymous with weakness, fault, imperfection, and as such is accompanied by feelings of self-rejection (self-contempt, humiliation, self-hatred). More precisely, in this patient, at different times it signified dependency or submission, a lack of self-sufficiency, masculinity at one time and femininity at another, loss of control, being less smart, or an intellectual means of dominating others. Even genuine emotional health was conceived of as sickness, since it meant acceptance of normal aches and pains of everyday life. During the analysis, as each of these elements came up and was worked upon, another would follow.

A second quality I have found in these patients is a characteristic type of intellectualizing, which Horney has described as a general measure to relieve tension.[4] It is not the total intellectual detachment seen, for example, in some schizoid individuals, where the existence of the emotional-body is denied psychologically or put out of consciousness. In such cases, where supremacy of the mind predominates to an extreme, or there is extreme living in imagination, I have found somatization reactions infrequent; feelings are more completely transformed into thoughts.

In these patients, where there is a partial, conflictive appeal to intellectual ability, the body functions are admitted to awareness but are felt to intrude. The intellect is often experienced as a means of controlling. In the self-image it becomes associated with perfectionistic standards: knowing is willing away body functions. This patient had "shoulds" involving both her intellectual ability and her emotionalism. In her self-concept she was both smart and feelingful. In the healthy individual these qualities are complementary aspects of the total personality. Here each was compartmentalized and compulsive, and therefore mutually contradictory. She had to be both, but could be neither, having moved away from the conflict thereby generated. Through her somatization she was able to effect a satisfaction of both, comprising something between a total form of intellectualization and a full emotionality.

BODY IMAGE AND SOMATIZATION

A third characteristic of such patients is an attitude toward their body which is basically a distortion of their body image. The child begins to develop a self-concept, the sense of "I" very early. It derives from the first awareness of his inner stimuli and movements, and from his outer surface stimuli. An important part of this self-concept is the body-image which has two aspects: a physical and an emotional, both of which interrelate and influence each other. The former involves appearance and outer and inner configuration. The latter consists of feeling–tone and emotional value associated with the various body parts and functions.

Although many authors have emphasized that adequate and healthy external stimuli are necessary for the normal development of the self-concept, comparatively little attention has been devoted to the body-image development, or the relationship of this body-image to the total self-concept. A few workers, following the Freudian approach such as Hoffer,[5] Greenacre,[6,7] Linn,[8] and Keiser,[9] have focused on the inclusion of particular body parts—the mouth, the hand-arm, the skin, the genitals—into the body-ego. They have postulated that these organs may remain or later become detached from the body-image, which would thus explain the appearance of somatic symptoms therein. But the attempts to relate this process solely to the psychosexual development and libidinal vicissitudes inevitably limits their purview. The body image thus not only becomes "genitalized," but fragmentary, or of less isolated parts, rather than a unitary whole related to a total individual. Keiser's observations on patients in an analysis who show compulsive, concretizing intellectualization are most astute and correct. They indicate his awareness of this body-image-self relationship when he notes, for instance, that "the body-image was not part of, nor blended with, nor identical with the idea of the self. . . . The pathological body-image was separated from the real self. Although this did not ward off anxiety, it did permit the patient to retain the feeling that he was safe." In addition he observed that "the body image never coalesced into a unitary whole, but persisted as a number of discrete parts which functioned independently of each other."

Using a more holistic approach, Schilder[10] has described the various and numerous factors—including developmental, libidinous and social—which enter into the formation of this image, and has related various clinicopathological states to it. L. Bender[11] has extensively studied distortions of the body-image in hospitalized children, as evidenced in their drawings of themselves. In fact, she holds that some distortion of this physical self-image is a basic condition for childhood schizophrenia, which is thus seen as a "soft" organic condition.

Zuger has described the earliest stage of self-development as the "phase of self-discovery," followed by the "phase of self-possession,"[12] which continues through adolescence. He thereby stresses the importance not only of external emotional stimuli, but of the formation of a physical self-image through discovery and awareness of the body; and of then assimilating or incorporating (taking possession of) this body-image into the total self-concept. He has suggested that certain early psychosomatic conditions may be the result of undue or distorted emphasis upon the body part involved—the bladder and enuresis, for instance—so that it is excluded from or otherwise distorted in the body-image. This approach has the advantage of going beyond the purely libidinal factors, and of pointing out that there is such a process as self-acceptance.

The Freudian psychoanalytic explanation of such somatization as distorted libido-fixation, or the Adlerian one of organ inferiority, are not adequate to explain many clinical observations. For instance, they cannot account for such phenomena as the rapid shifting of somatic symptoms (unless we postulate a singularly loose energy cathexis), or for the simultaneous somatic involvement of different systems, whether in more fixed patterns, somatic diseases,[13] or in more transitory patterns, as seen during analysis.

I feel that a more inclusive explanation must be sought in the distortions of the body-image, not only during early childhood development but later as well, during neurotic personality development. This image is constantly changing during both physical and emotional growth, throughout the entire lifetime. It is influenced by internal modifications, such as sexual drives, illnesses, physical defects, and by external perceptual and conceptual relationships (such as in the case presented here), by mothers' attitudes toward illness, and by self-generated neurotic patterns—namely, self-idealization and self-rejection. Abnormal emotional development is accompanied by distorted body-image development, each affecting the other mutually, both as cause and effect. Alienation from the real includes the physical self also. While every neurotic person is more or less estranged from his self, in these somatizing patients the body-image is peculiarly implicated.

Especially dramatic examples selected from many such cases include one man with a slight, congenital hyperhidrosis of his palms, who pictured himself as having a small body with large hands, although he was really quite tall. Requiring tremendous control as a solution of the conflict between his idealized concept of himself as considerate, charming, and suave on one hand, and exploitative and scheming on the other, his hands became the predominant expression of any emotion which did not correspond to the picture he wished to present at the time; anything which might get through his control and give him away. He had frequent dreams of being enclosed in boxes, or cemented in concrete or submerged in water, with only his hands sticking out. His somatic symptoms consisted of intermittent tremor, acrocyanosis with paresthesias, and dermatitis, all confined to his hands. After two years of analysis, his pattern began to change to include headaches and palpitations.

Another such patient, who had had an eye surgically removed for a tumor during late childhood, had a body-image of herself as having tremendous eyes, a large plump body, and small extremities, although she was fairly thin with long limbs. Her somatic symptoms included headache, dizziness, and itching or tearing in her remaining eye. In her idealized self-concept she was a kind, self-sacrificing, motherly woman, helpless in an abusive world. In her real attitude to others she was extremely manipulative, arrogant, vindictive, and sexually seductive. Although she had some intellectual knowledge of these latter feelings, they were in an emotional sense largely unconscious. And her psychosomatic symptoms would recur when such feelings came into awareness and threatened her idealized image.

The patient described previously in this paper had idealized strength and bigness, and associated it with idealized maleness. Her normal attributes of femaleness—breasts, menses, pregnancy—were associated with weakness and rejected. Alienated from her real inner experiental center, yet subject to the compulsive "shoulds" of having proper emotional-physical reactions like other people, such as crying, she had to find a means of expression that would at once be emotional inside and more physical outside. Somatic reactions, in the sense of being more superficial, more "surface" than direct emotional experience, while still easily relatable to herself, would best serve this purpose. They would thus be a way of both experiencing qualities emotionally unpleasant to her, and also keeping them at a distance—the greatest possible distance—while still belonging to her. She is at once saying "I have and I have not emotions and a body."

SOMATIC SYMPTOMS AND DUPLICITY

The easy visibility and accessibility of somatic symptoms to perceptual experience permits a greater lack of openness, with more pretense (duplicity) on the part of the individual. Thus, this patient was able to demonstrate to others (and herself, as well) that she had a means of controlling them, for instance, when she might be feeling helpless; or to show that she was feeling suffering or some other emotion, in the absence of any profoundly experienced real affect. With such manifest evidence, she could convincingly feel herself to be honest and real and thus avoid awareness of her fundamental duplicity. By the same token, however, accessibility is important in a constructive sense. It provides an index of inner processes otherwise difficult to obtain. For this patient it was part of testing her tolerance of anxiety and conflict-situations. Somatic symptoms thus constitute an essential, though distorted, way of self-experience when more direct ways are not available.

SPECIFICITY

The psychic (emotional) factor varied at different times in connection with the same somatic symptoms, and vice versa. Many different dynamisms were manifested during these variations of particular somatic symptoms. For example, her respiratory symptoms were exacerbated when she experienced needs for attention and/or affection, needs to dominate or to distance herself, when experiencing self-frustration of these needs; or later in the analysis as she was taking a stand against her "shoulds," with disintegrative shifts in her idealized image of herself, and while experiencing self-hate and self-contempt. Nevertheless, it is difficult to affirm from the apparent concurrence in these dynamisms how valid the connection really is or whether there is any direct one-to-one specificity of psychic-physical function. In analytic therapeutics we attempt to ascertain and select from our awareness of the patient's total communicated context whatever underlying feeling or theme is evident at a particular moment in the process of analysis, in order to further that analysis. As part of analytic technique, whenever such psycho-physical relationships can beneficially be brought to the patient's awareness (either spontaneously or through interpretation), it might be indicated to do so. In the case under discussion, the patient's anxiety at times was diminished by so doing—and at other times was not. Therefore, in context, her asthma, for instance, appeared at one point as a conflictual crying-out for help. At another, it appeared with sneezing as an ambivalent laughing, or as a conflict over breathing freely. It appeared with her sneezing as a pleasure-giving "throat tickling"; with her eye "burning" as a question of emotionally "seeing"; with her nausea as self-disgust; with her dysmenorrhea as a conflict over "womanness"; and with various sphincteric openings or closings as emotional letting go or holding back.

However, I feel that even such symptomatic improvement does not validate the assumption of a specific psycho-physiological relationship between the apparent emotional process and the somatic symptom appearing at the same time.

In the first place, every "trait" or attitude, as a dynamic tendency or movement, is in direct relation to other reinforcing or opposing traits, to the conflict so produced, and to the anxiety resulting therefrom. This was emphasized by Schilder[14] in his concept of inner functional "sphere" or group of unconscious interrelated affects. It is a moot question whether any particular "trait" can be isolated from the constellation of total inner experience it is embedded in, and more conclusively related to the somatic symptom, than can some other concurrent trait.

Secondly, the anxiety-relieving effect may be due to other mechanisms. For instance, it may be due to focusing awareness on a body part in relation to inner activity, as enlarging the total experience of the self. One focusing of such symptoms that was often permitted with good therapeutic results was to relate their tempo and rhythmic changes to psychic shifts and other body rhythms.

ANXIETY AND SOMATIZATION

Many investigators have attempted to qualify the "nature" of anxiety. Some have claimed that by definition it is a pathological affect. Some have distinguished between defensive and signal anxiety,[5,7] between neurotic or healthy anxiety,[15] between rational or irrational anxiety.[8] Recently an existential anxiety was described, which is neither healthy nor neurotic, but an essential attribute of normal existence today.[16] While it is beyond the scope of this paper to dwell on the details involved in such considerations, I feel that such a blanket qualification tends to confuse rather than clarify, particularly insofar as it relates to psychosomatization. The investigators do this because they try to describe quite different aspects of anxiety at the same time. Thus, healthy or neurotic anxiety may refer to its experiential nature; to its intensity and quality; to its sources—whether it is produced by rational or irrational, or by healthy or compulsive forces; to its effects—whether it produces effective action or indecisiveness and paralysis; or to its social values—whether it is appropriate or not in the context of the situation. We could speak of anxiety in a healthy or neurotic individual, produced by compulsive conflict, but not of neurotic anxiety. This is particularly pertinent in relation to the appearance of somatic symbols.

We have seen that although in this patient the somatic symptoms at times seemed to be related to the presence of anxiety (limited specificity), this was not a simple or direct quantitative relationship. There were intense somatic symptoms with a minimum or absence of anxiety, or no symptoms with considerable anxiety. This agrees with the observations of Reid[15] that the degree of somatic involvement does not correspond necessarily either to the intensity of the conflict or of the anxiety. In other words, although body participation is a normal physiological component of any effective state, including anxiety, the presence of anxiety or conflict per se does not lead to a predominant somatic expression. In order to explain the latter state, various conditions have been implicated.

According to Freudian theory,[17,18] there must not only be strong repressive forces, so that the active instinctual impulses will seek a devious circuit of expression, but also a "libidinization" or "genitalization" of body parts which become the focal point of expression. Martin[19] enlarged the concept of conflict inherent in repression to include the active opposition of any compulsive tendency. Somatization may occur when the conflict becomes an acute "dilemma" by emerging into consciousness. Weiss[20] emphasized that not only may opposing neurotic character traits conflict, but also that the total idealized self-image exerts a conflictual "clamping-down" effect. Somatization is seen to be, in effect, a compromise solution when other defensive solutions do not work. As such, the patient would have to "hold on" to his somatic symptoms to avoid the anxiety he could not otherwise cope with.

None of these theories adequately clarifies the particular nature of the conflicts insofar as they relate to the selection of the body for expressing the solution in preference to some other form of expression, such as dreams. While the notion of compromise solution is valid, what imports is not the special character traits in conflict, but rather the compulsive emotionality-intellectualization conflict.

Thus, the qualitative nature of their anxiety is of special importance in these patients, regardless of the particular conflicts which may have engendered it. There seems to be a distortion of their total experience of anxiety. This is not the simple blocking or damming up of its adequate discharge, as is claimed by some psychoanalytic authors.[21] This distortion involves two faculties.

First, it is a blurring of the experiential awareness of the anxiety as an existent inner emotional impulse. This is a part of the self-alienation characteristic of the neurotic process in general, including all inner processes. Such an awareness is both perceptual and conceptual, though not necessarily intellectual. It does not refer to either conscious or unconscious anxiety as these terms are conventionally used. Briefly, it is an inability of these patients to identify their anxiety.

Secondly, it is a decrease of the capacity to assimilate or become freely involved with the anxiety as emergent, affective experience, however it may be distortedly felt. In this sense, the somatic symptom is at once a limited and limiting expression of anxiety. Accordingly, as the patient in analysis becomes less estranged from his inner qualities and more able freely to experience them all, including his anxiety, the somatic symptoms may also be expected to diminish. At the same time the intensity of his anxiety may be decreasing through resolution of his neurotic conflicts. This occurred in the case under discussion here. The somatization tends to decrease, as the anxiety can be more tolerated and more freely entered into. The appearance and evolution of any somatic symptom during analysis is a composite function of the interplay between two factors: the emergence of anxiety into experience (itself depending on emotional awareness of conflict, the capacity to resolve it, and other neurotic defenses), and the ability to freely tolerate the anxiety.

PSYCHOSOMATIZATION AS RESTITUTIVE FUNCTION

Implicit in the foregoing is the notion that the presence of anxiety may be a normal phenomenon as well as a neurotic one.

This might apply in several ways. The anxiety might result from non-compulsive personality factors (what is often termed, incorrectly, healthy anxiety). The ability to tolerate anxiety may be greater (healthier) or lesser (neurotic). The anxiety may occur during movement in an obstructive (neurotic) or constructive direction.

The presence of psychosomatic symptoms would at first glance appear to be only pathological, or indicative of neurotic process. However, I feel that another type of function could be indicated, which is neither solely neurotic nor solely healthy. This I would designate as restitutive. By this I mean a way of maintaining and affirming the integrity of the organism. Certainly not only somatization, but other organismic functions may represent this type of function, whether it be neurotic or healthy, or destructive or constructive at some other biological or psychic level.

Restitutive function as evidenced in the case under discussion here had three characteristics. First, it seemed to be a self-regulating process, comparable to the feedback mechanism of cybernetics in which inner variations of parts of the circuit (body parts or changing states of tension) influenced other parts and the total state of tension. Clinically, this tendency could be sensed in connection with the patient's somatic symptoms, as a testing both of her healthy strengths or her neurotic resistances.

Second, psychosomatization was an equilibrium-seeking process, comparable to the homeostatic tendency of Cannon.[22] It tends to bring the organism to a uniform state of tension throughout, and to that level of tension which will be optimally tolerated and acceptable—given whatever level of over-all activity at which the organism is then functioning, and whatever the local conditions are. In this property there can be no distinction between internal and external milieu as psychophysiological experience. Both form an interacting dynamic unity.

Third, these two properties are not inconsistent with the direction inherent in constructive growth. Equilibrium-seeking at any level of anxiety, conflict, or tension, is neither static nor regressive. It does not necessarily imply a lessening, although this may temporarily occur. In this characteristic it differs from what is usually considered as the psychological mechanism of defense or solution. These latter dynamisms are directed at avoiding psychologically painful experience. This patient on the contrary was constantly moving toward a higher level of tolerance at the same time that she was experiencing qualitative changes in the mode of experiencing. Periods of somatic symptoms permitted a plateau, a pause for the consolidation of previous intrapsychic movement, and a temporary experiencing of a newer psychic organization. Periods of freedom from somatic symptoms had often indicated movements in the direction of neurosis, and more successful resistances, such as distancing herself or other neurotic solutions. Occurring after longer periods of consistently low-level anxiety or somatization, they indicated that she was now ready to proceed further into the conflict-producing sphere.

Restitutive function, as expressed in somatization in this case, is a basic pattern of psychological expression, which differs from neurotic patterns in not necessarily being compulsively adopted for security-safety needs, although it may become imbricated with neurotic development and take on a compulsive quality. It could be either constructive or obstructive, depending on the way we view it. What is retarding or destructive to one point of reference, or at one level, may be constructive at another.

Although this concept is in some ways similar to Goldstein's concept of optimal behavior,[23] it has a significant difference. He maintains that in cases of impairment of partial function (whether by internal or external inhibitory stimuli) the organism will behave in the best possible way, so as to avoid "disorderliness" or "catastrophic reactions" (anxiety) in its total activity related to the external causal environment. This type of behavior implies a teleology, the "best possible" having as its goal a certain adjustment relationship with the external milieu. That is, although he admits the inherent faculty of "direction" toward the actualization of its capacities in all living things, the optimal quality of its behavor is judged by its relation to the outside. I would see the directiveness of restitutive function as being, perhaps, influenced by external stimuli, but definitely not depending upon them. It may sometimes manifest itself, through symptoms, in spite of the external situation, or in ways which, while optimally consistent with the patient's impaired capacities, are not optimal to the external situation.

PROCESS OF SOMATIZATION

The question of *how* somatization is produced cuts across motivational factors. The process refers to the psychological mechanisms through which the various personality elements—the idealization and rejection of attitudes and self-aspects, body-image distortions, functioning in restitutive direction—are translated in somatic symptoms.

I have presented elsewhere the concept of modes of reflexive presentation of inner experience.[24] In brief, according to this notion, all stimuli arising within the organism, regardless of their nature or source, whether primary (affects, instinctual urges, etc.) or secondary, in reaction to external stimuli, are available to awareness and are self-directed. The mode of experience is the total pattern-process in which such stimuli present themselves to the individual. This self-presentation is neither conscious nor unconscious in the usual sense, but rather, a total self-reporting. It is neither ego function nor id activity, but more inclusive than either. And the self has constant awareness of this process at the same time that it is directing it. The various modes of experience constitute what we ordinarily experience as attitudes, subject-object polarity, conception or imagery, thought or ideation, affects, or action.

Externalization is an important mechanism of self-presentation. The self brings its inner events to its own total awareness by seeing them as external occurrences, completely or in part. The means by which these various modes are brought about, is through the symbolizing faculty of the organism, taken in its broadest sense as the representation of one event by another. Externalization is but one form of the more inclusive mechanism of spatialization, which may be used to insure the optimal representative value to the symbolizing process. Other such mechanisms are objectification and temporalization. But it is particularly important insofar as somatization is concerned, since inner space is as significant as the external world. The body, as it is conceived by the individual (body-image and body-concept) becomes the framework for the externalized inner stimuli.

Configurational distortions in this image will result in spatial distortions and symptoms related thereto—phantom limb, pain asymbolia. Conceptual distortions may give rise to psychosomatic symptoms. Since the symbolization process operates at many levels of self-experience, and at varying degrees of complexity, and since the body image appears to be relatively more stable than psychic changes, somatic symptoms will vary less than psychic events. Moreover, the same somatic symptom may express many intra-organismic stimuli, from the more simple to the more complex. Similarly, several modes of presentation may be operative at the same time. For instance, gut-pain may be experienced simultaneously with a mental image as an association to a particular emotional stimulus. We might say that the reflexive circuits are of different directness, more or less distorted. The patient who has a shift in somatic symptoms from headache to respiratory to intestinal is expressing a shift in the configuration of his constellation of psychic factors.

The various body symptoms are thus not only the direct overflow of one or several affects or affectively changed ideas, but also self-presentations of the inner organization (configuration) of this psychic-affective state. The individual who has contradictory, compulsive, energy-charged attitudes may experience anxiety. His somatic symptoms express not only the anxiety, but more specifically represent his way of becoming aware of the anxiety in a particular inner context. Somatic symptoms are thus symbolic, but not object-symbols. They are rather *symbolizings* of psychic movements.

SOMATIZATION AS A PREFERRED PATTERN

In this patient, somatization was an important pattern of symbolized self-presentation of inner experience. In other patients it may be in such different channels as reasoning, acting-out, or dreaming. For instance, one of my borderline schizophrenic patients laces innumerable dreams into his accounts of waking experiences, without separation, so that it is difficult to distinguish where one leaves off and the other begins. To him, both experiences are equally real and equally representative of what is occurring within himself. This is his pattern of being, in the same way that predominant somatization may be a pattern of being in the existential sense, if you will. These must be distinguished from neurotic personality orientations developed as solutions to inner conflicts.

Although temperamental factors may influence these patterns, compulsive anxiety-driven personality trends (such as supremacy of mind) or other neurotic distortions (such as alienation from the self) may contribute to the adoption of such patterns. But as holistic forms of function they must be seen as being selected. This is because any particular one provides the greatest possible self-representative awareness of inner process, given the personality organization at the time, and because that one selected is most familiar to the person. "Familiarity" would involve many factors. Among these might be mentioned the ease with which the pattern is learned; the emotional state at the time of learning—that is, the degree of freedom from conflict, and degree of closeness to one's experiential self; its effectiveness in most consistently satisfying healthy or neurotic needs at the time of learning and thereafter; and the degree to which the pattern is consistent with the symbolizing systems of the person. Cultural or family influences would thus be important in making available, or emphasizing, particular patterns to be later used as channels of symbolic expression. As one example, Symonds,[16] has noted among adolescents hospitalized for varying emotional disturbances a greater percentage of somatic symptoms among those of Italian descent, and fewer symptoms but a greater hypochondriacal preoccupation among those of Jewish descent.

SUMMARY

Present theories are inadequate to explain the origin, different clinical forms and changes, or significance, of psychosomatic symptoms. This is so, partly because they study such symptomatology from a developmental (historical-genetic) viewpoint too exclusively, and partly because they are based on the concept of a duality of psychic and somatic entities, with a cause-effect relationship between more or less specific psychic (emotional) and physical constellations. By contrast, study of the occurrence and variations in such somatic symptoms during psychoanalysis, in correlation with changes in the dynamics of the neurotic process, permits a greater understanding of the factors involved in somatization.

The case of a woman who is representative of a large number of grossly similar patients was discussed. She has a record of prominent psychosomatic symptoms during her lifetime, but has shown important variations in these symptoms in about five years of analysis. While in analysis, the symptoms occurred in cycles. They affected varying somatic systems, and could be related to dynamic intrapsychic movements. It is felt that particular dynamic qualities observed in this patient can be applied to the process of somatization in general.

Conclusions pertained to three areas: dynamic forces which predisposed to somatization (motivational-causal); functional characteristics of the somatic symptoms; and a theory of psychophysical transformation.

As to the first, a predominant tendency to somatization reactions is seen to result from several dynamic personality factors acting together:

1) A pride-invested idealization of physical health, with contempt for and rejection of "sickness." The latter is associated with various emotionally charged attitudes and self-concepts depending on specific conflicts and solutions thereof, in each patient.

2) A partial, conflictual form of control of emotional expression through supremacy of the mind. Somatization is a compromise between compulsive emotional body-expression and compulsive intellectualization.

3) A distortion of the body-image in which particular body parts are either overvalued (idealized) or rejected, thereby being selectively involved in the alienation from the self that is characteristic of general neurotic development.

From the viewpoint of psychophysiological function, somatic symptoms were found to be:

1) Non-specific insofar as a particular symptom might relate to a particular personality trait or profile. Although a suggestive correlation (which could be used analytically) occasionally appeared, it could not be stated whether the symptom was primarily related to the apparent psychic trait, to its functional antagonist in conflict, to the conflict itself, to the anxiety so produced, or to some related dynamic force.

2) Not quantitatively related to the intensity of the anxiety experienced.

3) Related to the quality of the anxiety experience. Symptoms diminished as the patient was better able to identify her anxiety and remain more totally involved with it.

4) Restitutive. Somatic symptoms could not be considered as pathological in themselves, nor as indicating movement in a healthy or neurotic direction. Instead, they seemed to be part of a self-regulating, equilibrium-seeking, organismic process, leading toward a greater accommodation to anxiety.

Finally, a theory is advanced as to how the various abovementioned motivational forces (personality traits, needs, conflicts, etc.) are transformed into somatic manifestations. This postulates that the individual presents to himself (reflexively) all inner experience as best he can, within the limits of any neurotic distortion. This is done through the symbolizing capacity of the self. Projection (external or internal) is one of the mechanisms in this symbolizing process, and spatialization is one of the means used. Since the body-image has inner spatial dimensions, it is used as a framework for such projection. Psychosomatization is thus seen as a symbolized self-presentatory mode of experience in inner psychic events.

REFERENCES

1 KAPLAN, H. I. & KAPLAN, H. S.: "A Psychosomatic Concept," *Amer. Journ. Psychotherapy,* 11, 16, 1957.

2 BLAZER, A.: "The Psychosomatic Character," *N. Y. State Journ. Med.,* 1587, July, 1950.

3 KELMAN, H.: "A Unitary Theory of Anxiety," *Amer. Journ. Psychoan.,* 17, 127, 1957.

4 HORNEY, K.: *Neurosis and Human Growth,* New York: W. W. Norton, 1950.

5 HOFFER, W.: "The Development of the Body-Ego," *Psychoan. Study of the Child,* New York: International Univ. Press, 1950.

6 GREENACRE, P.: *Trauma, Growth and Personality,* New York: W. W. Norton, 1952.

7 GREENACRE, P.: "Early Physical Determinants in the Development of the Sense of Identity," *Journ. Amer. Psychoan. Assn.,* 6, 628, 1958.

8 LINN, L.: "Some Development Aspects of the Body-Image," *Int'l Journ. Psychoan.,* 36, 36, 1958.

9 KEISER, S.: "Disturbances in Abstract Thinking and Body-image Formation," *Journ. Amer. Psychoan. Assn.,* 6, 628, 1958.

10 SCHILDER, P.: *The Image and Appearance of the Human Body,* New York: Int'l Univ. Press, 1950.

11 BENDER, L.: Organic Brain Conditions Producing Behavior Disorders, *In Lewis & Pacella's Modern Trends in Child Psychiatry,* New York: Int'l Univ. Press, 1945.

12 ZUGER, B.: "Growth of the Individual's Concept of Self," *Amer. Journ. Dis. Children,* 83, 719, 1952.

13 MOSCHCOWITZ, E. & ROUDIN, M.: "The Association of Psychosomatic Disorders and Their Relation to Personality Types in the Same Individual," N. Y. State Journ. Med., 1375, June, 1948.

14 SCHILDER, P.: *Medical Psychology,* New York: Int'l Univ. Press, 1953.

15 REID, J. R.: "The Concept of Unconscious Anxiety," *Amer. Jour. Psychoan.,* 16, 42, 1956.

16 SYMONDS, A.: Personal communication.

17 FLESCHER, J.: "A Dualistic Viewpoint on Anxiety," *Journ. Amer. Psychoan. Assn.* 3, 415, 1955.

18 RANGELL, L.: "On the Psychoanalytic Theory of Anxiety—A Unitary Theory," *Journ. Amer. Psychoan. Assn.,* 3, 389, 1955.

19 MARTIN, A.: "The Body's Participation in Dilemma and Anxiety Phenomena," *Amer. Journ. Psychoan.,* 5, 28, 1945.

[20] WEISS, F.: "Neurotic Conflict and Physical Symptoms," *Amer. Journ. Psychoan.*, 6, 35, 1946.
[21] ZETZEL, E. R.: "Anxiety and the Capacity to Bear It," *Int'l Journ. Psychoan.*, 13, 1, 1950.
[22] CANNON, W. B.: *Bodily Changes in Pain, Fear, and Rage,* Boston: Chas. Brandford, 1953.
[23] GOLDSTEIN, K.: *The Organism.* New York: Amer. Book Co., 1939.
[24] RUBINS, J. L.: "Notes on the Organization of the Self," *Amer. Journ. Psychoan.*, 18, 171, 1958.

Observations on Male Homosexual Object-Relationships

by Carlos Carillo, M.D.
Postgraduate Center for Psychotherapy

Carlos Carillo, M.D.

Since writing the paper presented herein, Dr. Carillo has served as Director of the Special Clinic on Alcoholism for the Westchester Community Health Board in White Plains, N. Y. He is presently Associate Professor in Psychiatry at the College of Medicine, Downstate Medical Center, State University of New York, and has continued in private practice.

THE concept of object-relationships refers not only to cathexes of the external object but also to cathexes of the self, the body and the introjects. Therefore, when speaking of pathological object-relationships, self-representations, body-representations and the broad concept of self-identity may also be disturbed. Since concepts such as self, ego, self-representations, etc. will be used throughout this presentation, it seems necessary to define these terms. I follow Jacobson [32] and others [5,28,29,55] in their elaboration of these concepts.

"The term 'ego' has been used to define the 'subject' in contradistinction to the 'object,' or one's own person as opposed to other persons or even to include the entire psychic apparatus." [5] The term "ego" means "that part of the psychic system which is distinguished from the id and superego.[28] "Self-representation refers to the endopsychic representations of our bodily and mental self in the system ego." [32] The term "self" is used in contradistinction to the term object." Spiegel [55] suggests confining the term "self" to the totality of self-representations as opposed to object-representations within one mind.

In this paper I used the term "self-representation" as the endopsychic representation of the psychic self, and the term body-representation" as the endopsychic representation of the somatic self.

It is generally agreed [1,8,9,23,24,25,38,40,49,57] that any lasting object-relationship requires a combination of several factors, among which the availability of neutralized energy to the ego-system plays a dominant role. This means that unneutralized libidinal and aggressive discharges must be limited, that the residual aggressive and libidinal energies must be neutralized and fused. The nature of the homosexual conflict results in the expenditure of large amounts of energy in countercathexes, as well as in a reduced amount of neutralized energy. This is a consequence of ego-splitting brought about by the early introjection of objects invested with unresolved primitive ambivalence.

In the exposition that follows, I base my views primarily on those of Klein [34,35,36,37] and Sychowsky.[8,9,10]

Klein asserts that the roots of male homosexuality are to be found in the boy's "feminine position," brought about by the loss of the external breast which intensifies the identification with the mother. According to her, the boy wishes to incorporate the father's penis (at first equated with the breast), not only in a passive manner (suck it, swallow it, etc.), but also actively (entering the father's body with his penis). When this feminine phase is strongly governed by aggression, the introjection of the father's penis will also be charged with equal aggression. As a consequence of the fantasies of the mother's breast and body having been attacked and destroyed by the father's penis and his own, the introjection of the father's penis arouses the fear that his own body may be exposed to the same dangers from within as he imagines his mother's is. This displacement, in which all that is aggressive is located in the interior of the woman's body, needs to be accompanied by another factor, the displacement of the value of his penis onto that of another male, in order to establish a homosexual position. This other penis now serves as counter-proof against all his fears concerning the penis inside him and the body. The incorporated object is used by the ego as a defense against the destructive impulses within the organism. The more sadism which prevails in the process of incorporating and the more the ego is felt to be fragmented, the more the ego is in danger of being split in relation to the internalization of the object. The corollary is that the part of the ego denying the bad object is also denied: a splitting of the object implies a splitting of the ego itself. Homosexuality is then seen as a protective device against a persecuting and damaging mother.

From an economical angle, and according to Bychowsky,[8,9,10] splitting of the ego is accomplished by erecting barriers of counter-cathexes, which separate one introject from the other, thus limiting the use of neutralized energy by the ego-system. The introjects preserve their original instinctual charge (libidinal and aggressive), and the counter-cathexes necessary to keep this state of splitting can be easily weakened by situations offering libidinal gratifications. Under this impact, the ego yields the unneutralized energy used in the counter-cathexes and is employed to cathect the external object. However, because of the undifferentiated nature of the object-cathexes, the relationship established is only momentary. On the other hand, with the weakening of the counter-cathexes, the dissociated introjects within the ego are freed and displaced (externalization) onto the external object. In this manner the external object is at once cathected with aggressive and libidinal charges from the counter-cathexes and also becomes a reservoir for the externalized introjects. These processes aim at restoring some of the experiences that existed between the infantile ego and its original objects. Homosexual object-relationships are predominantly limited to incorporation, not only because the cathexes are maintained on an oral level, but because of the narcissistic and pre-narcissistic disposition of the homosexual ego.

We can see, then, "the attitude toward the homosexual partner may emphasize the tender or the sadistic aspect of the externalized strivings toward the parental images." [8]

Similar conclusions are offered from a socio-anthropological angle. Devereux [12] distinguishes between normal sexuality and perversion as follows: From the intrapsychic point of view, he maintains that in normal sexuality the conscious purpose of foreplay is to increase tension and to cathect the partner, whereas the purpose of the perversion is to release tension and to decathect the partner. From the point of view of object relationships, normal sexuality is characterized by true object cathexes, in which the partner matters as an individual, is not used as a means to an end, is highly cathected and is valued in the subject's and the partner's sexual gratification. The pervert's love is never perceived as a total object. He remains a partial object.

Huensterberger [12] also agrees that a perversion is based on regression to infantile sexuality. Rado,[12] on the other hand, using a socio-biological approach, arrives at the conclusion that homosexuals (male pairs) reactivate a child-parent relationship.

It has been mentioned that, although libidinal cathexes are the first ones mobilized in the attempt to establish an object-relationship, aggressive charges are concomitantly discharged. Hence the peculiar destructiveness of homosexual relationships. This is mainly due to the lack of fusion of the unneutralized drives.

It appears that there is general agreement with respect to the failure of homosexuals to establish a complete, lasting object-relationship because the cathexes useful for it cannot be bound to the object for a long period of time, since they are urgently needed for counter-cathexes. A problem arises when one is faced with the many male homosexual couples who have been living together for as many years as one finds among heterosexuals.[1] What factors may account for these lasting relationships? It is the thesis of this paper that a general explanation may be found in a relatively successful exchange of externalized introjects in a basically sado-masochistic personality with a certain ability to use projective identification. This kind of relationship is symbiotic in nature. In this paper I present some observations that give basis to the above-mentioned hypotheses, observations derived from the study of male homosexual couples.[2]

II

A general trend of sado-masochism, in a greater or lesser degree, was found in the object-relationships of all the patients seen. This is not a surprising finding, if we bear in mind what we said about the homosexual's use of unneutralized energy. Hartman [26] says, "The internalization of non-neutralized energy in the ego may be the hallmark of a masochistic ego."

We will present in some detail the case history of one of the couples studied. Their histories reveal an abundance of traumatic situations, difficult conflicts and a preponderance of regressed pregenital and sado-masochistic stringings. Conditions for the formation of good object-relationships and healthy identifications were far from favorable.

Peter and John were 25 and 28 respectively. They had been living together for the past six years. Almost from the beginning they began to have serious difficulties in adjusting to each other, but they had stayed together despite many problems. They quarreled frequently, and the fighting was intense. John inclined towards leaving Peter. There had been short separations brought about by these fights, which never lasted more than one or two days. For the two months before Peter started treatment, the fights had been more intense, and finally John decided to leave the country. This precipitated a panic-stricken behavior in both of them. Then they made up and decided to seek treatment. I saw both of them separately in the beginning and then Peter began treatment with me, and John was referred to another therapist.

Peter was intelligent, (I.Q. 146), sensitive and reliable. Characteristic was his manner of ingratiation and conformity, his inability to make up his mind about his behavior and a constant searching for the opinions of John. He was slightly effeminate and very moody. Projective tests showed schizophrenic-like features in the manner of ideas of reference and a tendency to withdraw. Clinically, he had several paranoid trends (an exaggerated tendency to use projection and splitting), and when first seen he was manifestly withdrawn and sad. His prominent tendency to react with extreme anxiety approaching a panic state, associated with self-derogatory feelings, precipitated by the threat or actual separation from John soon became apparent. He threatened to kill himself during these episodes, and he did in fact attempt this, the first time an actual separation occurred, four years before starting treatment. It is important to note, though, that these reactions were so severe only when the separation was the result of a fight.

If the separation was caused by other reasons—job, vacation and so on—his reaction was less severe, although anxiety was mobilized. The extreme dependence on John's physical presence was thereby evident. Moreover, during the treatment period, there were further threatened separations that permitted a closer observation of Peter's reactions. During the sessions Peter had been able to furnish important material concerning himself and his relationship with his parents and brother. When separated, Peter could not speak of himself any more; all the material dealt with John's neurotic problems and his "badness." The content of his statements about John's badness concerned the same defects he had constantly denied within himself. During these episodes, Peter offered himself as a "victim" of John's badness and simultaneously as an all-good, naive, innocent person. As soon as the separation ended, Peter would continue speaking of himself. Nevertheless, his tendency to present an "all-good," pure image of himself, in which there was no envy, hostility, competitiveness nor selfishness, persisted. All aggressive drives considered by him as evil and dangerous were denied and displaced onto John. In contrast, his body-representation was completely devaluated. Although a striking, good-looking young man, he felt his body to be ugly, poorly developed, deformed. On the other hand, he perceived John's body as beautiful, well-developed, "the handsomest I have ever seen." This dichotomy between self-representation and body-representation turned out to be an important factor in the understanding of the nature of Peter's and John's object-relations.

Another feature of Peter's behavior during the separation periods was the quality of his thought processes and affects. He tended to think in a sluggish manner; his associations tended to be loose and fluid; his affects had a flat flavor. There never were indications of actual psychotic breakdown, but the symptoms already described suggest a borderline functioning.

Peter was the younger of two siblings. His older brother, 3 years his senior (as was John), was his parents' favorite. His physical characteristics, both as described by Peter and as seen in some photographs, bore a close resemblance to John's. His parents had hoped for a girl before Peter's birth. He remembers his mother telling him that she wanted a girl because they are less troublesome than boys. Peter's father was a New England farmer with strong puritan attitudes. No smoking or drinking was allowed; there had been stern talks about the evils of sex, and the general atmosphere was one of restriction. At the beginning of his treatment he constantly referred to his father as a sexless individual, until he was able to remember an episode of his early childhood.

Peter was 7 or 8 when one day he discovered, in one of his father's drawers, photographs of pin-up girls. He was taken aback by what he considered hypocrisy in his father's life and reacted with a masochistic fantasy in which he was being drowned and his father rescued him. This was the onset of this kind of fantasy, which was expressed in his adult life as the fantasy of being kept by an older man, this latter a fantasy he strongly rejected (and which John has acted out as we see later).

Peter's mother, a submissive and most likely masochistic woman, did not spare Peter her complaints about the difficult time she had had when he was born, which resulted in her inability to have more children. "She was built small, and apparently I was a large boy; if I had been a girl, she said, the labor would not have been so difficult."

The rivalry between our patient and his brother was excessive and was solved by the parents in a most unusual manner, namely, by rejecting Peter. There were constant fights between the two brothers, which obviously ended with the defeat of the younger. When Peter was about 5 or 6, he attempted to defend himself by throwing different objects at his older brother. This behavior provoked the rage of his father, who proceeded to beat Peter for his "dirty tricks." Our patient promptly inhibited this reaction and only resorted to flight whenever his brother started a fight. Nevertheless, as this was not successful most of the time, Peter would be beaten and would go to his parents with a black eye, bruises and so on. He consciously expected to make them feel guilty. As the fights between the brothers continued, the attitude of the parents was completely devoid of any criticism of the older brother.

It is probable that Peter provoked many of these fights, but it is also probable that his exaggerated submissiveness (partially the result of guilt for his mother's imagined damage) triggered his brother's reactions. At any rate, the situation became increasingly intolerable and quite dangerous to Peter, so the parents decided that he should leave and stay with some relatives. Peter was 7 or 8. It was during this time that he discovered his father's inconsistency. From that time on Peter lived with different aunts until he went to a boarding school, when he was 11. The aunts lived in the same town as Peter's parents. He would see them off and on. There was a constant feeling of humiliation and of puzzlement over his parents' weakness in dealing with his brother.

Masturbation had started while he was at school, probably around his tenth or eleventh year. However, there were memories of his fascination for his father's penis much earlier in his life, as well as sexual plays with his brother when Peter was 4 or 5, which consisted in a mutual display of their genitals and an unsuccessful attempt at anal relations on his brother's part. The contents of the fantasies accompanying masturbation were the masochistic fantasies already described and occasional heterosexual fantasies with girls of his school.

It was about the time he left his parents' home that Peter began to feel that his body was inadequate, ugly and not virile enough. This situation was reinforced by acne on his face and his back. As was to be expected, he reacted to his acne with a masochistic pattern, breaking them and causing scars which increased his feelings of bodily inadequacy. This behavior was in part the repetition of the exhibition of his bruises after a fight with his brother.

When Peter began college, he was 20. He was interested in the theatre and decided to become an actor. He was a good student, conscientious and able, which earned him a scholarship. Although basically withdrawn, he made good friends and had several heterosexual affairs of short duration and without sexual intercourse. He found himself unable to be sexually aroused by women. On the other hand, he had not acted out his homosexual impulses, which he indulged only in his fantasies while masturbating. It was at this time that he met John, also a drama student. He felt attracted to him from the start, and it was only a matter of days before his first homosexual acting-out took place. He saw in John the epitome of physical beauty; at the same time, he felt contempt for John's effeminate friends, his superficiality and glibness. (John was, therefore, his inverted body/self representation.) His first sexual experience began with fellatio performed on him by John; he became frightened and tried to stop it. He rationalized his fear by saying that his penis was ugly and deformed (as he felt his body was), and couldn't stand the idea of "this Greek god" performing fellatio.

Unconsciously, he was afraid both of damaging John with his bad penis and of being damaged in retaliation. Impulsively, then, he performed fellatio on John simultaneously. He saw John's penis as large, beautiful and potent (like John's body). From then on this was the usual pattern of sexual activity between them. As frequently seen among male homosexuals, they felt that this relationship was fully satisfying, that each was the object the other had been longing for all his life.

But, after a week or so, Peter began to feel that John was excessively demanding, selfish and unreliable. He felt he had been generous and concerned over John. Not only did he give John all kinds of material gifts, particularly food and clothes, but he also did his homework and his laundry. By this zealous activity he could rationalize his control over John, who soon started to have promiscuous homosexual affairs, at first on the sly, but soon unconsciously inviting discovery. Then the fights began: they ranged from a brisk exchange of mutual recrimination to actual physical combat in which Peter always managed to be beaten.

For Peter, John was cruel, bad and deceiving, whereas Peter was for John a depriving, controlling figure. Before proceeding with the history of their relationship, some material about John seems pertinent.

John was a bright, alert, sensitive man. His more than ingratiating behavior was cunningly seductive. He appeared to be charming, considerate, polite and generous, and yet one had the feeling that all this was a facade. It was these characteristics that made John extremely successful in persuading others to do things for him. He presented himself as the capable person, but, at the same time, one unable to fulfill his potential because of alleged reality problems that assailed him. This attitude and behavior accounted for the innumerable "benefactors" whom John had found in his life. After he had obtained what he wanted, he felt no gratitude and reacted as if he had done his "benefactors" a favor by accepting their help. In this manner, John had received money, paid vacations, clothes, home and board. At the beginning of such relationships he "paid" by performing fellatio or having passive anal relations with the "benefactors," always older men. Later on, he dismissed them or made them dismiss him by refusing to have sexual relations and/or by becoming overtly promiscuous. He was aware of his behavior and said, "I make people fall in love with me . . . and it's so wrong . . . and so cruel and selfish." Despite this promiscuity, John felt extremely attached to Peter and perceived him as the best oral object he had ever met: "Nobody I know *has* as much as he does" (a provider).

It became clear that his basic anxiety was connected with his fear of being orally deprived and that he was dealing with this fear by depriving others at the same time that he was proving to himself that he had not been deprived. As soon as the object gratified John's oral needs and began to demand a response for its care, anxiety would strike him and compulsive acting-out would come to the surface. The acting-out consisted in searching for partners who would provide him with oral gratification. John's conscious desires were to be cared for, to be given things, to be admired. If he was refused, he would steal or lie in order to obtain what he wanted.

We can see that his passivity had the deeper meaning of having deprived the object of all its goodness (father's penis, and ultimately his mother's breast), and that the already incorporated object would retaliate at him. Thus, as soon as the good object was incorporated, it became bad, and the need to search for more good objects was compulsive. The structure of his acting-out may be better seen in what follows.

Like Peter, John was the younger of two siblings. His brother was 5 years older.[3] The financial situation was unstable at home because John's mother spent money beyond her means. As a result, both parents had endless arguments and an unhappy marital relationship. It was shortly after John's birth that his father began to drink excessively and died of cirrhosis of the liver

16 years later. John was frightened of his father and constantly wished for his death. It was typical of John to say to his father as he was dying, "I hope this is your last breath." This was related to a fear of respiratory incorporation.[21]

After these fights, John's mother came to sleep with him, crying how awful his father was. Her behavior was openly seductive towards John: after her husband's death she told John they should live together and they would share the same bed. When John had expressed reluctance to sleep with her, she answered, "But why? You are wearing pajamas and I, a nightgown . . ."

When he was 6, he discovered a prophylactic on his mother's bed. He did not want to believe it, but he had to admit his disappointment. It was then that he had his first homosexual experience: he performed fellatio on an adolescent from his neighborhood. (John has jokingly said that his life has been an open prophylactic. He used to collect used prophylactics from nearby alleys, take them home and masturbate into them.)

He spent his first 5 years practically alone (except for his first two years of life), since both parents were working and his brother was going to school. He recalled the loneliness of those years and his feelings of helplessness. His mother used to give him money to go to the movies, and it was there that he learned about masturbation. After his first homosexual experience at the age of six, he continued having them more or less frequently. When he was 13 he already belonged to a "gay circle." He felt his mother was possessive and controlling, and that she tried to create guilt in him by giving him things. "My mother was giving me everything, and then she would complain . . . didn't want me to work while I was at college, and yet she was always telling me of her sacrifices to send me money . . . I felt guilty about it. My brother said I was a parasite, but my mother wanted me that 'way.' She always liked to degrade me. Sometimes I think she wants to make of me what she made of my father . . ."

The close relationship between these feelings and his homosexual acting-out is especially apparent here.

Another important characteristic of John's personality was his need to be *the* favorite, the center of admiration. He envied anyone who might be better off than he. In social situations he displayed all his powers of seduction, particularly through the use of his body.

This trend turned out to be related to an unconscious equation, body-phallus. He had feelings of sexual potency while he was seducing. It also showed attempts to reassure himself that his body had not been damaged, a denial of castration fears.[4] These exhibitionistic impulses appeared to be connected with his mother's permission to exhibit himself, in the form of the "superego lacuna," also described by Johnson et al.[33]

> When he met Peter, he had not had any lasting object-relationships. Peter was seen as a handsome boy, but particularly he was considered a generous, warm, conscientious person. However, "As soon as *I got him,* I found him very possessive, controlling . . . always checking on me . . . He called on the telephone every 15-20 minutes . . . always so innocent. I felt he would make *small* anything I might do . . . sort of degrading me . . . I never felt he gave me love." The provider good-object had become as controlling and dangerous as he felt his mother was. He expressed this feeling of receiving things from Peter by saying he was "trapped." He attempted to cope with this anxiety by compulsive fellatio in a very promiscuous way, which was the reason for endless fights with Peter.
>
> John's body-representation was libidinally hyper-cathected. He thought of himself as a handsome, well-developed man. In contrast, his self-representation was aggressively hyper-cathected: he felt thoroughly evil. He said of himself, "I'm all shit . . . a selfish shit . . . I've never really been in love . . . I've no character, no morals. I need somebody to dominate me . . . to control me . . . I'd like somebody to look up to."

In their relationship, Peter and John acted out towards each other their relationships with their parents. As mentioned above, John was for Peter a cruel, tormenting object. He was both his father and brother. On the other hand, Peter represented for John his depriving, over-possessive, controlling mother. By externalizing these introjects, both had been able to displace their aggressive drives vested in the original objects. Both Peter and John were afraid of having injured each other, and both tended to use gifts as a means of reparation. In Klein's formulation,[36,37] one could say that both patients tried to master their paranoid situation by projected identification ("a process by which other objects became possessed with one's own aggressive self"), which resulted in their ego-splitting. They appeared to be living a "relative fusion of ego and super-ego, a relative union with the parents," as Brody[7] puts it. They had placed their fate in each other's hands because this maneuver enabled them to imagine their autarchy and, thereby, control the external object. What Brody states about patients with a conflict of ambivalence also applies to Peter and John: "Should the object withdraw his love, the ambivalent person can retaliate by also withdrawing love, thus forcing the object to bestow love."

III

Inter-dependence of the kind described may survive because of its symbiotic nature, which provides a change in the intrapsychic energy balance and allows a relatively less destructive relationship.

Mahler [43,44] states that in symbiosis, "The mental representation of the object is not separation from the self," and that "unneutralized libidinal and aggressive forces have remained narcissistically vested in fused systems of object-subject unit:" Another important consideration in such relationships is the one of communication between the primitive object and the child's unconscious.

If our assumptions are correct, then, when the symbiosis is broken, we should be able to see all its components in their nakedness. We should expect that the projected part of the self that was fused with the self of the external object, should return to the self; that is, a re-internalization of the projected introject is to be expected. On the other hand, since we are assuming a relative object-subject fusion and since one part of the self has been, as it were, separated, feelings similar to those of dissolution should appear. And this is indeed the case. We have said that the members' behavior following a separation was panic-like, and we feel that can justly be called separation-anxiety.

We have mentioned the clinical picture of ego impoverishment that both members of the couple (described in this paper) presented following a separation. From Freud's "Mourning and Melancholia," [16] we know that such a picture, following the loss of the object, is the result of the tremendous energy consumed in the ego's anticathectic task of freeing the libido, bit by bit, from each memory trace of the lost object, so that little is left for investment in the surroundings and in new objects; or, under other circumstances, we know that a pathological introjection of the lost object may occur, resulting in a psychotic depression, in which the aggression is turned against the self.

The withdrawn narcissistic cathexes (both aggressive and libidinal) are employed by the ego to reinforce its splitting by strengthening the counter-cathexes for the purpose of isolating the internal object. This analysis reveals the real persecutory nature of the chosen object.

But this is only one side of a complex reaction. Although it is true that the couple attempts to maintain the isolation of the internal dangerous object by turning the external one into all badness, at the same time they set out the role attributed to the external object. In our couple, for example, following a separation they acted out with new objects in the same faulty manner they had so readily criticized in the partner.

So, after all, the lost object had been introjected, but, in contrast with the melancholiac, the aggressive drives were here acted out rather than felt. I think that an explanation for this situation may be found by bearing in mind that the object is being predominantly cathected with aggressive drives, and that the re-internalization is an incomplete one, thus enabling the object to be kept separated from the self.

This analysis reveals the persecuting nature of the external object and a *mutual* projective identification, by means of which that split part of one member's self is "completed" by the self of the other. In accordance with our thesis, a separation should affect this symbiosis and engender feelings similar to those of dissolution.

In attempting to cope with such feelings a twofold activity is used: first, a particular kind of sexual activity, the homosexual orgy, through which an effort to achieve self-identity is attempted; second, acting out the role of the lost object.

It was found that during a separation the anxious symbiotic couple invariably had engaged at least once during that period in a simultaneous multi-partners' sexual activity, the homosexual orgy.[5] Without entering into all the details of this behavior, which are described in another paper,[11] one may say that in an atmosphere devoid of external and internal control, homosexuals gratify their pregenital drives with several partners, who are, in fact, only partial objects, simultaneously or successfully. The most important areas gratified are those connected with the component instincts: the scoptophillic/exhibitionistic pair and the sado-masochistic pair, as well as passive and active oral and anal drives. Two conclusions are apparent from the study of this behavior. One is a sudden, massive, more apparent release of pregential drives, which appears to be related to the loss of an external control, until then relatively capable of preventing an overwhelming discharge of these drives. The other is related to the feelings of dissolution of the self, as a consequence of the break of the symbiotic relationship. Compensatory over-cathexes of the body are anxiously sought in an attempt to achieve self-identity. The situation seems to me to be similar to Mahler's cases [43,44] (See also Peppenheim-Sweeney [48])—children who searched for paroxysms of jumping, cringing and twisting to enforce compensatory cathexes. Also, in this sense, Keiser finds that "The libido withdrawn from the body during intercourse becomes concentrated in the genitals, which maintain contact with the partner. This serves to fix the body image." [30]

The analysis of the structure of Peter's and John's acting out the role of the lost object offers more light. The following is an outline of the material obtained. A full description of their acting-out would enlarge this paper even more.

> Following a separation, Peter reproduced exactly what he had condemned in John's behavior. He seduced older men. If the man proved to have money, he would accept his gifts (usually clothes) and then would perform fellatio on him, despite his "repugnance for old men"; if not, he would entice him and then leave him. His teasing activities were numerous, and interestingly enough, he never went to bed with a young man. He

was completely unaware of his deceiving, cruel behavior. When this was pointed out to him, he was able to see its relation to John's. Later on, when another separation came, his acting-out showed the relationship with his internalized father-brother objects. He felt the need to be beaten up, and found the right partner for this without difficulty. The beating consisted of his partner's mildly slapping Peter's gluteal regions and was followed by anal relations. He reacted with severe guilt and immediately initiated a period of reparation by overwhelming John with expensive gifts: a seduction of the aggressor, as Niederland has described.[47] With an understanding of the meaning of his behavior, his acting-out after the next separation was more ego-syntonic. He felt the need to redecorate the bathroom of his apartment. It was a time- and energy-consuming activity and very frustrating, because he sensed that he could never attain the ideal he had in mind.

When analyzed, the following material was brought to the surface. Peter had the unconscious fantasy that his "ugliness" would disappear if he had a nice apartment; the bathroom was the one place in the home where one becomes "beautiful." Then he was able to recall an early memory: "We did not have a bathtub at home until I was 5 or 6 years old. So my father and mother would wash me once a week every Saturday night. It is really the only beautiful thing I remember from my childhood."

This was followed by a dream: "I am in a house, a country house. I am on the fifth floor, in my room. The house is on fire. There are other people in the house. The walls of my room are on fire. I think, "What should I do? Then I decided to throw all my possessions (my furniture) out the window. They fell on the grass; all the things were all right, nothing was broken."

From the wealth of associative material obtained, I want to mention only the relation he established between his feeling of ugliness and the discharge or organization of his introjects. He could feel bodily adequate only with those loved objects (his parents washing him, for instance). This is in line with the Kleinstein concept that, "Ugliness expresses the destruction of good and whole objects and their change into persecutory fragments."[57]

His compulsive re-decoration of the bathroom symbolized his attempt to organize his part and whole objects within himself, the isolation of which had become endangered as the result of the sudden flow-back of unneutralized cathexes. By this time some of the aggressive and libidinal object-cathexes were becoming neutralized as a result of treatment and his ego system was beginning to receive neutralized object cathexes. This was manifested, among other things, in his finding a more suitable job and in his first verbal desires for heterosexual relations.

> John, apart from the homosexual orgy, on the other hand, acted out the role ascribed to his internalized mother. He adopted a pseudo-passive attitude, and actively seduced young or older men. His pattern with older men has been described—to render them harmless. However, because he felt like robbing their penises, he feared that they would turn into retaliatory objects, so that he would engage in an endless search for penises. All this time John refused to let any older man perform fellatio on him. He deprived them of what they wanted. The pattern was to receive everything and to give nothing; in his fantasy, he wanted all his bodily orifices to gratify his oral needs, including his urethra. He was being "over-possessive, controlling and depriving," his descriptions for Peter and his mother.
>
> Contrasted to this, his behavior with young men was one of giving. He let them perform fellatio on him and had active anal relations. Of course, they represented John himself, while he was the generous mother.

In the relationship between Peter and John we found a constant interaction of aggression and counter-aggression, of hostility and yet inability to let each other go, and a clear communication between their unconsciousness. Peter became the mother-figure for John; John became the father-brother figure to Peter. Peter could enact his relationship with his father and brother and, at the same time by externalizing these introjects onto John and identifying his split self with John's self, he could get rid of the dangerous introject, exert control over him and obtain control from him. In other words, John served the purpose of receiving the aggressive drives channeled away from Peter's self. Such a projective identification had the defensive function of warding off the anxiety produced by the dangerous internalized object by transforming it into an external danger more easy to control. Because of the libidinization of the unpleasure of his original object-relationships, Peter's relationship with John was also pleasurable, despite the persecutory nature of the object.

On the other hand, John enacted with Peter his early relationship with his mother, also externalizing his dangerous devouring mother, thus being able to exert a better control and at the same time gratifying his pre-Oedipal fantasies with her. As Bychowsky [8] says, "The splitting . . . serves the purpose of deceiving the vigilance of projected enemies, eliminating the patient from retaliation, while permitting him to preserve his infantile sexuality and his inhibited aggression. This becomes even clearer when the child has as much interest in drawing attention to itself as it has in making himself inconspicuous." Let us remember how John made Peter aware of his promiscuity at the same time that he tried to hide it.

From the several elements that, differently blended, make up such a symbiosis, I want to examine only the following three elements which I found to be more basic:

a) Exchange of introjects; projective identification
b) Exchange of body-self representations
c) Exchange of external control

a) *Exchange of introjects:* This item has already been partially discussed in the previous considerations of symbiosis. The mutual externalization of the introject leads to a mutual projective identification with the external object. The fact that the external object does not become an enemy (except during a separation) may be due to sado-masochistic gratifications and super-ego appeasements, but principally has to do with the reality of the external object. It is the conspicuous characteristic of these couples that each member's real behavior partially coincides with the one ascribed to the externalized object, and ultimately with the unconscious of the parents. Furthermore, each member can find in the other an over-evaluation of that part of the self devaluated in himself.

(b) *Exchange of body-self representations:* Splitting not only affects the introjects in the ego; it also affects the self-representations. We have mentioned, for instance, that Peter had split his self-representations in such a way that his body-representation was unrealistically considered ugly and deformed, while his self-representation was perceived as having only "good" qualities, that is, without hostility.

When studying such a split, it becomes evident that both parts correspond to original libidinal and aggressive, narcissistic cathexes turned inward, fortified by unhappy relationships with early love objects. The masochistic character of the behavior also becomes apparent. As Jacobson puts it, "A libidinous hypercathexis of the object, along with an aggressive hypercathexis of the self . . . , will correspond to masochistic behavior." [52]

The split, however, is not only employed with onesself, but also with the object. The symbiotic object is also split to fit in an inverted body-self representation. In other words, one part of the self is over-evaluated or devaluated by the object itself and by the other object. What is exchanged is the self-devaluated part, that part of the self hypercathected with aggressive energy. Both attempt to get rid of that part of their selves that they despise and, through a symbiotic relationship, acquire an idealized one. The relationship so established is predominantly narcissistic [15] and the main characteristic is that the object takes the place of an ego-ideal. Freud writes [14] about love and being in love. "The real essence of the matter is whether the object is put in the place of the ego or the ego-ideal." Jacobson's observations [52] on self-esteem are pertinent here. She says that the emotional and ideational evaluation of the body and the self is called self-esteem. It also means the expression "of the corresponding more or less neutralized libidinal and aggressive cathexis of the self-representations." She adds, "Self-esteem is expressive of the discrepancy of harmony between the self-representations and the wishful concept of the self. Hence, the disturbances of self-esteem may originate from many sources and represent a very complex pathology: on the one hand, a pathology of the ego-ideal and of the self-critical ego and super-ego functions; on the other hand, a pathology of ego functions and of the self-representations."

In general, there is agreement [22,29,42,52,53] in believing that the greater the degree of unneutralized energy invested in the self-representations, the greater is their distortion. Manaker finds that, "Self-depreciation is characteristic of one type of moral masochism. The ego-image is built principally from two sources: first, through the experiences and awareness of the ego's functioning; second, through identification with the attitudes and judgements of significant love objects." [46] And, further, ". . . self-conception derived from the earliest oral level through the ego's elaborations of the perception and experience of its own inadequate functioning. (which) is then reinforced with identification with the mother's attitude towards the child as weak, helpless, dependent . . ."

The case material of John and Peter is striking in this sense. John's over-evaluation of his body and his exhibitionistic traits are in great part the result of his mother's unconscious desires to gratify her own exhibitionism. John's hypercathected body is the counterpart of and corresponds to his mother's bodily preoccupations and fantasies. In the case of Peter, the opposite holds true. His aggressively hypercathected body-representation (devaluation) and his looking for opportunities to be "beaten up" are the counterpart of his father's unconscious fantasies and behavior. John and Peter could then "complete" themselves. Peter's hypercathexis of John's body permitted him to "complete" his body image with the idealization of John's. John, on the other hand, obtained the gratification of his exhibitionistic trends with a mother-substitute.

The above outline indicates, once more, a repetition of the original symbiosis in the present one. Also, I want to mention that these findings coincide with those of Johnson [33] in regard to perversions and unconscious parental attitudes.

Lastly, and only briefly, it will be mentioned that in the member with body devaluation, the symbolic equation body-phallus was found.

Fenichel says,[19] "In cases in which the symbolic equation body-penis holds, this relation to the penis stems from pregenital antecedents . . . The penis thus is only the final member of the series of introjects."

This whole process of exchanging body-self representations found as a basic component in the homosexual symbiotic relationship is similar to Shilder's concept of "appersonation," cited by Berman. "Whole or parts of another's body (or personality) are incorporated into the body image to such an extent that one's own body image is not possible without the body image of the other's."[4] The symbiotic relationship resembles closely the classical biological symbiosis: one creature unable to move protects with its shell an uncovered and unprotected creature capable of movement and able to obtain food; or, as Balint says, "a perpetual dependent identification."[2]

c) *Exchange of External Control:* This point has been discussed previously. The symbiotic member demands external control and obtains it through externalizing the introject he feels he must obey. He certainly gets rid of its aggressiveness, but by displacing the introject onto the external object, he is also inviting this control. On the other hand, the control of the external object is easier than that of the introject. A separation represents, then, the sudden loss of this control, and the anxiety aroused is similar to the one felt by the desertion of the super-ego and recalls a relative fusion between ego and super-ego, as described by Brody.[7]

In conclusion, we think that an explanation for the lasting duration of object-relationships in many male homosexual couples is found in the particular kind of symbiotic relationship they establish. We believe that many of the items discussed in this paper, blended in various proportions, account for similar lasting relationships among heretosexual couples.

On the other hand, it seems clear that the symbiotic members re-enact the original symbiosis with their parents. The behavior of the couples studied here appears to be a repetition of an Oedipal relationship on a pre-Oedipal level.

We feel that a sado-masochistic personality is essential in order to make the symbiosis relatively successful.

Finally, I want to emphasize the protective element, the survival function as it were, of those symbioses which lessens the self-destructive drives and permits the acquisition of some kind of love, albeit a very primitive one.

FOOTNOTES

[1] Devereux (12) feels that a sexual relationship in which the behavior is normal but the object-relationship defective, is essentially perverted. In this reasoning he encompasses the vast majority of human sexual relations, and he says that it is regrettable, but "only an infinitesimal fraction of mankind is capable of behaving and experiencing even occasionally in a mature manner befitting genital characters."

[2] Of course those studied had problems in the area of object relationships. I cannot say, however, that they necessarily represent the larger group of male homosexuals who do not seek treatment and who appear to be functioning as well as any heterosexual couple which does not request treatment.

[3] It may be of interest to mention that Peter's and John's brothers are both married.

[4] This is a complex subject into which we will not go more deeply for several reasons. Interesting suggestions on the subject may be found in Fenichel (19), Greenacre (22), Keiser (39), Rosen (50) and others.

[5] Hang band sex, as it is called. The sound of the words, as well as the associations obtained from the persons involved in such activity, suggest once again "the coalescence of acts of loving and beating," as Niederland (47) has described it. It is, however, beyond the scope of this paper to go deeper into this subject.

BIBLIOGRAPHY

1 Abraham, K.: "A Short Study of the Development of the Libido." Selected Papers on Psychoanalysis. Hogath Press. London, 1948.

2 Aaron, A.: "A Study on Perversion and an Attendant Character Disorder." Psychoanalytic Quarterly, Volume XX, No. 4, 1959.

3 Balint, M.: "On Love and Hate." J. of Psychoanalysis.

4 Berman, L.: "Depersonalization and the Body Ego." Psychoanalytic Quarterly, Volume XVII, No. 4, 1948.

5 Bing, J. F., McLaughlin, F. and Marburg, R.: "The Metapsychology of Narcissim." The Psychoanalytic Study of the Child, Volume XIV, 1959.

6 Brody, E.: "Clinical Manifestations and Ambivalence." Psychoanalytic Quarterly, Volume XXV, No. 4, 1956.

7 ———: "Superego, Introjected Mother in Schizophrenia." J. of the American Psychoanalytic Assn., Volume VI, No. 3, 1958.

8 Bychowsky, G.: "The Ego and the Introjects." Psychoanalytic Quarterly, Volume XXV, No. 1, 1956.

9 ———: "The Structure of the Homosexual Acting-Out." Ibid., Volume XXIII, 1954.

10 ———: "The Ego of Homosexuals." J. of Psychoanalysis, Volume XXVI, No. 1, 1945.

11 Carillo, C.: "On the Meaning of the Homosexual Orgy." To be published.

12 Devereux, G.: "Panel on Perversion." The Annual Survey of Psychoanalysis, Volume V, 1954.

13 Freud, S.: "On Narcissism." Collected papers. Volume V, Hogarth Press, London.

14 ———: "Being In Love and Hypnosis." In Group Psychology and the Analysis of the Ego. Hogarth Press, London, 1948.

15 ———: "On Negation." Collected papers. Volume V, Hogarth Press, London.

16 ———: "Mourning and Melancholia." Collected papers. Volume IV.

17 ———: "Instincts and their Vicissitudes." Collected papers. Volume IV.

[18] FEDERN, P.: "Ego Psychology and Psychosis." Basic Books, New York, 1952.

[19] FENICHEL, O.: "The Symbolic Equation: Girl-phallus." Psychoanalytic Quarterly, Volume XVIII, No. 3, 1949.

[20] GREENACRE, P.: "Pregenital Patterning." J. Psychoanalysis, Volume XXXIII, 1952.

[21] ________: "Respiratory Incorporation." The Psychoanalytic Study of the Child.

[22] ________: "Fetichism and Body Image." Ibid.

[23] GUSHMAN, H.: "Compulsive Homosexuality." Am. Journal of Psychoanalysis, Volume XVII, No. 1, 1957.

[24] GRAUER, D.: "Homosexuality and the Paranoid Psychosis as Related to the Concept of Narcissism." Psychoanalytic Quarterly, Volume XXIV, No. 4, 1955.

[25] GLAUBER, P.: "Panel on Perversions." Ann. Survey of Psychoanalysis, Volume V, 1954.

[26] HARTMAN, H.: "Notes on the Theory of Aggression." The Psychoanalytic Study of the Child, Volumes III and IV.

[27] ________: "On the Psychic Structure." Ibid. Volume II.

[28] ________: "On the Psychoanalytic Structure of the Ego." Ibid.

[29] ________: "Comments on the Psychoanalytic Theory of Instinctual Drives." Psychoanalytic Quarterly, Volume XVII, 1949.

[30] HOFFER: "Development of body-ego."

[31] JACOBSON, E.: "On Psychotic Identifications." J. Psychoanalysis, Volume XXXV, No. 2, 1954.

________: "The Self and the Object World." The Psychoanalytic Study of the Child. Volume IX, 1954.

[32] JENSEN, V., and PETTY, T.: "The Fantasy of Being Rescued in Suicide." Psychoanalytic Quarterly, Volume XXVII, No. 3, 1958.

[33] JOHNSON, A.: "The Genesis of Antisocial Acting-Out in Children and Adults." Psychoanalytic Quarterly, Volume XXI, No. 3, 1952.

[34] KLEIN, M.: "Psychoanalysis of Children." Hogarth Press. London, 1950.

[35] ________: "Contributions to Psychoanalysis." Ibid. 1948.

[36] ________: "Developments in Psychoanalysis." Ibid. 1952.

[37] ________: "New Directions in Psychoanalysis." Basic Books, New York, 1955.

[38] KOLB, L., and JOHNSON, A.: "Etiology and Therapy of Overt Homosexuality." Psychoanalytic Quarterly, Volume XXLV, No. 4, 1955.

[39] KAISER: "Body Ego During Organism." Psychoanalytic Quarterly, Volume XXI, No. 2, 1952.

[40] LEWINSKY, H.: "Features from a Case of Homosexuality." Psychoanalytic Quarterly, Volume XXI, No. 3, 1932.

[41] ________: "Two Features in a Case of Homosexuality." J. of Psychoanalysis, Volume XXX, No. 1, 1949.

[42] LACAN, J.: "Some Reflections on the Ego." J. Psychoanalysis, Volume XXXIV, No. 1, 1953.

[43] MAHLER, M.: "On Child Psychosis." The Psychoanalytic Study of the Child.

[44] ________: "Disturbances of the Ego and Infantile Psychosis." The Psychoanalytic Study of the Child."

45 MUENSTERBERGER, W.: "Panel on Perversion." Annual Survey of Psychoanalysis, Volume V, 1964.

46 MENAKER, E.: "Masochism—A Defense Reaction of the Ego." Psychoanalytic Quarterly, Volume XXII, No. 2, 1953.

47 NIEDERLAND, W.: "Linguistic Observations on Beating Fantasies." J. of Hillside Hospital, Volume VII, 1958.

48 PAPPENHEIM and SWEENEY: "Separation Anxiety in Mother and Child." The Psychoanalytic Study of the Child, Volume VII, 1952.

49 ROSENFELD, H.: "Remarks on the Relation of Male Homosexuality to Paranoia, Paranoid Anxiety and Narcissism." J. of Psychoanalysis, Volume XXX, No. 1, 1949.

50 ROSEN, V.: "Reconstruction of a Traumatic Event." J. of Psychoanalysis, 1955.

51 RADO, S.: "Panel on Perversion." Am. Survey of Psychoanalysis, Volume V, 1954.

52 SCOTT, C.: "Libidinal and Aggression Instincts." J. of Psychoanalysis, Volume XXXV, 1954.

53 SZASS, T.: "A contribution to the Psychology of Bodily Feelings." Psychoanalytic Quarterly, Volume XXVI, No. 1, 1957.

54 SAUL, L.: "Two Observations on the Split of Object Choice." Psychoanalytic Quarterly, Volume XX, No. 1.

55 SPIEGEL: The Psychoanalytic Study of the Child.

56 THOMPSON, C.: "Changing Concepts of Homosexuality." In A Study of Interpersonal Relations. Edited by P. Mullahy, Evergreen Books, New York, 1949.

57 THORNER, H. A.: "Notes on a Case of Male Homosexuality." J. Psychoanalysis, Volume XXX, No. 1, 1949.

The Role of Olfaction in Sexual Development

by Michael G. Kalogerakis, M.D.
New York Medical College

Michael G. Kalogerakis, M.D.

At present the author is clinical instructor in psychiatry at New York University, and Psychiatrist in Charge of the male adolescent ward at Bellevue Hospital. In addition to research on aggressive delinquent youngsters, he is engaged in private practice.

HAVELOCK ELLIS' the *Psychology of Sex*[9] was one of the earliest and most elaborate attempts to compile existing information dealing with the relationship between olfaction and sexuality. Ellis assumed that the sexual significance of personal odors was less important in man than in animals and noted that the focus of olfactory attractiveness in the body of man was not in the sexual region, as usually among animals, but had been transferred to the upper part of the body, specifically the axilla, skin and hair. Ellis also wrote that, "personal odors," not only, "fail to exert any attraction, but rather tend to cause antipathy, unless some degree of tumescence has already been attained."

Throughout the voluminous work that Freud left to posterity, there appear only five references to olfaction: two references in 1897 in letters to Wilhelm Fliess,[11] some remarks at the end of the "Rat Man history," [13] a footnote added to the "Three Essays on the Theory of Sexuality," [14] and some remarks in two longer footnotes in chapter IV of "Civilization and its Discontents." [15]

Freud thought that smell was the principal sense in animals for sexual as well as other purposes. However, as a result of the assumption of an upright posture by man, "a number of what had formerly been interesting sensations connected with the earth became repellent." Freud wondered whether this organic repression of man's pleasure in smell . . . "may not have had a considerable share in the origins of his susceptibility to nervous diseases," and he linked sexual repression to the loss of the sense of smell. He also cited his clinical observations that the tendency to take pleasure in smell, ordinarily extinct since childhood, seems to arise anew in neurotic patients, especially the obsessional and hysterical types.

Ferenczi [10] and Jones [17] remarked briefly on the coprophilic significance of smell, the former chiefly in connection with his investigation of the interest in money, the latter as part of a psychoanalytic review and interpretation of folklore.

Bromberg and Schilder [5] made an extensive study of olfactory imagination and hallucinations. The association between sex and smell was infrequent. Body-connected odors were nearly universally present in the verbal productions of 40 patients seen at Bellevue Hospital. The researchers related that one of their patients felt that his father and brother exuded an odor after sexual intercourse which placed him in a "trance." As anyone who has worked with psychotic patients is aware, this is frequently a highly symbolized association, and often females report that odors have access to their "insides," an intrusion often accompanied by ideas of impregnation. The authors mention that one of the functions of smell is to conduct the individual toward heterosexual satisfaction.

C. D. Daly and H. Senior White [7] collaborated on a study of "Phychic Reaction to Olfactory Stimuli." They stated that, "It seems to us that the instinctive responses of man have not been so completely repressed as not to be reactive in varying degrees to the same or similar tropisms which influence the greater part of the animal world. Possibly these may exert a very much greater influence on our lives than with our present knowledge we are prone to suppose." C. D. Daly, drawing from his own psychoanalytic studies of mythology wrote:

> "There is evidence . . . of odors of a subtle nature operating directly in the service of the functions of reproduction which are to be differentiated from the coprophilic odors. . . . I believe . . . this hypnotic sex-attractiveness smell was lost to man because of the inhibition of the sexual impulse from causes which were the inevitable result of the severity of the primary law of incest and the taboos."

Direct clinical reference to the importance in the child of odors emanating from the mother was first made by A. S. Brill. He told of a patient, who was sensitive to odors, especially that of his mother. "During his early boyhood he would rush to occupy a chair vacated by his mother because the odor she left attracted him." [4]

In two other cases of compulsive neurosis the chief symptom of halitosis was traced to early pleasure in odors emanating from the mother (or mother substitute).

In a group of three other patients, who all had jobs involving the sense of smell, two mothers of the patients had suffered long illnesses during the patients' childhoods, characterized by the presence of offensive odors. These observations led Brill to remark: "The vocations of the patients . . . represent the final adjustment of a disturbance of mother cathexis . . . these . . . olfactory occupations . . . represented the last links of the earliest mother cathexis in which the sense of smell played a predominant part." Brill summarized by writing, "although the sense of smell has been almost completely superseded by sight and touch, it surely continues to play a part, albeit an unconscious part, in the mental life of man."

Peto examined nearly 400 children at a clinic in Budapest and arrived at the conclusion that children do not begin to distinguish between agreeable and disagreeable smells until the age of five. At this age,

> "The child is obliged to submit to the demands of culture and more attention is paid to his odorlessness. He is also at this time brought gradually to curb his wish for bodily intimacies . . . It is the age when the whole education in and outside the family aims at repressing bodily manifestations." [22]

Thus, according to Peto the child learns which smells are "bad" through association with adult attitudes and prohibitions.

Stein, Ottenberg and Roulet [24] corroborated the findings of Peto in an experiment which determined the reaction of 300 children, ages 3-12, to the odor of synthetic sweat, synthetic feces and amyl acetate. They found that children 3 to 4 found these odors pleasant but that at 5 there was a sharp drop in favorable responses to the odors of sweat and feces. The authors speculated that the drop in the number of favorable responses might be due to the "pan-repression of erotic drives that is initiated by the Oedipal conflict."

Irving Bieber [2,3] reported the dreams of patients in analysis in which olfaction appeared directly or symbolically. It was his experience that these dreams almost always referred to incestuous objects. He inferred from his observations that olfaction plays an important part in the oedipal stage of sexual organization. He felt that the onset of heterosexual reactivity ushers in the oedipus complex between the second and fifth years and that the response is mediated through one or more of the sensory modalities which must undergo change at this time. The child, through the development of his gonads and central nervous system becomes capable of reacting with excitation to sexual odors and is able to identify "the source of the exciting odors as the total person and the specific odiferous parts."

Further evidence of the relationship between olfaction and the oedipal period of development was presented by Rosenbaum,[23] who discussed three cases in which the appearance of olfactory experiences in treatment were followed by the working through of Oedipal material, much of which was linked to the transference.

Best and Taylor,[1] listed nine reasons for presuming a physiological relationship between sex and olfaction:

1. The mucosa covering the conchae has a cavernous structure suggestive of the erectile tissue of the penis and clitoris.
2. Olfactory stimuli and psychic aspects of sex are very closely associated.
3. Nasal congestion (with epistaxis) occurs in many women, commonly at the time of the menses and in both sexes at puberty.
4. Changes in the nasal mucosa (swelling and reddening)

are common in women during pregnancy and in monkeys during the estrus cycle.

5. Stimulation of the interior of the nose in rats changes the periodicity of the estrus cycle.

6. Excision of the conchae in young rats produces hypoplasia of the sex organs.

7. Castration has produced degenerative changes in the nasal mucosa of rats, changes which are reversed by estrogen injections.

8. Pseudopregnancy has been induced in rats by removal of the sphenopalatine ganglion and by nasal application of silver nitrate solution.

9. All 11 members of a French-Canadian family had atrophic rhinitis which was successfully treated by the nasal application of the follicular hormone.

Le Magnen [18] has written that 50-60% of the men he tested were anosmic to exaltolide, a musklike substance, while the remainder were sensitive to the odor of one part in a million. Women, on the other hand were sensitive to one part in a billion with a significant increase, 100-100,000 times, at the time of ovulation with regard to the menstruation period. Six ovariectomized women were 100-1000 times less sentitive to exaltolide than normal women. However, estrogen treatment restored four of the women to normal sensitivity. Le Magnen [19] also demonstrated the presence of a sex-specific and species-specific odorous substance given off by white rats. The response to and production of this substance varied with the sexual state of an animal.

David et al [8] found that electrical stimulation of the olfactory bulbs of female cats during the interestrus period increased the rhythm of the cycles, with a lengthening of the proestrus, a shortening of the proestrus, and an elimination of the interestrus. Stimulation during proestrus modified pituitary ovarian function, eliminating the estrus and creating a permanent proestrus. These and other physiological investigations were summarized by Le Magnen.[20]

Recently Bruce and Parrott [6] demonstrated that it is the olfactory sense that determines the blocking of pregnancy in female mice which occurs when they are placed in the vicinity of a strange male. Bruce and Parrott also noted that regression of the ovaries and uteri, alternations in mating behavior and other disturbances of reproduction occurred in female mice whose olfactory bulbs had been removed.

CLINICAL OBSERVATIONS

The following clinical material was reported to the writer by a patient in treatment. It consists of carefully recorded observations of this patient's son between the ages of 2 and 5 years.

Jackie is an alert, healthy youngster, the only child of a young professional couple. At the age of 2, he could consistently distinguish the sounds of several musical instruments being played in concert. From the age of 2½, he demonstrated considerable sensitivity to odors, frequently asking, "What smells?," on entering a room where no odor was immediately apparent to the adults who were with him. This was usually accompanied by a grimace, occasionally of displeasure, as in the case of onion, garlic, or other strong food smells. This response was apparently influenced by his maternal grandmother who cared for him during the day and herself habitually over-reacted to strong odors in similar fashion. Jackie's comments and observable reactions to odors were at this time confined to household odors, with no mention of body or toilet odors. Shortly after his third birthday, he developed a special interest in feet. This apparently began during play with his youthful aunt; as they watched television, he would take off her slippers and play with her feet. He sometimes remarked that they "smelled," grimacing in apparent displeasure but this did not interfere with his desire to handle them. A few weeks later, as he glanced through the Sunday newspapers and saw advertisements depicting stockingless little girls wearing pyjamas or underclothes, he would ask why they were without shoes and socks. He seemed dissatisfied with the explanation he received and saved the newspaper. He would frequently look at these pictures with a quiet but intense fascination. This interest shortly returned to the living specimen, so that with company at the house he would sometimes sit under the table gazing at some footweary woman's shoeless foot. Invariably his focus of interest was a female, generally young. This activity continued for some months but had disappeared by the time he was 3½. He showed no reaction when summer arrived and he was exposed to the barefoot multitudes at the beach.

When 3½ years old, he first reacted to bedroom odors; approaching his mother as she was arising one morning, about to embrace her, he suddenly pulled away. Grimacing, he commented that something smelled and indicated that the smell emanated from his mother. The parents were aware of an odor which they identified with sexual secretions resulting from coitus several hours earlier. This experience was subsequently repeated many times. He had an identical reaction to his father on these occasions. Invariably, he could respond in this way hours after intercourse had been completed, even when his parents had washed or bathed in the interim. In one remarkable instance on joining his father in the shower as the latter was preparing to leave, he suddenly bolted and vociferously insisted on getting out, complaining that his father's penis smelled. This was again coincident with coitus the night before. In fact, it is important to note that, for a time (3-4 months), Jackie showed none of these responses except when parental intercourse had occurred the previous night, and he invariably showed the response when they had had intercourse. There was no awareness at other times of other odors emanating from his father's genitalia (e.g. of smegma), despite ample opportunity to detect these while observing his father urinating. It was evident that the boy was reacting specifically to the odor of one or more of the numerous substances secreted during coitus.

Gradually, his olfactory responses diminished, becoming less clear-cut. There were still frequent evidences—usually in the form of wincing or gulping—that early-morning body odors emanating from his parents were evoking unpleasant feelings. This no longer specifically followed coitus, however, and usually appeared only when the boy came quite close to either parent. Interestingly, by the time he was 3 years and 8 months old, he seemed generally to prefer his mother when detecting such odors, tended to become more "cuddly" than uusal, and was also quieter, seeming almost preoccupied. Confirmation of a growing differentiation of his responses to his mother and father came a few months after his fourth birthday. Again, it was the morning on awakening. Jackie's father had gone into his room as the boy lay in bed, and began to play with him. He was gently nuzzling his head in the boy's abdomen when the latter suddenly retched, spat as though sick to his stomach. He would not speak when asked what had bothered him, wanting only to go to his mother, clambering up into her arms, head on her shoulder, and acting very much as was his wont when ill. No such reaction of revulsion had ever before been observed in the boy, from any kind of stimulus. Though very resistive at first, the boy was gradually able to clarify what had happened. Nodding assent or shaking his head in denial to specific questions asked by his father, he indicated that he had reacted to an odor; that the odor seemed to issue chiefly from his father's armpit, although the hair too seemed to be involved; that the perception made him sick to his stomach.

Two or three weeks after this episode, the father had once again gone in to the boy in the morning, embraced him, and had been pushed away. This exchange then took place:

Father: What's the matter, Jackie, don't you like to hold Daddy close?

Jackie: I like to hold you close but not too close.

Father: And how about Mommy?

Jackie: Oh, I like to hold her very close.

At last report, the boy, who had by then passed his fifth birthday, had had a recrudescence of the reaction of revulsion to his father. After many months, during which only minimal responses were noted, Jackie again began to complain, now very articulately, of odors, emanating from his father's body. The complaints and accompanying reactions were generally made in the morning or when the father was in a relative state of undress. Generalization of the response, probably by way of a conditioning process, had occurred, so that the visual perception of seminudity evoked a reaction immediately after the father had showered, although minutes earlier, before he showered, no response to the bathrobe-clad father was observed. It should be noted that the above reactions occurred in the context of a very close relationship between father and son, which included considerable body contact in the form of wrestling, riding piggy-back, etc. And the reaction was specific to the father, inasmuch as the boy denied that any other person in his entourage (this included an adult uncle) had a similar odor. These were distinctions, ostensibly on an olfactory basis, which could not be made by any of the adults involved. In the final incident reported by the father, Jackie, now 5½ had come to him while he was still lying in bed, nude but covered to the waist. The boy sat on the edge of the bed comfortably talking with his father. When the latter raised his arms, placing his hands behind his head, the boy turned away, apparently to conceal a grimace. His father smiled and said, "Ah-ha! As soon as I lift my arms you smell something and turn away, right?" The boy smiled in return, nodding assent. This represented a significant change from earlier responses. Though still reacting with avoidance to his father's body odors, the response was milder and he was able to talk about it and smile. It would appear that some resolution of the emotional significance of these olfactory experiences had taken place.

DISCUSSION

The difference in sensitivity to the odor of exaltolide between men and women or between oophorectomized and nonoophorectomized women, and the change in sensitivity recorded during normal menstrual cycles, as reported by Le Magnen, point to a hormonal basis for the olfactosexual relationship. This hormonal basis was also evident in the studies on animals. Sexual behavior in animals is clearly mediated through the olfactory sense more than any other. No other sense could lead the male to the female in estrus one mile away.

The role of olfaction in human sexual behavior is less clearly defined. A certain number of individuals are consciously aware of being attracted by sexual odors. A larger percentage are aware of sexual odors but react negatively to them. Some deny any awareness at all. Hormonal variations may account for relative degrees of anosmia, quite apart from any psychogenic factors. Nonetheless, it is clear that odor can play an important part in determining object-choice. This was amply illustrated by Brill, whose patient would run to occupy the chair vacated by his mother, attracted by the odor she left. Brill's other cases had formed definite associations to odors (not necessarily sexual), emanating from the mother.

Bieber's observations of analytic patients further underscore the relevance of odor to object-choice, laying emphasis on the Oedipal roots of such selection and bringing the whole question of sexual *development* into focus. The dream material he has collected from his patients consistently demonstrates the connection between odors and incestuous objects. As noted, this connection was usually a symbolic one.

Bieber's hypothesis that olfaction may be the very modality which under usual conditions determines initial heterosexual orientation and brings on the Oedipus complex finds support in the observations of the boy, Jackie. Although they have been made on only one child, one may speculate that a child, from about the age of two and one-half years:

1. Is capable of perceiving adult sexual odors, specifically those associated with coitus.
2. Is not indifferent to those odors but reacts affectively.
3. Distinguishes between his parents in the quality of his responses.
4. Reacts with avoidance which is more marked and more consistent with the parent of the same sex.

This olfactory perception of evidence of the primal scene is not a unique experience. As noted earlier, it was reported by one of the patients in the Bromberg and Schilder group. Recently, it was reported to me by an adult patient who, at the age of 8-10, always knew when his parents had had intercourse by the odor in the room. As was the case with Jackie, he was particularly aware of an odor emanating from his father and reacted negatively to him.

Jackie continued to respond negatively to his father but not to his mother. (There is one exception to this not noted above—and this occurred at a time when the mother was wearing her husband's bathrobe!) This persistent negative response raises an interesting question: Might not this differentiation in responses to mother and father be a part of the boy's growing sense of identity as a male? We know, of course, that the development of sexual identity proceeds along many lines. The clothes he wears, the toys he plays with, the activities he is encouraged to engage in, all help the child's growing sense of maleness or femaleness, as the case may be. The parents' differentiated relatedness to the child is of paramount importance in the entire process. But we are here suggesting a possibly *biological* basis for the establishment of sexual identity, in which olfaction would play a crucial role. Specifically, this would involve attraction to the body odors of the heterosexual parent, and concomitantly, repulsion from the odors emitted by the parent of the same sex. In the data presented above, there is considerable support for the presumption of a biologically-determined, olfactorily-mediated antagonism between members of the same sex. There is also evidence for heterosexual attraction, for example, in Jackie's attraction to his aunt's feet. In an excellent monograph on the human apocrine sweat gland, Hurley and Shelley,[16] outline the evidence indicating endocrine control of its secretion and describe it as an 'atavistic scent gland,' having little known physiological importance. In contrast to the eccrine (e.g. sudoriparous) glands, it is not a thermoregulatory organ. It becomes functional at puberty and wanes after the climacteric. One of its pathological states, Fox-Fordyce disease, disappears dramatically with pregnancy, only to reappear in the puerperium. Anatomically, it is situated in the axillary region (site of the largest apocrine gland) in the perianal and inguinal areas, and in the mammary areola. The mammary gland itself is an apocrine gland. (We are reminded that Jackie's earliest olfactory responses to his parents were to the genital areas, later settling on the axilla). Though studies on the odor of apocrine sweat were done, only male subjects were used as sources of sweat. Attempts to evaluate apocrine response to emotional stimuli were inconclusive and, in any case, did not include sexual stimulation.

SUMMARY

A careful evaluation of the data relating olfaction and sexuality in child development seems to permit of the following formulation:

(1) That human adults give off odors characteristic of their sex and probably of the person.[9]

(2) That, to account for the uniqueness of the odors, they must be intimately related to the chemistry of the individual, itself unique.

(3) That these odors must be associated with substances secreted by the body or by the exocrine glands.

(4) To account for sexual differences the odoriferous substances must in some way be linked to the sex hormones. The exocrine gland which most qualifies in this regard is the apocrine.

(5) These sex-specific odors are discernible to the child who, when in the Oedipal period, reacts with attraction for the heterosexual parent [2] and *repulsion to the ipsisexual parent.*

(6) That these responses participate in the establishment of the child's sexual identity. They add a physiological component to the existing anatomical differences (which lead to body-image formation) and the acculturation as male or female already in progress. These reactions would not be expected to determine the child's over-all attitude to each of his parents but would form a basic biological substratum for the development of his sexual identity and sexual relatedness to the adult male and female.

REFERENCES

1 Best, C. H. and Taylor, N. B.: "*The Physiological Basis of Medical Practice*—6th edit. Williams & Wilkins Co., Baltimore, 1955, p. 895.

[2] BIEBER, IRVING: "Olfaction in sexual development and adult sexual organization." Am. J. Psychother. Volume 13, 4:851-853 (Oct., 1959).

[3] ________: "Olfaction in sexual development and adult sexual organization" in *Psychoanalysis and Human Values,* edit. by Jules H. Masserman. Grune & Stratton, Inc., 1960.

[4] BRILL, A. A.: "The sense of smell in the neuroses and psychoses." Psychoanal. Quart. 1:7 (April, 1932).

[5] BROMBERG, W., and SCHILDER, P. "Olfactory Imagination and Olfactory Hallucinations." Arch. Neurol. & Psych. 32:467-492 (Sept., 1934).

[6] BRUCE, H. M. and PARROTT, D. M. V.: "Role of Olfactory Sense in Pregnancy Block by Strange Males." Science Vol. 131, p. 1526 (May 20, 1960).

[7] DALY, C. D. and WHITE, R. SR.: "Psychic Reactions to Olfactory Stimuli." Brit. J. Med. Psych. 10:70 (1930).

[8] DAVID, R., THIERY, C., BONVALLET, M., and DELL, P. "Effets de la stimulation des bulbes olfactifs sur le cycle sexuel de la chatte." Compt. rend. soc. biol. 146, 670-672 (1952).

[9] ELLIS, HAVELOCK: *Studies in the Psychology of Sex.* Random House, New York, 1936. Vol. 1, Part 3.

[10] FERENCZI, SANDOR: "The Ontogenesis of the Interest in Money" in *Sex in Psychoanalysis.* New York, Basic Books, Inc. (1950).

[11] FREUD, SIGMUND: Fliess correspondence in *Origins of Psychoanalysis* letters 55 and 75. New York, Basic Books, Inc. (1954).

[12] ________: "Fragment of an Analysis of a Case of Hysteria." (1905) Standard Edit. Volume 7, p. 69.

[13] ________: "Notes Upon a Case of Obsessional Neurosis." (1909) Standard Edit. Volume 10, p. 247.

[14] ________: "Three Essays on the Theory of Sexuality." Standard Edit. Volume 7.

[15] ________: "Civilization and Its Discontents." Hogarth Press, London (1951) pp. 66 and 77.

[16] HURLEY, HARRY J. and SHELLEY, WALTER B.: *The Human Apocrine Sweat Gland in Health and Disease.* Chas C. Thomas, Springfield, Ill. 1960.

[17] JONES, ERNEST: "The Madonna's Conception Through the Ear" in *Essays in Applied Psychoanalysis.* Hogarth Press, London, 1951. Vol. II, pp. 314-18.

[18] LEMAGNEN, JACQUES: "Physiologie des sensations: Nouvelles données sur la phénomène de l'exaltolide." Compt. rend. 230, 1103-5 (1950).

[19] ________: "Les phénomènes olfacto-sexuels chez le rat blanc." Arch. Sci. Physiol. 6: 295-332 (1952).

[20] ________: "L'olfaction: le fonctionnement olfactif et son intervention dans les régulations psychophysiologiques." J. Physiol. & Path. Gén. 45: 285-326 (1953).

[21] ORBACH, CHARLES E., BARD, MORTON and SUTHERLAND, ARTHUR W.: "Fears and Defensive Adaptations to the Loss of Anal Sphincter Control." Psychoanal. Rev. 44: 121, 1957.

[22] PETÓ, E.: "Contribution to the Development of Smell Feeling." Brit. J. of Med. Psych. 15: 314-320 (1936).

[23] ROSENBAUM, JEAN R.: "The significance of the sense of smell in the transference." J. Amer. Psychoanal. Assn. 9:2 312-324 (1961).

[24] STEIN, M., OTTENBERG, F., and ROULET, N.: "Study of the Development of Olfactory Preferences." AMS Arch. of Neurol. & Psych. 80 (2): 264-6, August, 1958.

Psycho-Physiological Conditions and Psychotherapy

by Oskar Guttmann, M.D.
Postgraduate Center for Psychotherapy

Oskar Guttmann, M.D.

Prior to his recent death, the author was instructor and Supervising Psychiatrist, Metropolitan Hospital-New York Medical College, and a member of the staff of the Postgraduate Center for Psychotherapy, in addition to being engaged in private practice.

"PSYCHOSOMATIC medicine" is as old as medicine and philosophy. The development of the concept of the mind-body relationship reflects the entire evolution of the concept of illness and of the art of healing.

Though "psychosomatic" would seem to imply the fusion of "soul" with "body" it could also imply that "psychic medicine" and "somatic medicine" have separate existences. It is important to emphasize that no isolated psychogenic disorder exists, just as no such thing exists as a separate organic or physical disease. In every disease, both the mind and body are affected. Goldstein has stated: "Neither does the mind act on the body, nor the body on the mind, no matter how this may seem to be the case in superficial observation. We are always dealing with the activity of the whole organism, the effects of which we refer to something called 'mind' at one time and another time to something called 'body.'" Mind and body then are two behavioral aspects of an inseparable psychobiological unit of the organism.

A person suffering from cancer—a profound organogenic illness—will also display emotional and mental symptoms which may even produce a complicating serious depression, "pathoneurosis" or "pathopsychosis," and require special physiological attention.

Sequin, at the International Congress of Psychiatry in Paris in 1950, stated:

> "without accepting psychogenesis or somatogenesis as such, we may state that the total reaction of the organism may be produced by psychologic or somatic stimuli, which means that the stimulus setting in motion the psychosomatic total response may be an emotion or a physio-chemical alteration, but in either case the organism, responding as a unit, will show psychological as well as somatic alterations. We may refer to a psychogenesis of

somatic symptoms or a somatogenesis of psychological symptoms only as regards the 'stimulus,' but not the biologic process in itself. If this is so, in diagnosing all diseases psychosomatic by definition, we may use research methods which test either the psychologic or the somatic component."

A "psychosomatic" disorder, or a "psycho-physiological reaction," as the APA nomenclature designates it, is a mixed, mostly chronic clinical manifestation which superficially has the character of a so-called "somatic" illness, but when analyzed is found to derive from unconscious emotional disturbances. Such a psycho-physiological syndrome, called by some, "organ neurosis," could have the meaning of a manifestation of deep-seated, unconscious, neurotic conflict with the value of an unconscious gratification. In some cases, it may appear only as a physiological vegetative corollary of psychoneurotic disturbances, as an "affect equivalent," as Fenichel calls "a state in which the mental content of the affect has been warded off, whereas the physical concomitants of the affect do take place."

The psychosomatic symptom may well appear, either as a group of so-called "somatic symptoms," accompanied by all sorts of psychoneurotic disturbances and character disorders, or, when localized in one organ-system, as a specific illness, such as peptic ulcer, bronchial asthma, or ulcerative colitis. These diseases—though often referred to as "psychogenic" or "functional"—may even exhibit temporary changes in the affected organ-systems. For example: during an attack of bronchial asthma, severe spasms of originally unaffected bronchi create temporary life-threatening suffocation. Instead, with the passage of time, almost every psycho-physiological syndrome will result in actual morphological changes, due to an over-activity of a part of the entire vegetative nervous system.

In order that we may better understand the full effect of stimuli, it is necessary—using Seguin's phrase—to scrutinize "the total reaction of the organism."

The organism is a miraculously purposeful conglomerate of organ systems bound by static energy of structure and dynamic processes. Through it, from intracellular to intercellular relationships, from tissue to tissue, and from organ apparatus to organ apparatus, and finally from all organ systems to the superior whole, flows that curious vital force which has in it the tension necessary for the fulfillment of two basic needs: the self preservation of the organism and the procreation of the human species. For these ends, two types of organs have developed, the organs of our immediate economy and the genital apparatus. Linked with the outer world and cultural environment by a complex of perceptions, gratifications and deprivations, these organs are profoundly influential in the development of the total personality. They are the first objects of cathexis. From them derive the first primordial energetic imprints of the mind.

An entire symbolic central representation of all the organ systems will gradually be constructed simultaneously with the organization of the developing ego, from birth on—through the central integration of perceptions, of interoceptive sensations with their libidinous erotogenic components—that which we call the "body image." Its anatamo-physiological basis is mostly localized around the tempero-parietal cortical area number 40 of Broadman.

Our total growth is profoundly influenced and affected by "emotions" associated with all the stages of libidinous psychosexual development, and with all cultural influences. The body image must include, partially, the condensed reflections of preserved impressions, whose Repressed components will eventually manifest themselves, disguised and unconscious, either in the regressed expression of the psychosomatic symptom, or partially, in a psychoneurotic symptom. Since these impressions are related to the emotions, they have a psycho-physiological relation to their subcortical coordination centers.

When a need arises, our organism produces a "tension," a mild emotion which excites our cortical centers, and there depending on the stage of development, judgement evaluation of the ego, will decide the reactive response for the gratification. If these needs are of a so-called "higher intellectual, creative, aesthetic type," the stimulation remains more conscious and localized in the cerebral cortex, where the responses also will be elaborated, and only in part emotionally influenced.

If, however, the needs are so-called "basic" in relation to self preservation or to preservation of the species, the stimulus is automatically transmitted from the cortex to the subcortical centers of the thalamus and hypothalamus, which mostly on an emotional and subconscious level will elaborate a reactive response, in whose elaboration and coordination the cortex and the conscious ego-organization are of decisive significance.

In the hypothalamus (which also is connected to the cerebral cortex through a very complex archaic structure, the rinencephalon, called the "visceral brain") reside the highest centers of the autonomic vegetative, hormonal and metabolic regulatory mechanisms. It is this area which phylogenetically was first built up in the more complicated defense and adjustment systems. We consider these structures the highest coordination centers in the so-called psycho-physiological "circuit of the emotions."

The tension of our basic needs guarantees our survival through a regulatory rhythm of our inner economy, which is created by an intrinsic and ubiquitous regular alternation and succession of primordial life movement, and by automatic regular change between activity and inertia. This rhythm in our organism determines all our vital manifestations and the adequate utilization and direction of our energy, such as: the heart beat, respiration, ovulation, the anabolic and catabolic processes of metabolism, the psychic polarities—frustration and gratification, sleep and wakefulness.

This vital rhythm oscillates between the subcortical sensations of "depletion" and "satiation," which through "tension" stimulate moderately the hypothalamic centers of the sympathetic and parasympathetic nervous system. These two antagonize each other harmoniously for the smooth well-functioning of all our organ systems. They automatically regulate our inner visceral activities through two main biochemical substances, adrenalin and acetylcholine, which cause transitory and mostly reversible changes in the tissues of the effector organs.

Since for the fulfillment of our needs we must appeal to a constantly interacting environment, we may encounter resistance. This outside stimulus, considered as a threat to our existence and integrity, will be an obstacle to the gratification of our need and therefore produce an emotion. This, unlike the milder rhythmically determined tension, will cause a temporary, more intense psychophysiological upset. Here the homeostatic principles of Cannon, "fight, defense or flight," come into play. Essentially these are expressions of the "general adaptation syndrome" of Selye. The resultant emotions (rage, anger, anxiety, fear), and the readiness to attack and fight, pass the normal physiological threshold of acting stimuli and are experienced then in the consciousness, as a special reactive state called by Selye "stress" or "alarm" reaction.

Stimulating almost all of the hormonal, vegetative, and metabolic hypothalamic-pituitary-adrenalin centers, these stresses, through the secretion of ACTH and epinephrine with a following corollary of peripheral somatic phenomena, make the body ready to fulfill its needs and allow the organism to reestablish homeostatic equilibrium.

The translation of emotions into somatic symptoms in the peripheral effector organs (expressed mostly in spasms or dilations of the blood vessels, in arrest or stimulation of the glands, in contraction or relaxation of the smooth musculature) is called the "somatization of the emotions." The same somatic effects may also be produced by morphological alterations in the organ itself.

How the organism accomplishes the complicated process known as "somatization of the emotions" (analogous, but not equivalent to the mechanism of "conversion") is at present unknown. The manifest physical symptoms accompanying the emotions are transitory and disappear mostly without a trace as soon as homeostasis is reestablished. It is exactly this reversibility which characterizes the so-called functional disorders in contrast to organic illness where we mostly deal with irreversible changes.

Such a return to the normal is seldom seen, however, in those who suffer from what is known as "emotional disturbance." This is an unconscious chronic state of anxiety, hostility or guilt, characteristic of psychoneurotic or psychotic conditions, in which the consciousness is under constant attack by a mass of unconscious repressions and complexes. These will constantly attempt to invade the ego-awareness and cause the well known discomfort of "emotional disturbance." This continuous state of stress, called by Landis "morbid emotion or anguish," necessarily mobilizes all our protective mechanisms, including the neurotic conflict symptoms.

One type of neurotic conflict manifestation is the psychosomatic symptom, which is not the secondary physiological corollary of an emotion and which in this sense may be defined as follows: the psychosomatic symptom is the expression of a regressive unconscious psycho-physiological defense reaction of displacement against the anxiety produced by a disturbed and inappropriate manifestation of "somatization of the emotions," which translates bodily an unconscious gratification of repressed fantasies and painful memories.

In those cases where the unconscious distortions of the symbolic representation of the body image are displayed in a dissociative non-anatomical-physiological or bizarre fashion, we will observe the clinical picture of conversion hysteria. In this syndrome the means of expression utilizes the conversion defense mechanism and the somato-muscular sensory apparatus. With strong erotogenic components in fantasy, it will dominate an eventual vegetative nervous stimulation. On the other hand, in the psychosomatic syndrome it will be noticed as a predominant expression of the stimulation of the nervous vegetative system, the defense mechanism being an inappropriate and distorted "somatization of emotions."

In either condition, the emotional disturbance will produce in our organism:

1. A break in the balance of the vital rhythm, causing dysrythmia and inadequate energy utilization in our inner economy.
2. A varying degree of upset in the central symbolic representation of the body image.
3. A threat to disrupt the intrinsic cohesiveness of the holistic organization of the personality.

The dysrythmia disturbs the harmonious antagonism between the two main vegetative nervous systems. Thus one or the other of these systems, or both in varying degree, may receive a hyperactive continuous overstimulation, which can cause morphological changes in the effector organs.

Since in psychosis we rarely see clinical psychosomatic syndromes, we may assume that the typical psychosomatic syndrome is a "psychoneurosis" or a "neurotic character disorder," with an organ localization of the conflict and defenses. Mention, however, should be made that psychoses may often display very overt and gross somatic accompanying syndromes, mostly of a constitutional and endocrine nature which, etiologically, may have nothing or little to do with the illness, but may be secondary manifestations of regressive or primitive physiological dysfunctions, associated with narcissistic withdrawal and its consequences.

The attempt to describe systematically the psychosomatic syndromes by approaching single organ-systems and seeking a common denominator in psychodynamics and personality profiles, is more helpful and necessary for didactic purposes. In psychotherapy of these illnesses it represents a rather obsolete static method, which does not emphasize sufficiently the pathogenic significance of the holistic concept. It is more practical to follow the general genetic principles of psychopathology. The therapist will want to know what Hippocrates professed about 2400 years ago: "What person has a disease rather than what disease has a person."

Clinically, we can subdivide all existent illnesses into six main categories, which swing from one extreme to another through a gamut of various syndromes:

1. All psychoses, in which certain delusions and haptic hallucinations occur (with a defensive narcissistic localization of the organ cathexis) but in which we cannot find a somatization of the emotions. The bodily complaints of the psychotic appear to be severe mental disturbances, magic archaic imagery. These seem to result from a troubled body-image which in turn is distorted by deep-seated complexes.

2. The borderline states and hypochondriasis, in which the delusion-like symptoms are precipitated by an extreme sensitivity and vulnerability of an immature ego, as well as by increased narcissistic erotogenic contributions from bodily organs. These patients are haunted by exaggerated fear of incurable illness and death, in connection with masochistic unconscious guilt feelings. Magnified and distorted interpretations of vague body sensations in relation to physiological processes also play some role.

In this category also belong the obsessive-compulsive neurotics, who indulge in their bodily complaints in order to expiate, masochistically and in secret magic rituals, their unconscious guilt and punishment.

3. All psychoneuroses and neurotic character disorders, in which anxiety and conversion hysteria are in the first rank. In anxiety hysteria, a host of the most various bodily complaints may at times include disturbances of all organ systems from "head to toe." This category was known to the older psychiatrists as "neurasthenia" or "psycho-asthenia."

4. All transitory but permanently recurring psycho-physiological reactions, without permanent structural changes. These recur either under special unconscious emotional conditions or at general conscious stress. Examples of this kind include depressions, allergic conditions, nervous vomiting, fainting, migraine, pseudo-angina pectoris spells, and bronchial asthma. Patients of this group require physical medical treatment as an emergency and eventually also as support while undergoing psychotherapy.

5. All permanently existing psycho-physiological reactions which, in the long run, stem from the previous group and may already present structural physical changes. Here we find peptic ulcer, hyper-tension, coronary heart disease and the sickest psychosomatic patients—those affected by ulcerative colitis, who actually are suffering from an underlying schizophrenic disorder. It is mostly this group which will require a transitory or a permanent combined medical-psychological treatment.

6. The organogenic or physical illnesses, from pneumonia to cancer, in which the morphological pathology, transitory or permanent-progressive predominates. But here also deep psychology can help, explaining the meaning of symptoms and the involvement of the total personality, which modern physicians seem to appreciate more and more.

At this point we may also mention the problem of "organ-specificity," or what Freud called "somatic compliance."

Why one patient suffers from stomach troubles, whereas another complains of his heart, has not yet been explained. Adler spoke of an "inborn organ inferiority" and others claim a "regressive physiological infantilism." It seems very possible that here the unconscious central symbolic representation of the body-image plays an important role.

In such a case the choice of the affected organ-system was probably made in that libidinous stage, when the patient was most susceptible to traumatization. In a sense, then, he has, not growing out emotionally enough, remained fixated at, or he will regress to, this point, when it is felt necessary in his unconscious conflict. Beyond his awareness he will then use such organs as will best serve him in his narcissistic needs to translate his unconcious symbolic fantasies into body language. We may, therefore, assume that a person who for various reasons has an increase in cathexis or "organ representatives," will be predisposed to psychosomatic illness. If, for instance, traumata occurred predominantly in the oral stage, the patient will mostly have difficulties in the upper digestive tract; whereas traumata which derive from frustrated experiences during the anal stage are more likely to affect the lower tract. It is hardly necessary to add that traumata may occur in all stages, so that the symptoms will always overlap and mix.

The Greek "theraps" means "serve" and "therapeia" means "healing." How can we best "serve" and "heal" the patient with a psycho-physiological disorder? In order to do this adequately we should have to perform a complete "somatanalysis," as well as a psychoanalysis. The two would then be combined in an integrated understanding of a "holistic behavior synthesis." This, of course, is an ideal to keep in mind.

The first step, preceding the therapy, is the diagnosis. In case the patient was sent directly for psychotherapy, he must first be referred to an internist for a physical check-up.

It is desirable during psychotherapy to avoid numerous physical check-ups, since these may well arouse the apprehensions of the patient. If, therefore, a psychosomatic patient is in treatment with a psychologist or a social worker, it is good policy for the therapist to keep in touch with a colleague physician, with whom symptoms and complaints can be freely discussed.

The initial physical check-up will be followed by a psychiatric interview. We must try, at this point, to detect the anxiety and defenses behind the description of the psychosomatic complaint. At times this description will imitate the symptoms of organic illnesses. Often, however, it will reveal exaggerated or even bizarre unphysiological inconsistencies. If possible, we should obtain a longitudinal life history in the psychobiological sense of Meyer.

The diagnostic problem of psychosomatic medicine is immense and embraces the whole field of medicine. Between forty and sixty percent of all sick people (who are treated only with drugs, surgery, or a host of other physical therapies, by general practitioners or specialists, who often refuse to acknowledge the source of the illness) are in reality "psychosomatic" cases and require, primarily, psychotherapy.

On the other hand, psychotherapists—with the same blind resistance and omnipotence—often treat patients only with psychotherapy where other somatic therapies, including surgery, would be indicated.

Here we may pause for a moment to note that every therapist—if offered the opportunity to treat the whole person in successfully constructed analytic psychotherapy—will hope for certain results. He will doubtless expect, for example, to discharge and then redirect the energies of the patient (which were previously bound to repressions stored partially in the body image) so that they may be utilized more rationally. Likewise the therapist will expect (as the patient gains insight into the buried motivations of his behavior and into the formation of his emotional growth) that the unconscious gratification which he had derived from his psychosomatic symptoms will cease to be necessary. At the same time the therapist will expect the dysrhythmic vital manifestations of the "irrational body language" and the vegetative irrations to subside, and also that morphological alterations, such as those which occur in ulcer diseases, will eventually heal under the influence of a "quieter inner milieu."

In treating a psychosomatic patient, the therapist will doubtlessly employ essentially the same well-known principles of psychotherapy which he would apply to any other patient. He ought, however, to know and accept a few very important additional rules.

He will try not to concentrate too much, for example, on any single symptom, since the patient in his unconscious display of helplessness often manifests a symptom for the infantile purpose of getting attention. This tendency is notable especially in anxiety hysterias, which show the best therapeutic results and in patients afflicted with ulcerative colitis, which show the worst.

Often, in treating psychosomatic patients, the therapist must accept the idea of combined psychotherapeutic-medical treatment. For example, he should permit, when necessary, the administration of drugs (for headaches, insomnia, distressing heart burns and so on, and for tranquilizing effect). Indeed, any treatment which relieves anxiety—thus clearing our way to a possible deep psychotherapy—will often prove beneficial. This holds true for a few electric-shock treatments, especially in case of severe depressions. In administering ECT, however, great care should be taken not to affect the sensorium. Hypnosis—though useful in research—has only a limited therapeutic value. It may be cautiously applied in cases of anxiety hysteria, but only if the patient has attained a satisfactory ego-growth.

We are reminded here of the danger involved in any forcible effort to remove the psychosomatic symptoms. Fenichel even expresses the opinion that an organ-neurosis may be a defense against, or an equivalent of a psychosis. Since psychosomatic symptoms mostly represent disguised manifestations of an underlying, unconscious conflict, they therefore provide the patient with homeostatically unconscious gratifications. If his ego is still only weakly organized, the removal of these symptoms may therefore produce a breakdown. In this connection the therapist should also keep in mind that the apparent removal of a symptom may actually constitute nothing more than a displacement. The patient might shift from a diarrhea to a headache or from a spastic colitis to a tic. Or he may oscillate between intense bodily symptoms and flareups of emotional and mental difficulties. One of my patients with ulcerative colitis swings between her intestinal crises and episodes of intense paranoid outbursts of hostility.

No comment on psychosomatic medicine would be complete without reference to the "Sector Psychotherapy" of Felix Deutsch, a treatment particularly intended for psychosomatic illness. This is a dynamically oriented, active, goal-limited, symptomatic psychotherapy in which, through the so-called "associative anamnesis," we focus and direct the patient's associations onto a specific sector, "which is one of several parts of a total situation to which a neurotic or psychosomatic symptom belongs."

Here the patient, under skillful and cautious direction, begins to be the observer as well as the observed. In short, he gradually comes to understand the life situations of the past against which he has for so long protected himself, by means of unconscious defenses. Among these, of course, is the actual psychosomatic symptom which brought him to the therapist. With insight, then, he may find that he is living a new life in which he can now give up his psychosomatic symptom as superfluous. Again, we must repeat, the therapist at all times, in employing this technique, must evaluate the ego-strength of the patient.

Obviously, it must also be stated that no definitive evaluation of this method can be attempted until results of more experience with this method are available.

In my final words, I want to appeal to all professionals interested in the disturbances and vicissitudes of behavior to abandon the isolationism which has kept us apart so long, and to join readily in working teams. I can think of no better example for us to follow than that provided by Robert Heath at Tulane University, where specialists—including psychotherapists, neuropathologists, neuro-surgeons, biochemists—who formerly worked alone, are now cooperating, for the first time, in multi-disciplinary research teams.

Our own Institute, where professionals of three disciplines—psychiatry, psychology, and social work—function harmoniously together, is another good example of the possibilities of this direction.

Fully accepting psychoanalytical principles and the important contributions of the culturalists, it has been my intention in this paper to call on the great flexible biological spirit of Freud for the courage to overcome rigid attitudes so that we may accept and integrate all possible data, either psychic or bio-physiological. For the benefit of our patients, and also for the widening of our own horizons in the approach to the complicated human mind, we must utilize eclectic pluralistic formulations, not one or two, but all possible existing avenues, and, if necessary, we must discover new ones. It is high time to give up the Cartesian dichotomy of the Middle Ages which in modern times is called "Organicism" versus "Psychogeneticism."